CALCULUS:

a first course

Calculus: a first course

DAVID J. MOORE

Department of Mathematics
University of Glasgow

ARKLAY PUBLISHERS

Published by Arklay Publishers,
64 Murray Place, Stirling, Scotland. FK8 2BX.

Printed in Great Britain by Bell and Bain Ltd., Glasgow

Preface

This book, as its title suggests, provides a first course in Calculus. The aim of the book is to develop a facility in the basic operations of Calculus, differentiation and integration, and to show how these may be used in practical applications. We also examine how curve sketching can help in understanding the behaviour of functions.

This book presents the course which is currently offered to students attending Mathematics class 1B here at Glasgow University. Such students are primarily interested in studying one or more years of Mathematics, usually as a back-up to their main course of study. Their interest is in the application of Mathematics, rather than in the abstraction of Mathematics. This book reflects that interest.

In writing the book, I have adopted a non-rigorous approach. I have always strongly believed that the initial step for students learning Calculus is to learn to carry through the basic operations quickly and reliably, rather than becoming bogged down in the technicalities concerning limits, etc. The time for getting involved with such matters, vital as they are, is after the Calculus has been successfully mastered.

In adopting a non-rigorous approach, I have tried to write in an informal manner, trying to explain as we go along the ideas that we are using. I have also included rather more detail of the algebraic manipulations than is common with books of this level. This is an attempt to make it easier for readers to follow the working in the book. I hope that the many students for whom such detail is not necessary will skip over it, and forgive its inclusion.

This book owes a lot to the many fine teachers who have developed Calculus courses here at Glasgow University over the years. In particular I would like to thank my colleagues, Dr. J. B. Hickey and Dr. D. B. Webber, for their sterling efforts in reading the text in detail, and offering numerous suggestions for improvement. Inevitably, errors will remain in the text, but these have been minimized as far as possible, and of course such errors are my responsibility and not the responsibility of the checkers.

I would also like to record my thanks to Dr. I. S. Murphy for his considerable contribution to this project.

Finally, I must also thank my wife, my children and my parents for their contributions to the book, none of which have been mathematical.

David J. Moore

University of Glasgow
July, 1992

Contents

CHAPTER 1

Functions and Graphs.

A **function** f is a rule, often given by a formula, that associates with each permitted value of the independent variable (which is frequently denoted by x) a **unique** value of the dependent variable (often y).

For example, $y = x^2$, $y = 2x^3 + 5$, and $y = 9 - x^2$ all express y as a function of x, since, in each case, for each value of x there corresponds a unique value of y.

If we use the notation $f(x)$ to denote a function of x, then $f(a)$ will denote the value of the function when x is replaced by the specific value a. So, for example, if $f(x) \equiv 2x^3 + 5$, then $f(1) = 2 \times 1^3 + 5 = 7$, while $f(2) = 2 \times 2^3 + 5 = 21$ and $f(-3) = 2 \times (-3)^3 + 5 = 2 \times (-27) + 5 = -54 + 5 = -49$.

It is frequently useful to be able to represent a function by means of a graph. To do this we use the rectangular (or Cartesian) coordinate system.

In theory, to represent a function f graphically, we take each possible value of x, calculate the corresponding value $f(x)$, and then mark on the graph the point with coordinates $(x, f(x))$. So the point marked on the graph is the point which is a distance x along the x-axis (negative values of x being marked to the left of the origin) and a distance $f(x)$ above the x-axis (negative values of $f(x)$ being marked below the x-axis).

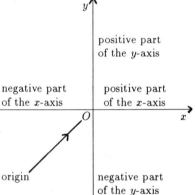

Since the above procedure is not practicable as it would take infinitely long to perform, in practice we choose a few points that we hope will prove to be typical, and hope to see a pattern emerging. It is sometimes difficult to decide which points to plot, and when sufficient have been plotted to give a good indication of the shape of the curve. Only experience can really help us in many cases. However one of our aims in this course is to obtain some feel for the behaviour of some typical functions.

Example 1. *Sketch $y = x^2$ and $y = (x-2)^2$ on the same diagram.*

Solution. To obtain an idea of the behaviour of these two graphs, we draw up a table of values.

x	-2	-1	0	1	2	3	4
x^2	4	1	0	1	4	9	16
$(x-2)^2$	16	9	4	1	0	1	4

Notice that the graphs have the same shape, but that the graph of $y = (x - 2)^2$ reaches its minimum value at $x = 2$, whereas $y = x^2$ has its minimum at $x = 0$. So the effect of replacing x by $x - 2$ is to move the graph 2 units to the right. *Note that it is what is subtracted from x that tells us how far to move the graph to the right.*

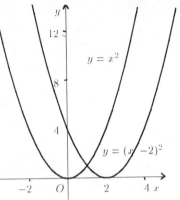

Each of the above graphs has an **axis of symmetry**. In the case of $y = x^2$ the graph is symmetric about the y-axis, while the line $x = 2$ is the line of symmetry of the graph of $y = (x - 2)^2$.

Example 2.   *Sketch the graph of $y = (x + 1)^2$.*

Solution.   We need to write $x + 1$ as $x - (-1)$, in order to see that we are subtracting -1 from x. As we saw above, this tells us that the graph of $y = (x + 1)^2$ will be the same as the graph of $y = x^2$, but moved -1 units to the right [which is the same as moving the graph 1 unit to the left]. Hence we see that the graph has its minimum value at $x = -1$, and that $x = -1$ is the axis of symmetry of the graph.

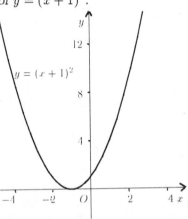

Example 3.   *Sketch $y = x^2$ and $y = 3x^2$ on the same diagram.*

Solution.   In this example, we see that every y-value for $y = x^2$ is multiplied by 3 to give the corresponding y-value on the graph of $y = 3x^2$. The result of this is to create a new curve, with a basic shape similar to the shape of $y = x^2$, and still symmetric about the y-axis, but rather steeper than was the case for $y = x^2$.

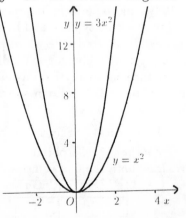

In preparation for the next set of examples, we consider the technique known as **completing the square.** Suppose we start with a typical quadratic expression $ax^2 + bx + c$, where we shall assume that a is not zero. The routine for completing the square involves taking the terms involving x, and re-writing them as the square of a single x-term, of the form $(x+?)^2$. So we write

$$ax^2 + bx + c = \underbrace{ax^2 + bx} + c$$

$$= a\left[x^2 + \left(\frac{b}{a}\right)x\right] + c,$$

on taking out as a factor a, the coefficient of x^2. To deal with the $[x^2 + (b/a)x]$-term, we need to take $x+$ one-half of the b/a-term, and square this. [The reason is that when we square $x+?$ then we obtain $x^2 + 2\times?+?^2$, and so we need to have $2\times?$ equalling b/a, or $? = b/2a$.] We also need to subtract the term $(b/2a)^2$, to compensate for having just added in this extra term. So we have

$$ax^2 + bx + c = a\left[x^2 + \left(\frac{b}{a}\right)x\right] + c$$

$$= a\left\{\left[x + \left(\frac{b}{2a}\right)\right]^2 - \left(\frac{b}{2a}\right)^2\right\} + c$$

$$= a\left\{\left[x + \left(\frac{b}{2a}\right)\right]^2 - \frac{b^2}{4a^2}\right\} + c$$

$$= a\left[x + \left(\frac{b}{2a}\right)\right]^2 - \frac{b^2}{4a} + c$$

$$= a\left[x + \left(\frac{b}{2a}\right)\right]^2 - \frac{b^2 - 4ac}{4a}.$$

You will notice that we have collected the $\{-b^2/4a\}$-term and the c-term over the common denominator $4a$, and taken a minus sign out, which leads to the compensatory $-$ before the $4ac$-term.

We shall now do a numerical example, which will help to clarify the above ideas.

Example 4. *Complete the square in $3x^2 + 12x + 5$.*

Solution.   Following the above routine, we see that

$$3x^2 + 12x + 5 = \underbrace{3x^2 + 12x} + 5$$

$$= 3[x^2 + 4x] + 5$$

$$= 3\left[(x + 2)^2 - (2)^2\right] + 5$$

$$= 3\left[(x + 2)^2 - 4\right] + 5$$

$$= 3(x + 2)^2 - 12 + 5$$

$$= 3(x + 2)^2 - 7.$$

Now we shall apply the idea of completing the square to help us to sketch the graphs of other quadratic functions.

Example 5.   *Sketch* $y = 2x^2 + 12x - 14$.

Solution.   If we apply the technique of completing the square, we have

$$2x^2 + 12x - 14 = \underline{2x^2 + 12x} - 14$$
$$= 2[x^2 + 6x] - 14$$
$$= 2\left[(x+3)^2 - 3^2\right] - 14$$
$$= 2\left[(x+3)^2 - 9\right] - 14$$
$$= 2(x+3)^2 - 18 - 14$$
$$= 2(x+3)^2 - 32.$$

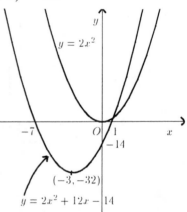

So we require to plot the graph of $y = 2(x + 3)^2 - 32$. As we have already seen in similar examples, the graph will be the same in shape as the graph of $y = 2x^2$, but centred around the line $x = -3$, and moved down by 32 units. Hence we obtain the graph shown.

To find where the graph cuts the x-axis, we need to find the values of x which make $y = 0$. We do this by factorising $2x^2 + 12x - 14$. Now

$$2x^2 + 12x - 14 = 2[x^2 + 6x - 7]$$
$$= 2\left[(x+7)(x-1)\right].$$

If you need further explanation of how we obtained the above factorisation, please see the chapter on Basic Techniques at the end of the book.

It follows that $2x^2 + 12x - 14 = 0$ when $2(x + 7)(x - 1) = 0$, which can only happen if one of the factors is zero. Hence we need either $2 = 0$ (which is impossible), or $x + 7 = 0$ (which happens when $x = -7$), or $x - 1 = 0$ (which means that $x = 1$). From this, we conclude that the graph cuts the x-axis at the values $x = -7$ and $x = 1$, as marked on the above diagram.

To find where the graph hits the y-axis is rather simpler. For this, we merely need to calculate the value of y that corresponds to $x = 0$. Obviously, if $y = 2x^2 + 12x - 14$, then when $x = 0$ we have $y = -14$, again as marked on the diagram.

Example 6.   *Sketch* $y = 8x - 7 - 2x^2$.

Solution.   Completing the square, we have

$$8x - 7 - 2x^2 = \underbrace{-2x^2 + 8x} - 7$$

$$= -2[x^2 - 4x] - 7$$

$$= -2\left[(x-2)^2 - (-2)^2\right] - 7$$

$$= -2\left[(x-2)^2 - 4\right] - 7$$

$$= -2(x-2)^2 + 8 - 7$$

$$= -2(x-2)^2 + 1.$$

This time we have to consider the graph of $y = -2(x-2)^2 + 1$. We have already looked at graphs like $y = x^2$ on several occasions. The graph of $y = -2x^2$ will be the same as the graph of $y = 2x^2$ but with every y-value multiplied by -1. The effect of this is to give the reflection of $y = 2x^2$ in the x-axis. Next, the graph of $y = -2(x-2)^2$ will be similar to the graph of $y = -2x^2$, but displaced 2 units to the right. The graph of $y = -2(x-2)^2+1$ will be the same as for $y = -2(x-2)^2$ but with all y-values increased by 1 unit. The result of this is to move the whole graph upwards 1 unit. Hence we obtain the graph shown in the diagram.

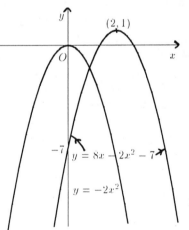

As in the last example, we see that the graph meets the y-axis at the point $x = 0$, $y = -7$.

From looking at the graph, we can see that the curve will meet the x-axis. However it is not at all easy to see how we can factorise the expression $8x - 7 - 2x^2$. In these circumstances, the best approach is to use the well-known formula for the solution of quadratic equations:

$$ax^2 + bx + c = 0 \quad \text{when} \quad x = \frac{-b \pm \sqrt{b^2 - 4ac}}{2a}.$$

[In this formula, a, b, and c are assumed to be constants, with $a \neq 0$.]

Applying this formula with $a = -2$, $b = 8$, and $c = -7$, we see that the roots are given by

$$x = \frac{-8 \pm \sqrt{8^2 - 4(-2)(-7)}}{2(-2)},$$

so that

$$x = \frac{-8 \pm \sqrt{64 - 56}}{-4},$$

or

$$x = \frac{-8 \pm \sqrt{8}}{-4}.$$

If we rewrite $\sqrt{8}$ as $\sqrt{4 \times 2}$, then we have $\sqrt{4 \times 2} = \sqrt{4} \times \sqrt{2} = 2 \times \sqrt{2}$. Hence, on dividing by -4, we easily see that the roots of the equation $8x - 7 - 2x^2 = 0$ are $x = 2 \mp \frac{\sqrt{2}}{2}$. Hence we deduce that the graph meets the x-axis at the points $x = 2 + \frac{\sqrt{2}}{2}$, $y = 0$ and $x = 2 - \frac{\sqrt{2}}{2}$, $y = 0$.

The expression '$b^2 - 4ac$' in the quadratic formula given above is known as the **discriminant**, and is often denoted by Δ.

If Δ is positive, then the equation $ax^2 + bx + c = 0$ has two distinct real roots. When Δ is zero, the equation has just one (repeated) real root. Finally, if Δ is negative, then the equation $ax^2 + bx + c = 0$ has no real roots (although there will be two distinct complex roots).

This means that the graph of $y = ax^2 + bx + c$ will meet the x-axis in two distinct points if $\Delta > 0$, will touch the x-axis at just one point if $\Delta = 0$, and will not meet the x-axis at all if $\Delta < 0$.

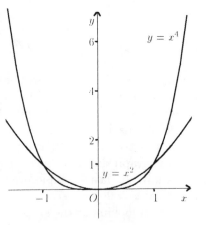

Having considered the graphs of quadratic functions for some time, let us now look at the graphs of $y = x^n$ when n is a positive integer larger than 1.

Firstly we consider the graphs of $y = x^n$ when n is an *even* integer. We find that the graphs are all symmetric about the y-axis (as for $y = x^2$) and that as n increases the graph of $y = x^n$ becomes flatter near the origin but is steeper further away from the origin. All of the graphs pass through the points $(0,0)$, $(1,1)$ and $(-1,1)$, and have the x-axis as a tangent at the origin.

These conclusions can readily be deduced from drawing up a table of values for the equations $y = x^2$, $y = x^4$ and $y = x^6$.

x	0	$\pm 1/4$	$\pm 1/2$	$\pm 3/4$	± 1	± 2	± 3	± 4
x^2	0	1/16	1/4	9/16	1	4	9	16
x^4	0	1/256	1/16	81/256	1	16	81	256
x^6	0	1/4096	1/64	729/4096	1	64	729	4096

Now we consider the graphs of $y = x^n$ when n is an *odd* integer. We find that these graphs are all symmetric about the origin, and, when $n > 1$, they all have similar basic shapes. Again for $n > 1$, the graphs are flatter near the origin the larger that n is, while they are steeper further away from the origin the larger n is. The x-axis is a tangent to the graph of $y = x^n$ at the origin for all odd $n > 1$. The pattern can be seen by tabulating the values of $y = x^3$ and $y = x^5$ against values of x.

x	-3	-2	-1	$-3/4$	$-1/2$	$-1/4$
x^3	-27	-8	-1	$-27/64$	$-1/8$	$-1/64$
x^5	-243	-32	-1	$-243/1024$	$-1/32$	$-1/1024$

x	0	1/4	1/2	3/4	1	2	3
x^3	0	1/64	1/8	27/64	1	8	27
x^5	0	1/1024	1/32	243/1024	1	32	243

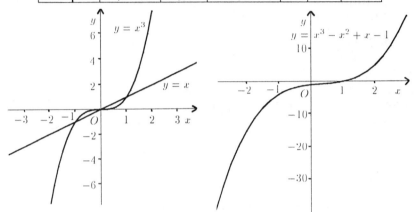

The graphs of **cubic functions** (that is functions where the highest power of x occuring is x^3) can also have the shapes exemplified in the following:

(a) $y = x^3 - x^2 + x - 1 = (x-1)(x^2+1)$, which meets the x-axis at the one point $x = 1$ and is a constantly rising curve as we look at it from left to right. We describe the function $y = x^3 - x^2 + x - 1$ as a **strictly increasing function**, because as x increases, so y increases.

(b) $y = x^3 - 2x^2 - 5x + 6 = (x+2)(x-1)(x-3)$, which meets the x-axis at the three points $x = -2$, $x = 1$ and $x = 3$. In this case there are portions of the curve which rise as we look from left to right, but also a portion of curve which is falling. We describe $y = x^3 - 2x^2 - 5x + 6$ as being a **strictly decreasing function** on a certain set of x-values, (from $x = a$ to $x = b$ in the picture) because, on these x-values, y decreases as x increases.

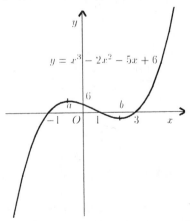

Besides the three shapes that we have seen above, there are also the reflections of these shapes in the x-axis. These can be distinguished from the above because the coefficient of x^3 in the equation of the curve would be negative.

We shall see shortly how Calculus helps us to distinguish between the possible shapes of cubic curves by telling us how many "turning points" a curve has, and also about the nature of the turning points.

In the meantime however we have to rely on the fact that a cubic curve can meet the x-axis at at most three points, and can have at most two turning points.

Example 7.   *Sketch the curve $y = x^3 - 12x + 16$ by noting that $x^3 - 12x + 16 = (x - 2)^2(x + 4)$.*

Solution.   From the equation of the curve in factorised form, we can see that $y = 0$ when $x = 2$ and when $x = -4$. We can also easily calculate that when $x = 0$, $y = 16$. To decide on the behaviour of the curve, and in particular where it is above the x-axis and where below, we shall use a **table of sign** for y. In this table we include those values of x for which y becomes zero. These are the x-values $x = 2$ and $x = -4$.

x	$\rightarrow$	-4	$\rightarrow$	2	$\rightarrow$
$x + 4$	$-$	0	$+$	$+$	$+$
$(x - 2)^2$	$+$	$+$	$+$	0	$+$
$(x + 4)(x - 2)^2$	$-$	0	$+$	0	$+$

In filling in the table of sign, it is a good idea in each row to fill in firstly the point for which the term in that row is zero (if there is one). For example, in the row labelled $x + 4$ we would start by putting the 0 under $x = -4$. After this, all we need to do is to decide whether the term is positive or negative to each side of its zero. Remember that *the square of any real number is positive unless it is zero.*

In interpreting the information from the table of sign, we must be clear that it is telling us about whether y is positive, negative or zero. In other words, it is telling us about whether the graph of the curve lies above, below or on the x-axis. It can be helpful to include an extra row in the table of sign for y to bring this out, as shown below.

x	$\rightarrow$	-4	$\rightarrow$	2	$\rightarrow$
$x + 4$	$-$	0	$+$	$+$	$+$
$(x - 2)^2$	$+$	$+$	$+$	0	$+$
$(x + 4)(x - 2)^2$	$-$	0	$+$	0	$+$
$(x + 4)(x - 2)^2$	below	on	above	on	above

As we see, the graph of $y = x^3 - 12x + 16 = (x - 2)^2(x + 4)$ will cross the x-axis (from below it to above it) at the zero at $x = -4$, while it will lie above the x-axis to the left and to the right of the zero at $x = 2$.

From this we see that the graph of $y = x^3 - 12x + 16$ is as shown in the diagram.

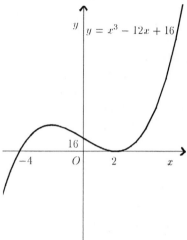

Let $f(x) \equiv x^3 - 12x + 16$. We can factorise the function f in the form $(x - 2)^2(x + 4)$, from which we see that f **vanishes** (i.e. it has the value zero) when x is -4 and 2. We can also use the table of sign to see that the function $f(x)$ is **(strictly) positive** ($f(x) > 0$) whenever x lies between -4 and 2 and also when x is larger than 2. We can express this in **interval notation** by saying that

$$f(x) > 0 \quad \text{precisely when} \quad x \in (-4, 2) \cup (2, \infty).$$

Here $(-4, 2)$ denotes the set of all real numbers which lie strictly between -4 and 2, *not* including the two end-points $x = -4$ and $x = 2$. The set of all real numbers which are strictly larger than 2 is denoted by $(2, \infty)$. The $\cup$ **(union)** symbol that connects these two sets of numbers indicates that we should take all the real numbers that belong either to the interval $(-4, 2)$ or to the interval $(2, \infty)$ (or to both of these intervals if there were any such points). The above intervals are both examples of **open intervals**.

The interval $[-4, 2]$ is an example of a **closed interval**. It denotes the set of all real numbers between -4 and 2, including these two end-points (in contrast to an open interval, from which the end-points are excluded).

From the graph we obtained above, it is easily seen that, when $f(x) \equiv x^3 - 12x + 16$, then

$$f(x) \leq 0 \quad \text{precisely when} \quad x \in (-\infty, -4].$$

(The interval $(-\infty, -4]$ denotes the set of all real numbers that are less than, or equal to, -4.)

There are a couple of conventions to be observed when using interval notation. Firstly, we usually write the numbers in an interval with the smaller number first (so for example $(3, -2)$ would not be allowed). Secondly we always use a round bracket at the end of an interval where there is either ∞ or $-\infty$. This is because there is no such real number as ∞, but rather we are using the ∞-symbol in an expression such as $(-\infty, -4]$ purely as a convenient notation.

A function that is sometimes useful is the **modulus**, or **absolute value**, function.

For a real number x, we define the modulus of x, denoted $|x|$, by

$$|x| = \begin{cases} x, & \text{if } x \geq 0; \\ -x, & \text{otherwise.} \end{cases}$$

[In words, the modulus of a positive real number is that positive number, the modulus of 0 is 0, while the modulus of a negative number is the positive number obtained by omitting the minus sign.]

For example, since 4 and 6/7 are positive, $|4| = 4$, and $|6/7| = 6/7$, whereas -8 and $-\pi$ are negative, so that $|-8| = 8$, and also $|-\pi| = \pi$.

By considering the four different possible cases, with $x \geq 0$, $x < 0$, $y \geq 0$ and $y < 0$, it can be shown that $|xy| = |x| \times |y|$, for any real numbers x, y.

The graph of $f(x) = |x|$ is the same as the graph of $y = x$ for $x \geq 0$, and the same as the graph of $y = -x$ for $x < 0$.

Example 8.   *Sketch the graph of $f(x) = |x-3|-2$, and determine the values of x for which $f(x) \geq 0$.*

Solution.   The graph of $y = |x - 3|$ would be the same as the graph of $y = |x|$, but centred on $x = 3$ rather than on the origin. The graph of $y = |x - 3| - 2$ will be the same as the graph of $y = |x - 3|$, but moved down by 2 units. So the graph is made up of two half-lines having $(3, -2)$ as their point of intersection.

Since the two half-lines have gradients ± 1, the lines will meet the x-axis 2 units in either direction from the point $x = 3$. Hence the lines meet the x-axis at $x = 1$ and at $x = 5$. It follows that

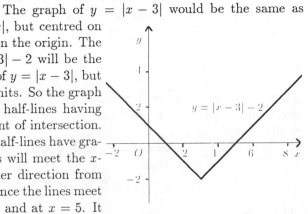

$$f(x) \geq 0 \quad \text{precisely when} \quad x \in (-\infty, 1] \cup [5, \infty).$$

EXAMPLES 1

1. Sketch the graph of
    (a) $y = (x-1)^2$,   (b) $y = (x+2)^2$,
    (c) $y = (x-2)^2 + 5$,   (d) $y = (x+1)^2 - 1$.

2. Sketch on the same diagram the graphs of

(a) $y = x^2$ and $y = 2x^2$,

(b) $y = -x^2$ and $y = -3x^2$.

3. Complete the square in each of the following quadratics:

(a) $x^2 - 6x + 7$;   (b) $x^2 + 4x - 4$;

(c) $3x^2 - 6x + 7$;   (d) $9 + 4x - 2x^2$.

4. For each of the following curves, use the technique of completing the square to find the point on the curve where y reaches its minimum value, and sketch the curve, showing clearly the point(s) where the curve cuts the coordinate axes:

(a) $y = x^2 - 4x$;   (b) $y = x^2 - 2x - 3$.

5. By considering discriminants, say whether each of the following quadratic equations has two distinct real roots, exactly one real root, or no real roots, and solve those equations which fall into either of the first two categories:

(a) $x^2 - 8x + 20 = 0$;   (b) $3x^2 + 11x - 4 = 0$;

(c) $2x^2 - 5x - 3 = 0$;   (d) $2x^2 + 8x + 9 = 0$.

6. For each of the following curves, use the technique of completing the square to find the point on the curve where y reaches its maximum or minimum value, and sketch the curve, showing clearly the point(s) where the curve cuts the coordinate axes:

(a) $y = x^2 - 4x + 3$;   (b) $y = 3 - 2x - x^2$;

(c) $y = 12x - 3x^2$;   (d) $y = 12 + 8x - 4x^2$.

7. Sketch on one diagram the graphs of

(a) $y = x^2$ and $y = x^3$,

(b) $y = x^4$ and $y = x^6$,

(c) $y = x^3$ and $y = x^5$.

8. By noticing that $x^3 - 2x^2 - 5x + 6 = (x + 2)(x - 1)(x - 3)$, sketch the graph of $y = x^3 - 2x^2 - 5x + 6$, and express as a union of intervals $\{x \in \mathbb{R} : x^3 - 2x^2 - 5x + 6 < 0\}$.

9. By noticing that $x^3 + 2x^2 - 11x - 12 = (x + 4)(x + 1)(x - 3)$, sketch the graph of $y = x^3 + 2x^2 - 11x - 12$, and express as a union of intervals $\{x \in \mathbb{R} : x^3 + 2x^2 - 11x - 12 \geq 0\}$.

10.   By noticing that $x^3 - 4x^2 - 3x + 18 = (x+2)(x-3)^2$, sketch the graph of $y = x^3 - 4x^2 - 3x + 18$, and express as a union of intervals $\{x \in \mathbb{R} : x^3 - 4x^2 - 3x + 18 > 0\}$.

11.   Sketch the graph of $y = |x-2| - 3$, and express as a union of intervals $\{x \in \mathbb{R} : |x-2| - 3 \geq 0\}$.

12.   Sketch the graph of $y = |3x - 6| + 2$. [Hint: You may find it helpful to draw up a table of the values of y for integer values of x from $x = -2$ to $x = 6$.]

CHAPTER 2

The Trigonometric Functions

In this chapter we shall introduce the trigonometric functions and meet some of the formulae that relate them, as well as applying the trigonometric functions to various problems.

The fact that underpins trigonometry is that if we have two **similar triangles**, that is, triangles in which the corresponding angles are equal, then the ratio of the lengths of each pair of sides of the triangles is independent of the triangle being considered and just depends on the angles involved in the triangle.

In the diagram shown, if the lengths of the sides of the one triangle are a, b and c, then there is a constant k such that the corresponding sides of the other triangle will have lengths ka, kb and kc.

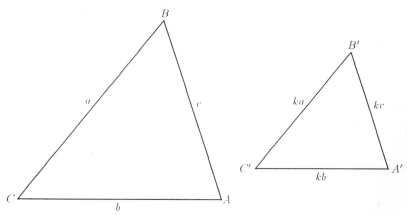

Our first consideration relates to how we should measure angles. Just as in measuring lengths, where there are two separate units in common use, namely feet and metres, and in the measurement of temperatures, where again there are two separate units in common use, this time Fahrenheit and Celsius, so there are two distinct ways of measuring angles. For applications such as surveying and navigation, angles are usually measured in **degrees**. In advanced mathematics, in contrast, it is usual to use **radian** measure for angles.

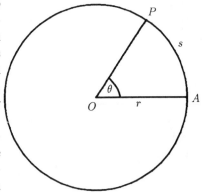

Suppose that we are given an angle θ which we have to measure. We draw a circle $\mathcal{C}$, of radius r and centre O. We also choose any point A on the circumference of the circle. Let P

be the point on the circle such that the angle AOP is the angle θ we were given. We then measure the distance from A to P *along the circumference of the circle*. If A to P along the circle is in the anti-clockwise direction we let s denote this distance. However, if A to P along the circle is in the clockwise direction we let s denote the negative of this distance. We then define the measure of the angle (in radians) to be given by

$$\theta = s/r.$$

Angles in the anti-clockwise direction are therefore positive, while clockwise is the negative direction.

We know that the circumference of a circle of radius r is $2\pi r$, so that it turns out that the radian measure of one complete revolution is $2\pi r/r = 2\pi$. Equally we know that one complete revolution measures $360°$. Hence we have the important relationship between the two methods of measurement:

$$360° = 2\pi \text{ radians} \qquad \text{and hence} \qquad \pi \text{ radians} = 180°.$$

From this we can see that $1\,\text{radian} = (180/\pi)° \approx 57°$. [Remembering of course that π is approximately $3.14159\ldots$.] Equally we can calculate that $1° = (\pi/180)\,\text{radians} \approx 0.01745\ldots\text{radians}$.

From the above relations, we can see that *to change degree measure to radian measure you multiply by $\pi/180$*, while in the reverse direction *to change radian measure to degree measure you multiply by $180/\pi$*.

In mathematics, some angles seem to turn up with great regularity. One reason for this is that they are convenient fractions of one complete revolution. It is useful to know the less familiar radian measure of these angles.

For example, $30° = 30 \times \pi/180 = \pi/6$, while we can easily see that $45° = 45 \times \pi/180 = \pi/4$, and $60° = 60 \times \pi/180 = \pi/3$. Also $90° = \pi/2$ and $180° = \pi$.

You will have noticed that we have given up writing 'radians' to denote when we are using radian measure for angles. This is because in Mathematics the convention is that we always use radian measure unless we indicate that we are using degree measure by including the ° symbol.

From the way we defined the radian measure of an angle, it follows that if we have an arc of a circle of radius r, subtending an angle of θ radians at the centre of the circle, then the length of the arc will be $r\theta$.

Also, since the area of a circle of radius r is πr^2, then the area of a circular sector, subtending an angle θ radians at the centre, will be

$$\left(\frac{\theta}{2\pi}\right) \times \pi r^2 = \frac{1}{2}r^2\theta.$$

Now we have come to the heart of this chapter—the definition of the trigonometric functions. There are six such functions, the sine, cosine, tangent, cosecant, secant and cotangent.

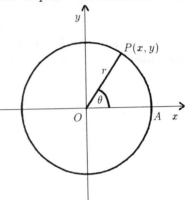

Let θ be a given real number, and let C be a circle of radius r and centre O. Draw a pair of perpendicular axes meeting at the point O. Let the positive part of the x-axis cut the circle C at the point A. Along the circumference of the circle, measure the distance $r\theta$, starting from A, in the anti-clockwise direction if θ is positive. Suppose we arrive at the point P, as shown in the diagram, so that by our earlier definition the angle AOP is θ radians. Let the coordinates of the point P be (x, y). Then we define the trigonometric functions by

$$\sin\theta = \frac{y}{r} \left(= \frac{\text{opp}}{\text{hyp}}\right)$$

$$\cos\theta = \frac{x}{r} \left(= \frac{\text{adj}}{\text{hyp}}\right)$$

$$\tan\theta = \frac{y}{x} \left(= \frac{\text{opp}}{\text{adj}}\right) \left(= \frac{\sin\theta}{\cos\theta}\right)$$

$$\text{cosec}\,\theta = \frac{r}{y} \left(= \frac{\text{hyp}}{\text{opp}}\right) \left(= \frac{1}{\sin\theta}\right)$$

$$\sec\theta = \frac{r}{x} \left(= \frac{\text{hyp}}{\text{adj}}\right) \left(= \frac{1}{\cos\theta}\right)$$

$$\cot\theta = \frac{x}{y} \left(= \frac{\text{adj}}{\text{opp}}\right) \left(= \frac{\cos\theta}{\sin\theta}\right) \left(= \frac{1}{\tan\theta}\right),$$

provided that the ratios in question exist. For example, we do not define $\tan(\pi/2)$, since from the construction given above, if the angle is $\pi/2$, then we would have P at the point where the positive y-axis meets the circle, so that $y = r$ and $x = 0$. Hence the ratio y/x would not exist in this case.

It is convenient to remember the values of the trigonometric functions for some of the more commonly used angles. These values are given in the following table, and *should be memorised*. The values can be verified by considering the diagrams given below.

θ	0	$\frac{\pi}{6}$	$\frac{\pi}{4}$	$\frac{\pi}{3}$	$\frac{\pi}{2}$
$\sin\theta$	0	$\frac{1}{2}$	$\frac{1}{\sqrt{2}}$	$\frac{\sqrt{3}}{2}$	1
$\cos\theta$	1	$\frac{\sqrt{3}}{2}$	$\frac{1}{\sqrt{2}}$	$\frac{1}{2}$	0
$\tan\theta$	0	$\frac{1}{\sqrt{3}}$	1	$\sqrt{3}$	ND

In this table the letters ND are used to denote that $\tan\theta$ is not defined when $\theta = \pi/2$. For a description of where the diagrams come from, please see the chapter on Basic Techniques.

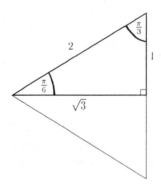
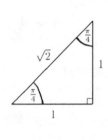

The coordinate axes divide the coordinate plane into four quadrants. From the definitions, we have the following pattern of signs for the main trigonometric functions.

A useful way to remember this pattern is to use the word 'CAST', which stands for Cos, All, Sin, Tan. This tells us which of the trigonometric functions is positive in which quadrant, listing them in the anticlockwise direction, *starting from the fourth quadrant.*

The signs of $\sec\theta$, $\operatorname{cosec}\theta$ and $\cot\theta$ are the same as those of $\cos\theta$, $\sin\theta$ and $\tan\theta$, respectively.

Pythagoras' theorem, applied to the right-angled triangle shown, gives

Sine positive cosine, tangent negative	All positive
Tangent positive sine, cosine negative	Cosine positive sine, tangent negative

$$x^2 + y^2 = r^2,$$

from which, on dividing by r^2, we obtain

$$\left(\frac{x}{r}\right)^2 + \left(\frac{y}{r}\right)^2 = 1.$$

In terms of the trigonometric functions this gives

$$\cos^2\theta + \sin^2\theta = 1.$$

Similarly, if $y \neq 0$, then dividing the above equation by y^2 and rearranging yields

$$\left(\frac{r}{y}\right)^2 = 1 + \left(\frac{x}{y}\right)^2,$$

which translates into

$$\operatorname{cosec}^2\theta = 1 + \cot^2\theta.$$

Similarly we also have

$$\sec^2\theta = 1 + \tan^2\theta.$$

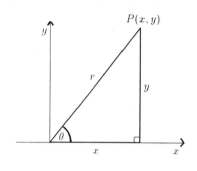

The above formulae hold for all values of θ, provided only that the trigonometric functions are defined.

In the above formulae, we have adopted a common convention. This is that it is normal to write $\sin^2\theta$, when we really should be writing $(\sin\theta)^2$. Similarly we write $\tan^3\theta$ rather than $(\tan\theta)^3$. The reason for this convention is to reduce the number of brackets that would otherwise be necessary to avoid ambiguity.

There is one exception to this convention. As we shall see later, $\tan^{-1}\theta$ has a completely different meaning to $(\tan\theta)^{-1}$. So if we mean $(\tan\theta)^{-1}$ then we must write this, or $1/\tan\theta$, or $\cot\theta$, but *not* $\tan^{-1}\theta$. The same remark applies to the other trigonometric functions.

If we imagine a point P travelling around a circle of radius 1, starting from the point A where the circle cuts the x-axis, then the sine of the angle subtended by AP at the centre of the circle is given by the perpendicular distance from P to the x-axis, with a positive sign if P is above the axis, and negative if P is below. If we draw the graph of $y = \sin\theta$ then we see that it is as given below.

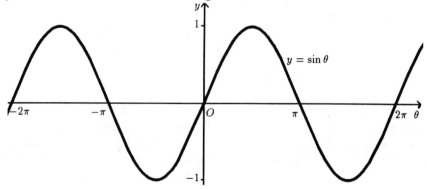

Similarly the graphs of $y = \cos\theta$ and $y = \tan\theta$ are as sketched below. For the cosine graph, the value of $\cos\theta$ is given by the perpendicular distance of P from the y-axis, this time with a positive sign if P is to the right of the y-axis and negative to the left. The value of $\tan\theta$ is given by the slope of the line OP.

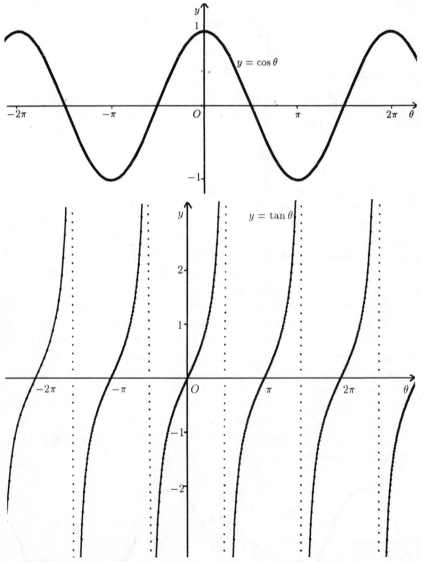

The sine and cosine functions are **periodic** with **period** 2π (which means that if we increase a real number θ by 2π to $\theta + 2\pi$ then the sine and cosine are unchanged). You can see this from the way in which the sine and cosine are defined. If, using the real number θ in the above construction, we arrive at the point P, then using the real number $\theta + 2\pi$ we will also arrive at the same point P, but after one further revolution of the circle. So we have the formulae

$$\sin(\theta + 2\pi) = \sin\theta,$$
$$\cos(\theta + 2\pi) = \cos\theta.$$

The tangent function is also periodic, but this time the period is π. Hence we have

$$\tan(\theta + \pi) = \tan\theta.$$

Furthermore we notice that the graphs of the sine and cosine functions are the same, except that they start at different points in the cycles. From what we saw in the last chapter, this corresponds to a shift in the θ-value. Hence the graph of $y = \cos\left(\theta - \frac{\pi}{2}\right)$ would be identical to the graph of $y = \cos\theta$, but centred on the line $\theta = \frac{\pi}{2}$. So we can easily see that the graph of $y = \cos\left(\theta - \frac{\pi}{2}\right)$ is the same as the graph of $y = \sin\theta$. In other words, we have

$$\cos\left(\theta - \frac{\pi}{2}\right) = \sin\theta.$$

The above are all examples of the **addition formulae**. These formulae, *which should all be learnt*, are

$$\sin(x + y) = \sin x \cos y + \cos x \sin y,$$
$$\cos(x + y) = \cos x \cos y - \sin x \sin y,$$
$$\tan(x + y) = \frac{\tan x + \tan y}{1 - \tan x \tan y}.$$

The proofs of the first two of these formulae can be deduced as shown in the chapter on Basic Techniques. The third formula is deduced from the first two as follows:

$$\tan(x + y) = \frac{\sin(x + y)}{\cos(x + y)}$$

$$= \frac{\sin x \cos y + \cos x \sin y}{\cos x \cos y - \sin x \sin y}$$

$$= \frac{\dfrac{\sin x \cos y}{\cos x \cos y} + \dfrac{\cos x \sin y}{\cos x \cos y}}{\dfrac{\cos x \cos y}{\cos x \cos y} - \dfrac{\sin x \sin y}{\cos x \cos y}},$$

(on dividing each term by $\cos x \cos y$,)

$$= \frac{\tan x + \tan y}{1 - \tan x \tan y},$$

as required.

If we take $x = y$ in these formulae then we obtain the formulae

$$\sin 2x = 2\sin x \cos x,$$
$$\cos 2x = \cos^2 x - \sin^2 x,$$
$$\tan 2x = \frac{2\tan x}{1 - \tan^2 x}.$$

Replacing $\cos^2 x$ by $1 - \sin^2 x$, or $\sin^2 x$ by $1 - \cos^2 x$, in the second of these formulae, we have the alternative forms

$$\cos 2x = \begin{cases} \cos^2 x - \sin^2 x \\ 2\cos^2 x - 1 \\ 1 - 2\sin^2 x. \end{cases}$$

These formulae are also very useful in the re-arranged form

$$\cos^2 x = \tfrac{1}{2}(1 + \cos 2x)$$
$$\sin^2 x = \tfrac{1}{2}(1 - \cos 2x).$$

All of the above formulae should be memorized. They are known as the **double angle formulae.**

Example 1.   *Use the double angle formulae to express $\cos 6x$ in terms of $3x$, and to express $\cos x$ in terms of $\dfrac{x}{2}$.*

Solution.   Applying the double angle formulae with x replaced by $3x$ we see that

$$\cos 6x = \begin{cases} \cos^2 3x - \sin^2 3x \\ 2\cos^2 3x - 1 \\ 1 - 2\sin^2 3x. \end{cases}$$

Again, if we use the double angle formulae, this time with x replaced by $\dfrac{x}{2}$, we have

$$\cos x = \begin{cases} \cos^2 \dfrac{x}{2} - \sin^2 \dfrac{x}{2} \\ 2\cos^2 \dfrac{x}{2} - 1 \\ 1 - 2\sin^2 \dfrac{x}{2}. \end{cases}$$

It is difficult to over-emphasise how important it is to know the trigonometric formulae. It helps us to see where some of the ideas we use are coming from, and also it helps us to know what formulae are available, and therefore what possible options we have in trying to simplify trigonometric expressions.

If we refer back to the graphs of the trigonometric functions, we see that the graph of the cosine function is **symmetric about the y-axis.** This means that the y-values corresponding to any two x-values which are symmetric with respect to the origin will themselves be equal. So, for any real x,

$$\cos(-x) = \cos x.$$

Equally, the graphs of the sine and tangent functions are **symmetric about the origin.** The meaning of this is that the origin is the mid-point of the line joining the points on the curves corresponding to the

x-values x and $-x$. Hence, for any real x for which the functions are defined, we have,

$$\sin(-x) = -\sin x,$$

$$\tan(-x) = -\tan x.$$

If we use these facts, and replace y by $-y$ in the addition formulae, then we obtain the formulae

$$\sin(x - y) = \sin x \cos y - \cos x \sin y,$$

$$\cos(x - y) = \cos x \cos y + \sin x \sin y,$$

$$\tan(x - y) = \frac{\tan x - \tan y}{1 + \tan x \tan y}.$$

As before, it is important to know the above trigonometric formulae, which will frequently be used without comment.

Example 2.   *Use the above formulae to show that*

$$\cos(\pi - \theta) = -\cos\theta,$$

and

$$\sin(\pi - \theta) = \sin\theta.$$

Solution.   Using the formula given above, with x replaced by π and y replaced by θ, we have

$$\cos(\pi - \theta) = \cos\pi\cos\theta + \sin\pi\sin\theta.$$

Since $\cos\pi = -1$ and $\sin\pi = 0$, it follows that $\cos(\pi - \theta) = -\cos\theta$, as required.

We obtain the other result we require by making the same substitutions in the formula

$$\sin(x - y) = \sin x \cos y - \cos x \sin y.$$

Example 3.   *If θ is an acute angle for which $\sin\theta = 5/13$, find $\cos\theta$, $\tan\theta$, $\operatorname{cosec}\theta$, $\sec\theta$ and $\cot\theta$.*

Solution.   One representation of the angle θ is shown in the right-angled triangle ABC, in which we have $\angle BAC = \theta$, $|AC| = 13$ and $|BC| = 5$. By Pythagoras' theorem, we know that

$$5^2 + |AB|^2 = 13^2$$

so that

$$|AB|^2 = 13^2 - 5^2 = 169 - 25 = 144.$$

Hence $|AB| = 12$. From the definitions therefore, we have $\cos\theta = 12/13$, $\tan\theta = 5/12$, $\operatorname{cosec}\theta = 13/5$, $\sec\theta = 13/12$ and $\cot\theta = 12/5$.

Example 4.   *Sketch the graph of $y = \cos 2x$ and also the graph of $y = 3\cos\left(2x + \frac{\pi}{3}\right)$.*

Solution.   As x varies from 0 to $\frac{\pi}{2}$, $2x$ will increase from 0 to π. Hence the graph of $y = \cos 2x$ will start at 1 and reduce to the value -1 as x varies from 0 to $\frac{\pi}{2}$. The graph of $y = \cos 2x$ will continue like this, tracing out the same set of y-values as $y = \cos x$, but at twice the rate. It follows that the graph of $y = \cos 2x$ will have the typical shape of the cosine curve, but will trace out two cycles for every one on the curve $y = \cos x$. Hence the graph is as shown in the diagram.

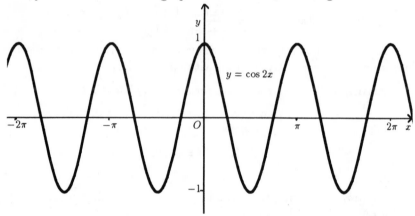

To sketch $y = 3\cos\left(2x + \frac{\pi}{3}\right)$, we note first of all that the basic curve will be similar to the graph of $y = \cos 2x$. The effect of the 3 is to multiply all the y-values by 3. This means that the graph will oscillate between the values 3 and -3, rather than between 1 and -1. We describe this situation by saying that the graph has **amplitude 3** rather than 1.

Now we have to see what the effect is of the $\frac{\pi}{3}$-term. To see this, we rewrite the function in the form

$$y = 3\cos\left(2\left(x + \frac{\pi}{6}\right)\right),$$

which is the same as

$$y = 3\cos\left(2\left(x - \left(-\frac{\pi}{6}\right)\right)\right).$$

Hence the curve $y = 3\cos\left(2x + \frac{\pi}{3}\right)$ will be the same as the curve $y = 3\cos 2x$, but translated so that it 'starts' from $x = -\frac{\pi}{6}$. We call $-\frac{\pi}{6}$ the **displacement** or **phase shift** of the curve. [Please note that there are several alternative definitions in use of the words displacement and phase shift. It is important, when using these words, to be certain that other people are using them with the same meaning as you.] The period of the curve will be $\frac{2\pi}{2} = \pi$, since the graph repeats itself after π.

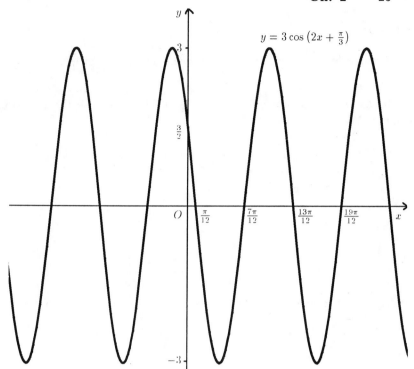

$$y = 3\cos\left(2x + \tfrac{\pi}{3}\right)$$

Example 5. *Express the oscillation $y = -\sqrt{3}\sin 3x + \cos 3x$ as a single sine curve, and determine the amplitude, displacement and period of this oscillation.*

Solution.   [When faced with an expression which has the form $a\sin px + b\cos px$, (where a, b and p are constants), we start by taking out as a factor the value of $\sqrt{a^2 + b^2}$. We then try to find a real number θ such that $\cos\theta = a/\sqrt{a^2 + b^2}$ and $\sin\theta = b/\sqrt{a^2 + b^2}$. We can then rewrite $a\sin px + b\cos px$ as $\sqrt{a^2 + b^2}[\sin px \cos\theta + \cos px \sin\theta]$, or as $\sqrt{a^2 + b^2}\,[\sin(px + \theta)]$, or as $\sqrt{a^2 + b^2}\,[\sin(p(x + (\theta/p)))]$, which has amplitude $\sqrt{a^2 + b^2}$, displacement $-\theta/p$ and period $2\pi/p$.]

If $y = -\sqrt{3}\sin 3x + \cos 3x$, then $\sqrt{\left(-\sqrt{3}\right)^2 + 1^2} = \sqrt{3 + 1} = 2$, and so $y = 2\left[(-\sqrt{3}/2)\sin 3x + (1/2)\cos 3x\right]$. Let the real number θ be such that $\cos\theta = -\sqrt{3}/2$ and $\sin\theta = 1/2$. Since $\sin\theta$ is positive and $\cos\theta$ is negative, we need to have θ in the second quadrant. By comparing the situation we have now with our earlier diagrams, we can see that the real number θ is $5\pi/6$. Hence we have

$$y = 2\left[\sin 3x \cos\left(5\pi/6\right) + \cos 3x \sin\left(5\pi/6\right)\right]$$
$$= 2\left[\sin\left(3x + 5\pi/6\right)\right]$$
$$= 2\left[\sin\left(3(x + 5\pi/18)\right)\right]$$
$$= 2\left[\sin\left(3\left(x - (-5\pi/18)\right)\right)\right]$$

Hence the sinusoidal oscillation has amplitude 2, period $2\pi/3$ and phase shift $-5\pi/18$.

Example 6. *Use the addition formulae to find* $\tan\frac{7\pi}{12}$.

Solution.   Since $\frac{7\pi}{12} = \left(7 \times \frac{180}{12}\right)^{\circ} = 7 \times 15^{\circ} = 105^{\circ}$, which we can break up as $105^{\circ} = 60^{\circ} + 45^{\circ} = \frac{\pi}{3} + \frac{\pi}{4}$, we can use the addition formula. We have

$$\tan\frac{7\pi}{12} = \tan\left(\frac{\pi}{3} + \frac{\pi}{4}\right)$$

$$= \frac{\tan\frac{\pi}{3} + \tan\frac{\pi}{4}}{1 - \tan\frac{\pi}{3}\tan\frac{\pi}{4}}$$

$$= \frac{\sqrt{3} + 1}{1 - \sqrt{3}}$$

$$= \frac{(\sqrt{3} + 1) \times (1 + \sqrt{3})}{(1 - \sqrt{3}) \times (1 + \sqrt{3})}$$

(multiplying top and bottom by $1 + \sqrt{3}$ to rationalise the denominator)

$$= \frac{\sqrt{3} + 1 + 3 + \sqrt{3}}{1 - \sqrt{3} + \sqrt{3} - 3}$$

$$= \frac{4 + 2\sqrt{3}}{-2}$$

$$= -2 - \sqrt{3}.$$

Example 7. *Simplify* $\dfrac{\cos 3x}{\sin x} - \dfrac{\sin 3x}{\cos x}$.

Solution.   Using the appropriate trigonometric formulae we have

$$\frac{\cos 3x}{\sin x} - \frac{\sin 3x}{\cos x} = \frac{\cos 3x \cos x - \sin 3x \sin x}{\sin x \cos x}$$

$$= \frac{\cos(3x + x)}{\sin x \cos x}$$

$$= \frac{\cos 4x}{\sin x \cos x}$$

$$= \frac{2\cos 4x}{2\sin x \cos x}$$

$$= \frac{2\cos 4x}{\sin 2x}.$$

Notice that it is very important that we should be able to use formulae such as $\cos 3x \cos x - \sin 3x \sin x = \cos(3x + x)$ in this "reverse" form. All formulae should be remembered in this form as well as in the more usual form $\cos(3x + x) = \cos 3x \cos x - \sin 3x \sin x$.

Example 8. *Establish the trigonometric identity*

$$\sin 8x = 4\sin 2x \cos 2x - 8\sin^3 2x \cos 2x.$$

Solution.   [When we require to establish a formula such as the above, we must start by trying to simplify one side of the equation (usually the more complicated side) into the form of the other side. The thing you should *not* do is to assume the identity holds and use it in the course of the proof.]

$$
\begin{aligned}
\text{The right hand side is} &= 4\sin 2x \cos 2x - 8\sin^3 2x \cos 2x \\
&= 4\sin 2x \cos 2x(1 - 2\sin^2 2x) \\
&= 2 \times (2\sin 2x \cos 2x)(\cos 4x) \\
&= 2\sin 4x \cos 4x \\
&= \sin 8x, \\
&= \text{the left hand side,}
\end{aligned}
$$

as required.

Again, notice the use of the formula

$$1 - 2\sin^2 \theta = \cos 2\theta \quad \text{with} \quad \theta = 2x$$

and the double use of

$$2\sin\theta\cos\theta = \sin 2\theta \quad \text{with} \quad \theta = 2x \quad \text{and with} \quad \theta = 4x.$$

Example 9. *In the diagram shown, which represents a kite, calculate the lengths (to the nearest centimetre) of the pieces of wood required to form the diagonals of the kite.*

Solution.   From the symmetry of the kite, $\angle AXD$ will be a right-angle. Hence in the triangle AXB we have $\sin \angle BAX = |BX|/|AB|$, and $\cos \angle BAX = |AX|/|AB|$. Hence we find that $|BX| = 71 \times \sin 25°$, and also that $|AX| = 71 \times \cos 25°$. We now need to calculate the distance $|CX|$.

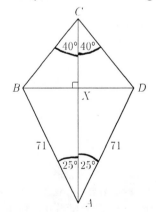

We find this distance by considering the right-angled triangle BXC. Now $\tan \angle BCX = |BX|/|CX|$, so we have $|CX| = |BX|/\tan \angle BCX = 71 \times \sin 25°/\tan \angle BCX$ which equals $71 \times \sin 25°/\tan 40°$.

We can now use our calculator to find the distances $|BD|$ and $|AC|$. By symmetry, $|BD| = 2\times|BX| = 2\times 71\times\sin 25° = 60\,\text{cm}$, to the nearest

B

centimetre. Also we can see that $|AC| = |AX| + |CX| = 71 \times \cos 25° +$
$71 \times \sin 25°/\tan 40° = 71 \times [\cos 25° + (\sin 25°/\tan 40°)] = 100\,$cm, to
the nearest centimetre.

If you know the Sine Rule, you will realise that it provides a much
easier way to find the distance $|AC|$. If you don't know the Sine Rule,
you might like to look in the chapter on Basic Techniques where it is
explained.

From the Sine Rule, we have $|AC|/\sin 115° = |AB|/\sin 40°$. Hence
$|AC| = |AB| \times \sin 115°/\sin 40°$, which gives the value we obtained before.

We could show that $\cos 25° + (\sin 25°/\tan 40°) = \sin 115°/\sin 40°$,
which is what is required to show that the above answers are the same.
This provides a useful exercise in the use of the trigonometric formulae.

EXAMPLES 2

1.   For each of the following angles θ, write down $\sin\theta$, $\cos\theta$, $\tan\theta$,
$\operatorname{cosec}\theta$, $\sec\theta$, $\cot\theta$, if these are defined. Write N.D. for any which are
not defined.

(a) $\frac{\pi}{6}$,   (b) $\frac{\pi}{4}$,   (c) $\frac{\pi}{3}$,   (d) $\frac{\pi}{2}$,   (e) $-\frac{\pi}{6}$,

(f) $\frac{2\pi}{3}$,   (g) $-\frac{2\pi}{3}$,   (h) π,   (i) $-\pi$,   (j) $\frac{4\pi}{3}$,

(k) $\frac{7\pi}{6}$,   (l) $\frac{5\pi}{4}$,   (m) $\frac{3\pi}{2}$,   (n) $\frac{7\pi}{4}$,   (o) $-\frac{\pi}{2}$.

2.   If $\sin\theta = \frac{1}{2}$ and $\tan\theta$ is negative, find the values of $\cos\theta$, $\tan\theta$,
$\sec\theta$, $\operatorname{cosec}\theta$ and $\cot\theta$.

3.   If $\tan\theta = \frac{3}{4}$ and θ is not in the first quadrant, find the values
of $\sin\theta$, $\cos\theta$, $\sec\theta$, $\operatorname{cosec}\theta$ and $\cot\theta$.

4.   Sketch the graphs of

(a) $y = 2\sin\left(x - \frac{\pi}{3}\right)$,   (b) $y = 3\cos 3x$,

(c) $y = -2\tan 2x$,   (d) $y = 3\sin\left(3x - \frac{3\pi}{4}\right)$.

Also give the period, phase-shift and (except for (c)) the amplitude of
each of the oscillations.

5.   A flag-pole CP is held in a vertical position by two guy-lines,
AP and BP, which are fastened to the ground at A and B so that the
base C of the flag-pole is directly between the points A and B, and so
that the distance between A and B is 30m. Given that the angle CAP
is 55°, that the angle CBP is 46° and that the ground between A and
B is horizontal, find the height of the flag-pole.

6.   A ship starts from a position A and travels a distance of 5.9 km
due East to a point B. It then alters its course through an angle of 45°
so that it is travelling in a North-Easterly direction. It continues on
this course for a distance of 7 km until it reaches the point C. The ship
again alters course, this time through an angle of 115°, so that now the

ship is heading slightly to the north of due West. The ship continues on this course until it reaches the point D, which is due North of the point A. Find how far north of the point A the ship is when it is at D.

7.   Twelve equally spaced marks are made on the circumference of a circular fly-wheel. Given that the straight-line distance between two adjacent marks is 3.52 cm, find the radius of the fly-wheel.

8.   A surveyor is standing at a point P and wishes to determine the height of a tall building ABC. The point A is at the base of the building and is at the same level as the surveyor. The point B is 20 ft vertically above the point A, while C is at the top of the face of the building. Given that the surveyor measures that the angles of elevation of B and C are 36° and 71° respectively, find the height AC of the buiding.

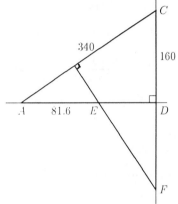

9.   Part of the pattern of roads in a particular town is as shown in the diagram. Given that from A to C is 340 m, that CD is 160 m and that AE is 81.6 m, find the distance DF.

10.   Use the fact that $\frac{\pi}{12} = \frac{\pi}{4} - \frac{\pi}{6}$ to find $\sin \frac{\pi}{12}$, $\cos \frac{\pi}{12}$, and $\tan \frac{\pi}{12}$.

11.   Use the fact that $\frac{7\pi}{12} = \frac{\pi}{4} + \frac{\pi}{3}$ to find $\sin \frac{7\pi}{12}$, $\cos \frac{7\pi}{12}$, and $\tan \frac{7\pi}{12}$.

12.   Use the fact that $\frac{\pi}{4} = \frac{\pi}{8} + \frac{\pi}{8}$ to find $\sin \frac{\pi}{8}$, $\cos \frac{\pi}{8}$, and $\tan \frac{\pi}{8}$.

13.   By writing $3\theta = 2\theta + \theta$, show that

$$\sin 3\theta = 3 \sin \theta - 4 \sin^3 \theta,$$

and

$$\cos 3\theta = 4 \cos^3 \theta - 3 \cos \theta.$$

14.   By writing $4\theta = 2\theta + 2\theta$, show that

$$\sin 4\theta = 4 \sin \theta \cos^3 \theta - 4 \sin^3 \theta \cos \theta,$$

and

$$\cos 4\theta = 8 \cos^4 \theta - 8 \cos^2 \theta + 1.$$

15.   Show that

(a) $\dfrac{\sin \alpha}{\tan \alpha} = \cos \alpha,$

(b) $\dfrac{\cos \alpha}{\cot \alpha} = \sin \alpha,$

(c) $\sin \beta \cot \beta = \cos \beta,$

(d) $\tan \beta \operatorname{cosec} \beta = \sec \beta.$

16.   Show that

(a) $\sin \theta \, (\operatorname{cosec} \theta - \sin \theta) = \cos^2 \theta,$

(b) $\sec \theta \operatorname{cosec} \theta - \cot \theta = \tan \theta,$

(c) $\dfrac{1 - \cos \phi}{\sin \phi} = \dfrac{\sin \phi}{1 + \cos \phi},$

(d) $\dfrac{\sec \phi + \operatorname{cosec} \phi}{\operatorname{cosec} \phi} = 1 + \tan \phi.$

17.   Show that

(a) $\sin (x + y) \sin (x - y) = \sin^2 x - \sin^2 y,$

(b) $\cos (\alpha + \beta) + \sin (\alpha - \beta) = (\cos \alpha + \sin \alpha)(\cos \beta - \sin \beta),$

(c) $\cos 2\gamma = \dfrac{1 - \tan^2 \gamma}{\sec^2 \gamma},$

(d) $\dfrac{\sin 3\gamma}{\sin \gamma} - \dfrac{\cos 3\gamma}{\cos \gamma} = 2.$

18.   In an investigation concerning the properties of light, the equation

$$A \left(\frac{\tan \beta}{\tan \alpha} - 1 \right) = B \left(\frac{\tan \beta}{\tan \alpha} + 1 \right)$$

was found. Show that this can also be expressed as

$$B \sin (\beta + \alpha) = A \sin (\beta - \alpha).$$

19.   The displacements, y_1 and y_2, of two waves travelling through the same medium are related to position x and time t by the equations $y_1 = A \sin \big((t/T) - (x/X) \big)$ and $y_2 = A \sin \big((t/T) + (x/X) \big)$. Find an expression in the simplest possible form for the displacement $y_1 + y_2$ of the combination of the waves.

20.   In Calculus, the expression

$$\frac{\tan (x + h) - \tan x}{h}$$

is discovered when using one method to find the derivative of $\tan x$. Show that this can be expressed as

$$\frac{\sin h}{h} \sec x \, \sec(x + h).$$

CHAPTER 3

The Inverse Trigonometric Functions

In this chapter we shall introduce the inverse trigonometric functions, which are introduced to provide an answer to questions such as

$$\text{if } \sin x = 1/2, \text{ what is } x?$$

If we look at the graph of $y = \sin x$, we see that there are a large number of values of x for which $\sin x = 1/2$. These are the x-coordinates of the points of intersection between the graph of the curve $y = \sin x$ and the line $y = 1/2$.

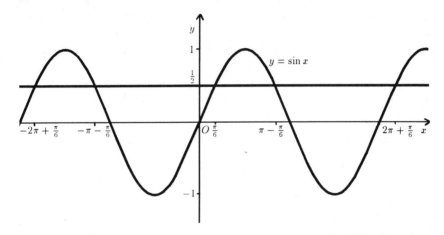

One of the points of intersection is given by $x = \pi/6$. Then from the fact that the curve repeats itself exactly every 2π, there will be roots at $2\pi + \pi/6$, $4\pi + \pi/6$, $6\pi + \pi/6$, ... Also from the fact that from $x = \pi/2$ to $x = \pi$ the curve descends exactly in the reverse of the way it ascended between $x = 0$ and $x = \pi/2$, we see that there will be a second series of solutions, given by $\pi - \pi/6$, $2\pi + \pi - \pi/6$, $4\pi + \pi - \pi/6$, $6\pi + \pi - \pi/6$, etc. Equally, there will be further roots to the left of the y-axis. These are given by $-2\pi + \pi/6$, $-4\pi + \pi/6$, $-6\pi + \pi/6$, ... and $-2\pi + \pi - \pi/6$, $-4\pi + \pi - \pi/6$, $-6\pi + \pi - \pi/6$, etc.

The set of all solutions of the equation $\sin x = 1/2$ can therefore be expressed as

$$\{\, x \in \mathbb{R} : x = 2k\pi + \pi/6 \text{ or } x = 2k\pi + \pi - \pi/6 : k \in \mathbb{Z} \,\}.$$

We can see that all of these solutions are related to the basic solution $x = \pi/6$.

Recall that our definition of a function required that, for every value of the independent variable, we obtain a unique value of the dependent variable. So in defining the inverse sine function we want to have a unique answer to the question 'if $\sin x = 1/2$, what is x?' We agree to concentrate our attention on the region of the graph of $y = \sin x$ for which $-\pi/2 \le x \le \pi/2$. [The reason for choosing this section of graph is that it is the region closest to the origin for which the function $y = \sin x$ takes on all the y-values between -1 and 1, exactly once each.]

We now come to the definition of the **inverse sine function**. For $-1 \le x \le 1$ we define $\sin^{-1} x$ or $\arcsin x$ to be the unique real number y with $-\pi/2 \le y \le \pi/2$ such that $\sin y = x$.

We can think of $\sin^{-1} x$ as giving us the real number y in the range $[-\pi/2, \pi/2]$ whose sine is x.

Since $\sin 0 = 0$ and $0 \in [-\pi/2, \pi/2]$, we have $\sin^{-1} 0 = 0$, while since $\sin \pi/2 = 1$ and $\pi/2 \in [-\pi/2, \pi/2]$, we have $\sin^{-1} 1 = \pi/2$. Again $\sin(-\pi/3) = -\sqrt{3}/2$ and $-\pi/3 \in [-\pi/2, \pi/2]$, so that we have $\sin^{-1}(-\sqrt{3}/2) = -\pi/3$. In each of the above examples, the angle chosen belongs to the interval $[-\pi/2, \pi/2]$, and so $\sin^{-1} x$ took the "obvious" value in each case. We shall later see an example where this is not the case.

By a similar argument to the one we used earlier, we see that, for any real number l with $-1 \le l \le 1$, the set of all solutions of the equation $\sin x = l$ is given by

$$\left\{ x \in \mathbb{R} : x = 2k\pi + \sin^{-1} l \text{ or } x = 2k\pi + \pi - \sin^{-1} l : k \in \mathbb{Z} \right\}.$$

The curly brackets we are using here denote that we are specifying a set. $x \in \mathbb{R}$ denotes that we are specifying x to be a subset of the set of all real numbers, while $k \in \mathbb{Z}$ denotes that k is allowed to vary through the set of all integers (including 0). The colon stands for 'such that'. Finally the condition $-1 \le l \le 1$ specifies all those real numbers that simultaneously satisfy the two conditions $l \ge -1$ and $l \le 1$. In interval notation, we could write the condition $-1 \le l \le 1$ as $l \in [-1, 1]$.

The definition of the **inverse cosine function** follows the same pattern as for the inverse sine function.

For $-1 \le x \le 1$, $\cos^{-1} x$, or $\arccos x$, is defined to be the unique real number y, with $0 \le y \le \pi$, such that $\cos y = x$. [The reason for imposing the restriction $0 \le y \le \pi$ is to obtain a set of values of y such that $\cos y$ takes on all the values between -1 and $+1$ precisely once each as y varies through the set of values we have chosen.]

Since $\cos 0 = 1$ and $0 \in [0, \pi]$, we have $\cos^{-1} 1 = 0$. Since $\cos \pi/2 = 0$ and $\pi/2 \in [0, \pi]$, we have $\cos^{-1} 0 = \pi/2$, while since $\cos 3\pi/4 = -1/\sqrt{2}$ and $3\pi/4 \in [0, \pi]$, we have $\cos^{-1}(-1/\sqrt{2}) = 3\pi/4$. The deductions we have made are valid here because the real numbers of which we are taking the cosines are all in the interval $[0, \pi]$.

By examining the graph of $y = \cos x$, we can see that for any real number l, such that $-1 \le l \le 1$, solutions of the equation $\cos x = l$ are given by $x = \cos^{-1} l$ (the value between 0 and π), and by $x = -\cos^{-1} l$. Then, since the graph repeats itself every 2π, there are the solutions

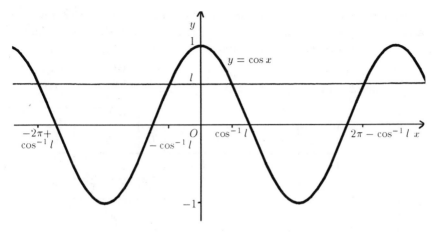

given by $2\pi+\cos^{-1} l$, $2\pi-\cos^{-1} l$, $4\pi + \cos^{-1} l$, $4\pi-\cos^{-1} l$, $6\pi+\cos^{-1} l$, $6\pi - \cos^{-1} l$, ...

In set notation, the set of all solutions of the equation $\cos x = l$ is given by

$$\left\{ x \in \mathbb{R} : x = 2k\pi \pm \cos^{-1} l : k \in \mathbb{Z} \right\}.$$

The **inverse tangent function** is defined in the following manner: for $x \in \mathbb{R}$, $\tan^{-1} x$, or $\arctan x$, is defined to be the unique real number y, with $-\pi/2 < y < \pi/2$, for which $\tan y = x$.

Since $\tan(\pi/3) = \sqrt{3}$ and $\pi/3 \in (-\pi/2, \pi/2)$, we can deduce that $\tan^{-1} \sqrt{3} = \pi/3$. Since $\tan(-\pi/4) = -1$ and $-\pi/4 \in (-\pi/2, \pi/2)$, we similarly see that $\tan^{-1}(-1) = -\pi/4$.

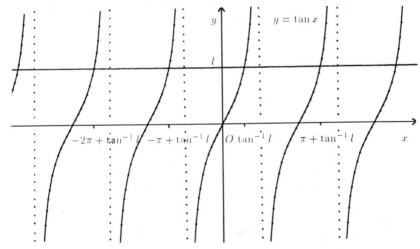

Given $l \in \mathbb{R}$, the set of all solutions of $\tan x = l$ is given by

$$\left\{ x \in \mathbb{R} : x = k\pi + \tan^{-1} l : k \in \mathbb{Z} \right\},$$

since there is the unique solution $\tan^{-1} l$ lying between $-\pi/2$ and $\pi/2$, and then the other solutions arising from the fact that the graph of $y = \tan x$ repeats itself with period π.

Now let us consider the graph of $y = \sin^{-1} x$. We start by drawing up a table of values to see what is happening.

x	$-\frac{\pi}{2}$	$-\frac{\pi}{3}$	$-\frac{\pi}{4}$	$-\frac{\pi}{6}$	0	$\frac{\pi}{6}$	$\frac{\pi}{4}$	$\frac{\pi}{3}$	$\frac{\pi}{2}$
$y = \sin x$	-1	$-\frac{\sqrt{3}}{2}$	$-\frac{1}{\sqrt{2}}$	$-\frac{1}{2}$	0	$\frac{1}{2}$	$\frac{1}{\sqrt{2}}$	$\frac{\sqrt{3}}{2}$	1
x	-1	$-\frac{\sqrt{3}}{2}$	$-\frac{1}{\sqrt{2}}$	$-\frac{1}{2}$	0	$\frac{1}{2}$	$\frac{1}{\sqrt{2}}$	$\frac{\sqrt{3}}{2}$	1
$y = \sin^{-1} x$	$-\frac{\pi}{2}$	$-\frac{\pi}{3}$	$-\frac{\pi}{4}$	$-\frac{\pi}{6}$	0	$\frac{\pi}{6}$	$\frac{\pi}{4}$	$\frac{\pi}{3}$	$\frac{\pi}{2}$

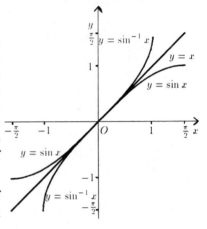

You will see from the table that the values of $y = \sin^{-1} x$ are obtained by interchanging the x- and y-values for $y = \sin x$. It follows from this that the graph of $y = \sin^{-1} x$ will be the reflection in the line $y = x$ of the graph of $y = \sin x$, or, to be more precise, the reflection in the line $y = x$ of that part of the graph of $y = \sin x$ for which $x \in [-\pi/2, \pi/2]$.

In a similar way, the graph of $y = \cos^{-1} x$ will be the reflection in the line $y = x$ of the part of $y = \cos x$ for which $0 \leq x \leq \pi$, while the graph of $y = \tan^{-1} x$ will be the reflection in the line $y = x$ of the part of the graph of $y = \tan x$ for which $-\pi/2 < x < \pi/2$.

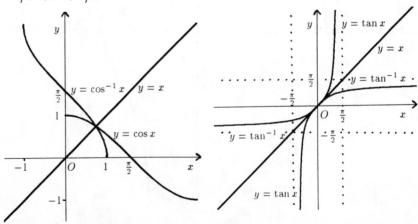

From the definitions of $\sin^{-1} x$, $\cos^{-1} x$ and $\tan^{-1} x$, it follows that

$$\sin\left(\sin^{-1} x\right) = x \quad (\forall x \in [-1, 1])$$
$$\cos\left(\cos^{-1} x\right) = x \quad (\forall x \in [-1, 1])$$
$$\tan\left(\tan^{-1} x\right) = x \quad (\forall x \in \mathbb{R}).$$

On the other hand the equation $\sin^{-1}(\sin x) = x$ only holds when $x \in \left[-\frac{\pi}{2}, \frac{\pi}{2}\right]$, while similarly $\cos^{-1}(\cos x) = x$ only holds when $x \in [0, \pi]$ and also $\tan^{-1}(\tan x) = x$ only holds when $x \in \left(-\frac{\pi}{2}, \frac{\pi}{2}\right)$.

To show that $\sin^{-1}(\sin x) = x$ is *not* always true, consider the value $x = 2$ radians. Then using a calculator we have

$$\sin^{-1}(\sin 2) = \sin^{-1}(0.9092974) = 1.1415927 \neq 2.$$

Example 1.   *For $x \in (-1, 1)$, express $\tan\left(\sin^{-1} x\right)$ in a form not involving the trigonometric functions.*

Solution.   We shall start by cosidering the case where $0 \leq x < 1$. Let $\theta = \sin^{-1} x$, so that we need to find $\tan \theta$. Now since $\sin \theta = x$, we need to consider the right-angled triangle shown. The lengths of the sides of this triangle have been chosen so as to give $\sin \theta = x$. In this diagram, we know that the third side is of length $\sqrt{1 - x^2}$, by Pythagoras' theorem. Hence $\tan \theta = x/\sqrt{1 - x^2}$, which can be rewritten in the form $\tan\left(\sin^{-1} x\right) = x/\sqrt{1 - x^2}$.

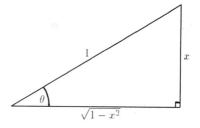

The case in which $-1 < x \leq 0$ is dealt with in a similar manner. In this case, the angle θ will be in the fourth quadrant and we have a similar, but not identical, diagram to consider. The final result is however the same. You might like to work through the details of this case yourself.

In both cases we finish up with the same answer,

$$\tan\left(\sin^{-1} x\right) = \frac{x}{\sqrt{1 - x^2}}.$$

Example 2.   *Solve the equation*

$$\sin\left(3x + \frac{\pi}{4}\right) = -\frac{\sqrt{3}}{2}.$$

Solution.   The routine that we are about to use in the following solution should be carefully noted. We shall find the general solution of the equation by using the formula for the general solution to obtain $3x + \frac{\pi}{4}$. We shall then solve for x to obtain the general solution for x.

If we were to start by trying to find a particular solution for x and then trying to get the general solution by just adding in multiples of 2π, we would find some, but not all, of the solutions.

Now

$$\sin\left(3x + \frac{\pi}{4}\right) = -\frac{\sqrt{3}}{2}$$

when

$$3x + \frac{\pi}{4} = 2k\pi + \sin^{-1}\left(-\frac{\sqrt{3}}{2}\right)$$

$$\text{or} \quad 3x + \frac{\pi}{4} = 2k\pi + \pi - \sin^{-1}\left(-\frac{\sqrt{3}}{2}\right) \qquad (k \in \mathbb{Z})$$

which is equivalent to

$$3x + \frac{\pi}{4} = 2k\pi - \frac{\pi}{3} \quad \text{or} \quad 3x + \frac{\pi}{4} = 2k\pi + \pi + \frac{\pi}{3} \qquad (k \in \mathbb{Z})$$

which holds when

$$3x = 2k\pi - \frac{\pi}{3} - \frac{\pi}{4} \quad \text{or} \quad 3x = 2k\pi + \pi + \frac{\pi}{3} - \frac{\pi}{4} \qquad (k \in \mathbb{Z})$$

which is the same as

$$x = \frac{2k\pi}{3} - \frac{\pi}{9} - \frac{\pi}{12} \quad \text{or} \quad x = \frac{2k\pi}{3} + \frac{\pi}{3} + \frac{\pi}{9} - \frac{\pi}{12} \qquad (k \in \mathbb{Z})$$

which we can express in the form

$$x = \frac{2k\pi}{3} - \frac{7\pi}{36} \quad \text{or} \quad x = \frac{2k\pi}{3} + \frac{13\pi}{36} \qquad (k \in \mathbb{Z}).$$

Hence the general solution of the equation is that

$$\sin\left(3x + \frac{\pi}{4}\right) = -\frac{\sqrt{3}}{2}$$

precisely when

$$x \in \left\{\frac{2k\pi}{3} - \frac{7\pi}{36} : k \in \mathbb{Z}\right\} \cup \left\{\frac{2k\pi}{3} + \frac{13\pi}{36} : k \in \mathbb{Z}\right\}.$$

Example 3.   *Solve the trigonometric equation*

$$2 \sin 2x \cos 3x = \sin 2x.$$

Solution.   Rearranging the equation, we see that

$$2 \sin 2x \cos 3x = \sin 2x$$

holds when

$$2 \sin 2x \cos 3x - \sin 2x = 0$$

which is true when

$$\sin 2x(2\cos 3x - 1) = 0$$

which is equivalent to

$$\sin 2x = 0 \quad \text{or} \quad 2\cos 3x - 1 = 0$$

which holds when

$$\sin 2x = 0 \quad \text{or} \quad \cos 3x = \frac{1}{2}$$

which is true when

$$2x = 2k\pi + \sin^{-1} 0 \quad \text{or} \quad 2x = 2k\pi + \pi - \sin^{-1} 0$$

$$\text{or} \quad 3x = 2k\pi \pm \cos^{-1}\left(\frac{1}{2}\right) \quad (k \in \mathbb{Z})$$

which can be expressed as

$$2x = 2k\pi \quad \text{or} \quad 2x = 2k\pi + \pi \quad \text{or} \quad 3x = 2k\pi \pm \frac{\pi}{3} \quad (k \in \mathbb{Z})$$

or as

$$x = k\pi \quad \text{or} \quad x = k\pi + \frac{\pi}{2} \quad \text{or} \quad x = \frac{2k\pi}{3} \pm \frac{\pi}{9} \quad (k \in \mathbb{Z}).$$

Hence the general solution of the equation

$$2\sin 2x \cos 3x = \sin 2x$$

is that x satisfies the equation precisely when

$$x \in \left\{ k\pi : k \in \mathbb{Z} \right\} \cup \left\{ k\pi + \frac{\pi}{2} : k \in \mathbb{Z} \right\} \cup \left\{ \frac{2k\pi}{3} \pm \frac{\pi}{9} : k \in \mathbb{Z} \right\}.$$

There are a couple of important points to make about the above solution.

(i)   Firstly we should note that we could not start the solution by dividing both sides of the original equation by $\sin 2x$. Had we done this then we would have thrown away a number of solutions of the equation. *You may only divide an equation by something if you know that the something is non-zero.*

(ii)   Secondly we should note that we used the fact that *a product is zero precisely when one (or more) of the terms in the product is zero.*

While this is valid, note that it is *not* true that if, for example, $(x - 3)(x + 1) = 5$ then either $x - 3 = 5$ or $x + 1 = 5$. The way to solve an equation such as $(x - 3)(x + 1) = 5$ is to expand the brackets, subtract the 5 from both sides of the equation, and then try to solve the resulting quadratic equation. If we do this, we would find that the solutions are $x = 4$ and $x = -2$.

Example 4. *A hemispherical bowl of radius 7.58 cm is filled with water to a depth of 5.52 cm. Assuming that the bowl starts from a level position, find the angle through which the bowl can be tilted before water begins to spill out.*

Solution.   Let α be the angle we require to find. Then if we consider the diagram, we see that $\sin \alpha = 2.06/7.58$, so that $\alpha = \sin^{-1}\left(\frac{2.06}{7.58}\right)$, and from the calculator we see that $\alpha = \sin^{-1}(0.27176781) = 0.2752$, to 4 significant figures.

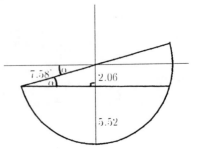

Notice that the final answer is given as a number of radians. Had we used the calculator in degree mode, we would have obtained an answer of 15.77°, correct to 4 significant figures.

EXAMPLES 3

1.   If $y = \sin 4x + \cos 4x$, express the oscillation as a single sine curve, and determine the amplitude, displacement and period of the oscillation.

2.   If $y = 8 \sin 2x - 15 \cos 2x$, express the oscillation as a single sine curve, and determine the amplitude, displacement and period of the oscillation. [You may assume that the angle θ in the first quadrant with $\sin \theta = \frac{15}{17}$ is 1.081 radians.]

3.   The current i in an electric circuit is expressed in terms of time t by $i = 4e^{-3t}\left(\sin 3t - \sqrt{3}\cos 3t\right)$. By re-expressing the term in the brackets as a single sine term, find the time when the current is first zero.

4.   Express $\cos\left(\tan^{-1} x\right)$ in a form which does not involve the trigonometric functions.

5.   Express $\cos\left(\sin^{-1} x\right)$ in a form which does not involve the trigonometric functions, valid for $x \geq 0$.

6.   If $\sin \theta = (x + 2)/3$, find $\cos \theta$ and $\tan \theta$ in terms of x.

7.   If $\tan \theta = (x - 3)/2$, find $\sin \theta$ and $\cos \theta$ in terms of x.

8.   Evaluate

    (a) $\cos^{-1}\left(\sin \frac{\pi}{6}\right)$,   (b) $\sin^{-1}\left(\cos \frac{2\pi}{3}\right)$,

    (c) $\sin^{-1}\left(\sin \frac{5\pi}{6}\right)$,   (d) $\tan^{-1}\left(\cot \frac{\pi}{3}\right)$.

9. Evaluate

    (a) $\sin\left(\sin^{-1}\left(\frac{\sqrt{2}}{3}\right)\right)$,   (b) $\cos\left(\cos^{-1}\left(-\frac{\sqrt{5}}{4}\right)\right)$.

10. Find the general solution of each of the following equations

    (a) $\cos x = \frac{\sqrt{3}}{2}$,   (b) $\sin 2x = \frac{1}{2}$,

    (c) $\sin 3x = \cos\frac{2\pi}{3}$,   (d) $\sin\left(4x + \frac{\pi}{3}\right) = \frac{1}{\sqrt{2}}$.

11. Find the general solution of each of the following equations

(a) $2\sin 2x \cos 3x = -\sqrt{3}\cos 3x$,   (b) $\sin 4x = \sin 2x$,

(c) $\sin x + \cos x = 1$,   (d) $\sqrt{3}\sin 2x - \cos 2x = 1$.

[Hint. In (c) and (d), start by expressing the left hand side of the equation in terms of a single sine term.]

12. A mathematics lecturer is trying to fasten together four pieces of wood of equal lengths to form the sides of a square drawer. The mathematician fastens together the pieces of the drawer so as to form a parallelogram. He checks whether it is a square by measuring the diagonals, and finds to his dismay that the diagonals measure 74 cm and 72.5 cm. Find the larger angle of the parallelogram, and hence find the angle through which the one side should be rotated in order to form the desired square drawer.

13. A rope of length 55 feet is fastened to a harbour wall at a height of 20 feet above sea-level. The other end of the rope is fastened to a rowing-boat, at a point which is 3 feet above sea-level. Assuming that a strong wind is blowing the rowing-boat away from the harbour wall, so that the rope remains taut, find the angle between the rope and the horizontal.

CHAPTER 4

Differentiation

Calculus has held pride of place for the past three hundred years as the most important branch of Mathematics, particularly with regard to applications. Calculus consists of the twin operation of differentiation and integration. These operations were introduced by Newton and Leibniz, working independently, at about the same time. There followed a long and acrimonious dispute between the supporters of these two great mathematicians, each group claiming that their champion was the true creator of this important branch of the subject.

In this chapter we shall study differentiation, leaving integration for later in the course.

Differentiation examines the way in which a change in the value of the independent variable x will affect the value of the dependent variable y, when y is given as a function of x.

We start by considering a particular example, in order to try to get an idea of what happens in the general situation. Let P be the point with coordinates $(2, 4)$ on the curve $y = x^2$. Let Q be the point with coordinates (x_1, y_1) on the curve, and let m denote the gradient of the line PQ passing through the points P and Q. It will be convenient to let $h = x_1 - 2$ and $k = y_1 - 4$, so that h and k represent the increments (or increases) in x and y respectively.

Consider the following table:

x_1	4	3	2.5	2.1	2.01
y_1	16	9	6.25	4.41	4.0401
$k = y_1 - 4$	12	5	2.25	0.41	0.0401
$h = x_1 - 2$	2	1	0.5	0.1	0.01
$m = \dfrac{y_1 - 4}{x_1 - 2}$	6	5	4.5	4.1	4.01

From this table we see that as Q approaches P, so that the value of h tends towards the value zero, then the gradient m of the chord PQ will approach very close to the limiting value 4.

The above table has simply suggested this as a deduction from calculations for the specific values of h we chose, all greater than zero.

Now let us try to establish the same fact in general, for any non-zero value of h, whether positive or negative.

Let Q be the point on $y = x^2$ with x-coordinate $2 + h$. Then the y-coordinate of Q will be $(2 + h)^2 = 4 + 4h + h^2$. Therefore $k = y_1 - 4 = (4 + 4h + h^2) - 4 = 4h + h^2$. Hence the gradient of the chord PQ through the points $P(2, 4)$ and $Q(2 + h, (2 + h)^2)$ will be

$$\frac{4h + h^2}{h} = 4 + h.$$

As we let $h \to 0$, so that Q approaches close to the fixed point P, the value of the gradient will become arbitrarily close to 4. This bears out the conclusion we drew from the table above.

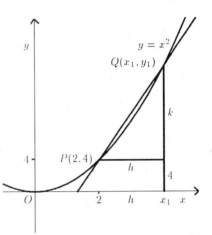

As the point Q approaches very close to the point P, then the chord PQ will become the **tangent** to the curve $y = x^2$ at P. We can think of the tangent as being a chord that touches the curve at two coincident points at P. The tangent to the curve $y = x^2$ at the point $P(2, 4)$ will have gradient 4, the value we obtained in the above process in the limit as h tended to 0.

We could obviously carry out the same calculation for different points on the curve $y = x^2$, in which case we would expect to obtain different values for the gradient m of the tangent.

We could also hope to carry through similar calculations in the case of functions other than $y = x^2$.

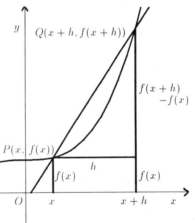

Assume that $y = f(x)$ expresses y in terms of x. Then the **derivative** of y with respect to x, denoted by $f'(x)$, or by $\dfrac{dy}{dx}$, is given by

$$\frac{dy}{dx} = \lim_{h \to 0} \frac{f(x+h) - f(x)}{h}.$$

From the diagram we see that $\dfrac{dy}{dx}$ gives us the gradient of the tangent to the curve $y = f(x)$ at the point $P(x, y)$. To find the tangent to the curve, we take the chord PQ, passing through the points $P(x, f(x))$ and $Q(x+h, f(x+h))$, and we let h become so small that the points P and Q are indistinguishable. Thus we can think of the tangent as meeting the curve at the two coincident points P and $Q = P$.

We describe the process of finding the derivative of a function as **differentiating** the function.

The following table gives the derivatives of the functions which arise most frequently in mathematics:

$f(x)$	$f'(x)$	comments
c	0	c constant
x^n	nx^{n-1}	$n \in \mathbb{R}$, $n \neq 0$, n fixed
$\sin x$	$\cos x$	x in radians
$\cos x$	$-\sin x$	x in radians
$\ln x$	$1/x$	$x > 0$
e^x	e^x	

There are various possible ways of combining together functions. The following rules tell us how to find the derivatives of these combinations. In these rules, $f(x)$ and $g(x)$ will denote any **differentiable functions**—that is, functions which have derivatives—and c will denote an arbitrary constant.

$$\frac{d}{dx}(cf(x)) = c\frac{df}{dx}.$$

$$\frac{d}{dx}(f(x) \pm g(x)) = \frac{df}{dx} \pm \frac{dg}{dx}.$$

The Product Rule.

$$\frac{d}{dx}(f(x) \times g(x)) = g(x) \times \frac{df}{dx} + f(x) \times \frac{dg}{dx}.$$

The Quotient Rule.

$$\frac{d}{dx}\left(\frac{f(x)}{g(x)}\right) = \frac{g(x) \times \dfrac{df}{dx} - f(x) \times \dfrac{dg}{dx}}{[g(x)]^2}.$$

Example 1.   Find the derivative of $x^3 + 4x^5 - 7 + \dfrac{9}{x^3}$.

Solution.   We shall think of $\dfrac{9}{x^3}$ as being $9x^{-3}$, and then we shall use the above rules for differentiating a sum of functions and a constant times a function. Then

$$\frac{d}{dx}\left(x^3 + 4x^5 - 7 + \frac{9}{x^3}\right) = \frac{d}{dx}\left(x^3 + 4x^5 - 7 + 9x^{-3}\right)$$

$$= \frac{d}{dx}\left(x^3\right) + 4\frac{d}{dx}\left(x^5\right) - \frac{d}{dx}\left(7\right) + 9\frac{d}{dx}\left(x^{-3}\right)$$

$$= 3x^2 + 4 \times 5x^4 - 0 + 9 \times (-3)x^{-4}$$

$$= 3x^2 + 20x^4 - 27x^{-4}$$

$$= 3x^2 + 20x^4 - \frac{27}{x^4}.$$

Example 2.   *Find the derivative of*
$$\left(7x^2 - 2x^{-5}\right)\cos x.$$

Solution.   Since this time we have a product of $\cos x$ with an expression similar to that in Example 1, we must use the Product Rule to differentiate the product. So we get

$$\frac{d}{dx}\left\{\left(7x^2 - 2x^{-5}\right)\cos x\right\}$$

$$= \left(14x + 10x^{-6}\right)\cos x + \left(7x^2 - 2x^{-5}\right)\left(-\sin x\right).$$

Example 3.   *Find the derivative of $e^x \sin x$.*

Solution.   Again using the Product Rule, we have

$$\frac{d}{dx}\left\{e^x \sin x\right\} = e^x \cos x + e^x \sin x.$$

Example 4.   *Find the derivative of*
$$\frac{x^2 + 3x}{x^3 + 4}.$$

Solution.   This time we must use the Quotient Rule, with $f(x) = x^2 + 3x$ and $g(x) = x^3 + 4$. So we have

$$\frac{d}{dx}\left(\frac{x^2 + 3x}{x^3 + 4}\right)$$

$$= \frac{(x^3 + 4) \times \dfrac{d}{dx}(x^2 + 3x) - (x^2 + 3x) \times \dfrac{d}{dx}(x^3 + 4)}{[x^3 + 4]^2}$$

$$= \frac{(x^3 + 4) \times (2x + 3) - (x^2 + 3x) \times 3x^2}{[x^3 + 4]^2}$$

$$= \frac{(2x^4 + 8x + 3x^3 + 12) - (3x^4 + 9x^3)}{[x^3 + 4]^2}$$

$$= \frac{2x^4 + 8x + 3x^3 + 12 - 3x^4 - 9x^3}{[x^3 + 4]^2}$$

$$= \frac{-x^4 - 6x^3 + 8x + 12}{[x^3 + 4]^2}.$$

We have quoted the Product and Quotient Rules without attempting to justify them. You might be interested in consulting the chapter on Basic Techniques, where we give an indication of how to prove these results. For now, we shall content ourselves with an example to show that if we ignore the Product Rule, then the rules for differentiation would not work.

If $y = x^2$, then we can show from the definition that $\dfrac{dy}{dx} = 2x$. However if we regard x^2 as $x \times x$ and differentiate by multiplying together the derivative of each term, then we would obtain the different, and wrong, answer $\dfrac{d}{dx}(x) \times \dfrac{d}{dx}(x) = 1 \times 1 = 1$.

We write $\dfrac{d}{dx}(???)$ to denote that we are differentiating what is contained within the bracket. A common notational mistake is to write down what is to be differentiated and then write '=' the derivative. If, for example, asked to differentiate x^2 please *never* commit a horror such as writing $x^2 = 2x$, when of course what is intended should have been written as $\dfrac{d}{dx}(x^2) = 2x$.

There is one further important way of combining together two functions, namely by **composition**. Suppose that $f(x)$ and $g(x)$ are two functions of x. Then the composition $(f \circ g)(x)$ is defined to be the function given by

$$(f \circ g)(x) = f(g(x)).$$

What this means is that we take a value of x, use the formula for g to calculate $g(x)$, and then we apply the formula for f to the value $g(x)$ to calculate the value of $f(g(x))$.

Suppose, for example, that $f(x)$ and $g(x)$ are the functions given by $f(x) = \sin x$ and $g(x) = 3x^3 - 5$, respectively. Then the composition $(f \circ g)(x)$ is given by

$$(f \circ g)(x) = f(g(x)),$$

so that

$$(f \circ g)(x) = f(3x^3 - 5) = \sin(3x^3 - 5).$$

This is because the function $g(x)$ acts by taking any number, cubing it, multiplying by 3 and then subtracting 5. The function $f(x)$ acts by taking any real number and taking the sine of that number. So the function f takes the real number $3x^3 - 5$ and gives us the real number $\sin(3x^3 - 5)$. Hence the effect of the composition $f \circ g$ is to start with the value x and to yield $\sin(3x^3 - 5)$.

Example 5.   *Find functions $f(x)$ and $g(x)$ such that each of the following can be expressed as a composition $(f \circ g)(x)$:*

(1) $h_1(x) = \tan(9x - 4)$;   (2) $h_2(x) = \ln(\tan^{-1} x)$;

(3) $h_3(x) = \sin^4 x.$

Solution.   (1) $h_1(x)$ is obtained by first calculating $9x - 4$ and then taking the tangent of this number. We will obtain precisely this if we take $g(x) = 9x - 4$ and take $f(x) = \tan x$.

(2)   To find $h_2(x)$ we first need to calculate $\tan^{-1} x$ and then take the natural logarithm of this number. It follows that we need to

take $g(x) = \tan^{-1} x$ and $f(x) = \ln x$. With this choice we see that $(f \circ g)(x) = h_2(x)$, as required.

(3)   To find $h_3(x)$ we need to recall that $\sin^4 x$ is a shorthand for $(\sin x)^4$. The calculation of $\sin^4 x$ will therefore involve finding $\sin x$ and then raising this to the fourth power. So we let $g(x) = \sin x$ and $f(x) = x^4$.

Students frequently confuse the product with the composition, and yet they are very different ways of combining functions. Note for example the difference between $(\sin x)(\tan x)$ and $\sin(\tan x)$. The first of these involves calculating $\sin x$ and $\tan x$ and then taking their product, while the second involves finding $\tan x$ and then taking the sine of this. So the second of these functions is a composition.

One way of distinguishing between the two is to imagine that you are using a calculator to evaluate a function. If you use the multiplication button, then you have a product. If on the other hand you simply use function buttons, then you will have a composition.

The rule for differentiating a composition is:
The Chain Rule

$$\frac{d}{dx}(f(g(x))) = f'(g(x)) \times g'(x).$$

So to differentiate a composition $f \circ g$, we firstly differentiate f with respect to its variable $g(x)$, and evaluate it at $g(x)$, and then *multiply by the derivative of $g(x)$*.

The Chain Rule can also be remembered in the form

$$\frac{df}{dx} = \frac{df}{du} \times \frac{du}{dx},$$

where u denotes the function $g(x)$ we used in the earlier version.

Example 6. *Differentiate each of the following functions:*

(1) $\ln(2x + 5)$;
(2) $\sin(2x^2 - 4x + 5)$;
(3) $\sin^3 x$.

Solution.   (1)   We should think of $\ln(2x + 5)$ as being the composition of the functions $g(x) = 2x + 5$ and $f(x) = \ln x$. Then we have $\frac{df}{dx} = \frac{1}{x}$, so that $\frac{d}{dg}(\ln(2x + 5)) = \frac{1}{2x + 5}$. Also $\frac{dg}{dx} = 2$, and hence we have, by the Chain Rule, $\frac{d}{dx}(\ln(2x + 5)) = \frac{1}{2x + 5} \times 2$, so on simplifying we have $\frac{d}{dx}(\ln(2x + 5)) = \frac{2}{2x + 5}$.

(2)   To find $\frac{d}{dx}(\sin(2x^2 - 4x + 5))$, we think of this function as the composition of $f(x) = \sin x$ and $g(x) = 2x^2 - 4x + 5$. Then

$\dfrac{df}{dx} = \cos x$, so that $\dfrac{d}{dg}\left(\sin\left(2x^2 - 4x + 5\right)\right) = \cos\left(2x^2 - 4x + 5\right)$, while

$\dfrac{dg}{dx} = 4x - 4$. Hence, using the Chain Rule, we have

$$\frac{d}{dx}\left(\sin\left(2x^2 - 4x + 5\right)\right) = \left(\cos\left(2x^2 - 4x + 5\right)\right) \times (4x - 4)$$
$$= 4(x - 1)\cos\left(2x^2 - 4x + 5\right).$$

(3)   To find $\dfrac{d}{dx}\left(\sin^3 x\right)$, we need to regard the function as the composition of $f(x) = x^3$ and $g(x) = \sin x$. Now $\dfrac{df}{dx} = 3x^2$, so that $\dfrac{df}{dg} = 3g^2 = 3(\sin x)^2$, and $\dfrac{dg}{dx} = \cos x$. Hence, by the Chain Rule, we have

$$\frac{d}{dx}\left(\sin^3 x\right) = 3\sin^2 x \times \cos x.$$

Normally when we have identified that we have to differentiate a composition, so that we have to use the Chain Rule, we do not bother formally to separate the component parts in writing out the solutions, but rather we try to figure out this decomposition mentally.

Example 7.   *Differentiate each of the following functions:*
(1) e^{3x-5};
(2) $\dfrac{1}{\sqrt{3x + 7}}$;
(3) $(5x^3 - 7x^2 - 4x + 8)^4$.

Solution.   (1) $\dfrac{d}{dx}\left(e^{3x-5}\right) = e^{3x-5} \times 3 = 3e^{3x-5}$.

(2)   Here we see that

$$\frac{d}{dx}\left(\frac{1}{\sqrt{3x+7}}\right) = \frac{d}{dx}\left((3x+7)^{-1/2}\right)$$
$$= (-1/2)(3x+7)^{-3/2} \times \frac{d}{dx}(3x+7)$$
$$= (-1/2)(3x+7)^{-3/2} \times 3$$
$$= (-3/2)(3x+7)^{-3/2}.$$

(3)   In this case we have

$$\frac{d}{dx}\left((5x^3 - 7x^2 - 4x + 8)^4\right)$$
$$= 4(5x^3 - 7x^2 - 4x + 8)^3 \times \frac{d}{dx}(5x^3 - 7x^2 - 4x + 8)$$
$$= 4(5x^3 - 7x^2 - 4x + 8)^3 \times (15x^2 - 14x - 4).$$

NOTE. It is important that we avoid writing things that can have more than one interpretation. To this end, we put in brackets to avoid any posssible misunderstandings. For example, in differentiating $\cos(2x - 3)$ we would obtain $(-\sin(2x - 3)) \times 2$. Had we missed out the brackets surrounding the $-\sin(2x - 3)$-term, then our answer could have been misinterpreted as $-\sin((2x - 3) \times 2)$, which is a very different answer.

There is a problem though in writing brackets to avoid ambiguity, and that is that we can finish up with expressions involving large numbers of brackets which are quite difficult to decipher. To reduce the numbers of brackets, we adopt some conventions.

We have already met the convention of writing $\sin^3 x$ rather than $(\sin x)^3$.

Another convention is that when taking a function such as sine, cosine, ln, etc., we interpret it as meaning the sine or whatever of the symbol immediately following the sine, except that where the symbol is multiplied by a number (and in multiplication we include division), or where the symbol is raised to a power, then we include the extra term or terms before taking the sine.

So for example $\sin 3x^2$ would mean that we should calculate $3x^2$ and then take the sine of this expression. However $\sin 3x^2 + 4$ would mean that we should again calculate $\sin 3x^2$ and add 4 on to this. In other words $\sin 3x^2 + 4$ would be better written as $4 + \sin 3x^2$. If we had meant to take first the value of $3x^2 + 4$ and then take the sine of this, then that would have to be written as $\sin(3x^2 + 4)$.

Note that e^{x^3}, for example, is taken to mean $e^{(x^3)}$, the exponential of x^3, rather than the other possible interpretation.

Using the rules for differentiation that have been given above, we can find the derivatives of some more of the elementary functions that we have met.

$f(x)$	$f'(x)$	comments
$\tan x$	$\sec^2 x$	x in radians
$\sec x$	$\sec x \tan x$	x in radians
$\operatorname{cosec} x$	$-\operatorname{cosec} x \cot x$	x in radians
$\cot x$	$-\operatorname{cosec}^2 x$	x in radians
a^x	$a^x \ln a$	$a > 0$
$\log_a x$	$\dfrac{1}{x \ln a}$	$x > 0,\ a > 0,\ a \neq 1$

We prove the above results as follows:

$$\frac{d}{dx}(\tan x) = \frac{d}{dx}\left(\frac{\sin x}{\cos x}\right)$$

$$= \frac{(\cos x)(\cos x) - (\sin x)(-\sin x)}{[\cos x]^2}$$

$$= \frac{\cos^2 x + \sin^2 x}{[\cos x]^2}$$

$$= \frac{1}{[\cos x]^2}$$

$$= \left(\frac{1}{\cos x}\right)^2$$

$$= \sec^2 x,$$

as required.

$$\frac{d}{dx}(\sec x) = \frac{d}{dx}\left(\frac{1}{\cos x}\right)$$

$$= \frac{(\cos x)(0) - (1)(-\sin x)}{[\cos x]^2}$$

$$= \frac{\sin x}{[\cos x]^2}$$

$$= \left(\frac{1}{\cos x}\right) \times \left(\frac{\sin x}{\cos x}\right)$$

$$= \sec x \tan x.$$

The proofs for the derivatives for $\operatorname{cosec} x$ and $\cot x$ are similar to the ones given above.

$$\frac{d}{dx}(a^x) = \frac{d}{dx}(\exp(x \ln a))$$

$$= \exp(x \ln a) \times \frac{d}{dx}(x \ln a)$$

$$= (a^x) \times \ln a,$$

as required. Note the use in the above of the formula for expressing a^x in terms of the exponential function. Note also that we have written $\exp(x \ln a)$ rather than the equivalent alternative form $e^{x \ln a}$, purely for the sake of variety.

If we use the formula for the change of base in logarithms to express $\log_a x$ in terms of $\log_e$, then we can differentiate, and obtain

$$\frac{d}{dx}(\log_a x) = \frac{d}{dx}\left(\frac{\log_e x}{\log_e a}\right)$$

$$= \frac{d}{dx}\left(\frac{\ln x}{\ln a}\right)$$

$$= \frac{1}{\ln a} \times \frac{d}{dx}(\ln x)$$

$$= \frac{1}{\ln a} \times \frac{1}{x}$$

$$= \frac{1}{x \ln a}.$$

The derivatives of the three inverse trigonometric functions are given by the following table:

$f(x)$	$f'(x)$	comments
$\sin^{-1} x$	$\dfrac{1}{\sqrt{1-x^2}}$	$x \in (-1, 1)$
$\cos^{-1} x$	$-\dfrac{1}{\sqrt{1-x^2}}$	$x \in (-1, 1)$
$\tan^{-1} x$	$\dfrac{1}{1+x^2}$	$x \in \mathbb{R}$

The proofs of all these follow a similar pattern. We shall illustrate the method by considering $\sin^{-1} x$.

Let $y = \sin^{-1} x$, so that $x = \sin y$. Hence

$$\frac{dx}{dy} = \cos y = \sqrt{1 - \sin^2 y} = \sqrt{1 - x^2}.$$

However, using the Chain Rule, it can be shown that $\dfrac{dy}{dx} = \dfrac{1}{\left(\dfrac{dx}{dy}\right)}$,

so that $\dfrac{dy}{dx} = \dfrac{1}{\sqrt{1 - x^2}}.$

Example 8. *Differentiate each of the following functions:*

(1) $\sin(\tan^{-1} x)$;   (2) $\cot^2(4x^2 + 7)$;

(3) $\dfrac{\log_3 x}{\tan x}$;   (4) $4^x \sin^{-1} x.$

Solution.   (1)   Using the Chain Rule to differentiate, we obtain

$$\frac{d}{dx}\left(\sin(\tan^{-1} x)\right) = \left(\cos(\tan^{-1} x)\right) \times \frac{d}{dx}\left(\tan^{-1} x\right)$$

$$= \left(\cos(\tan^{-1} x)\right) \times \left(\frac{1}{1 + x^2}\right)$$

$$= \frac{\cos(\tan^{-1} x)}{1 + x^2}.$$

(2)   If we use the Chain Rule twice over, we obtain

$$\frac{d}{dx}\left(\cot^2(4x^2 + 7)\right) = 2 \times \cot(4x^2 + 7) \times \frac{d}{dx}\left(\cot(4x^2 + 7)\right)$$

$$= 2 \times \cot\left(4x^2 + 7\right) \times \left(-\operatorname{cosec}^2(4x^2 + 7)\right) \times \frac{d}{dx}\left(4x^2 + 7\right)$$

$$= 2 \times \cot\left(4x^2 + 7\right) \times \left(-\operatorname{cosec}^2(4x^2 + 7)\right) \times 8x$$

$$= -16x \cot\left(4x^2 + 7\right)\operatorname{cosec}^2(4x^2 + 7).$$

(3)   Using the Quotient Rule we have

$$\frac{d}{dx}\left(\frac{\log_3 x}{\tan x}\right) = \frac{\tan x\left(\dfrac{1}{x \ln 3}\right) - \log_3 x \sec^2 x}{[\tan x]^2}$$

$$= \frac{\dfrac{\tan x}{x \ln 3} - \log_3 x \sec^2 x}{\tan^2 x}$$

$$= \frac{\sin x \cos x - x \ln x}{(\sin^2 x)(x \ln 3)},$$

on multiplying top and bottom by $\cos^2 x$ and using one of the laws of logarithms.

(4)   Using the Product Rule, we have

$$\frac{d}{dx}\left(4^x \sin^{-1} x\right) = 4^x \frac{1}{\sqrt{1 - x^2}} + \sin^{-1} x\, 4^x \ln 4.$$

EXAMPLES 4

1.   Differentiate with respect to x

    (a) $7x^5 - 4x^4 + 8x^3 - 5x^2 + 2x - 7,$

    (b) $4x^5 - 5x^3 + 7x^2 - 8x + 11,$

    (c) $6x^3 - 3x^2 + 5x - 8 + \dfrac{2}{x^2} - \dfrac{4}{x^3},$

    (d) $9x^4 - 8x^3 + 3x - 4 + \dfrac{4}{x} - \dfrac{2}{x^2} - \dfrac{5}{x^4}.$

2.   Use the Product Rule to differentiate with respect to x

    (a) $\left(x^3 - 5x^2 + 2x - 4\right)\left(x^4 - 2x^2 + 7\right),$

    (b) $\left(3x^4 + 7x^3 + 9x + 7\right)\left(5x^2 + 3x + 4\right),$

    (c) $\left(x^3 + 4x\right)\sin x,$

    (d) $\left(2x^5 - 9x^3\right)\ln x.$

3.   Use the Quotient Rule to differentiate with respect to x

    (a) $\dfrac{x^3 + 5x^2 - 2x + 4}{x^2 + 9},$ (b) $\dfrac{x^2 - 7x + 4}{x^2 - 3x + 4},$

    (c) $\dfrac{\sin x}{2 + x^3},$ (d) $\dfrac{\ln x}{3x^2 - 5}.$

4. Use the Chain Rule to differentiate with respect to x

(a) $\left(x^4 - 2x^3 - 5x^2 + 4x - 7\right)^{7/2}$,

(b) $\left(3x^5 - 4x^3 - 7x^2 + 3x + 2\right)^{5/4}$,

(c) $\tan^3 x$,

(d) $\sec^5 x$,

(e) $\cos\left(5x^2 - 4x + 7\right)$,

(f) $\sin\left(\tan\left(x^2 - 4x + 2\right)\right)$.

5. Differentiate each of the following with respect to x, simplifying your answer where possible:

(a) $(x-5)^8 (x+3)^6$;   (b) $(3x+4)^7 (7x-2)^3$;

(c) $\sin 3x \cos^3 x$;   (d) $\sin^4 x \cos 4x$;

(e) $\sin^6 x \cos^3 2x$;   (f) $\sec 2x \operatorname{cosec}^2 x$;

(g) $\tan^3 \sqrt{x}$;   (h) $\cos\left(x^{\frac{2}{5}}\right)$;

(i) $\operatorname{cosec}\left(x^{\frac{4}{3}}\right)$;   (j) $\left(1 - \tan^2 x\right)^{\frac{3}{2}}$;

(k) $\dfrac{x \cos x - \sin x}{x \sin x + \cos x}$;   (l) $\dfrac{\sin^3 x}{\cos 3x}$;

(m) $\dfrac{\sin 5x}{\cos^5 x}$;   (n) $\dfrac{\cos^2 3x}{\sin^3 2x}$;

(o) $\sin^{-1} 3x$;   (p) $\cos^{-1} 5x$;

(q) $\sin^{-1}(3x + 2)$;   (r) $\tan^{-1} 4x$;

(s) $\left(\sin^{-1} x\right)^3$;   (t) $\tan^{-1}\left(\dfrac{x+3}{2}\right)$.

6. Differentiate each of the following with respect to x:

(a) $\ln(3x - 5)$;   (b) $\ln\left(2 + 4x^3\right)$;

(c) $\ln\sqrt{6 + x^2}$;   (d) $\ln\left(3x^2 - 7\right)^{\frac{4}{3}}$;

(e) $\ln(\cos x)$;   (f) $x^2 \ln 2x$;

(g) $\tan(\ln x)$;   (h) $\ln(\sin 4x - \cos 4x)$;

(i) $\left(x^3 - 5x^2\right)\ln\left(x^2 + 3\right)$;   (j) $\left(x^2 + 7x\right)\ln\left(2x^3 - 5x\right)$;

(k) $\ln\left(\dfrac{x^2 + 4}{x^4 + 7}\right)$;   (l) $\log_{10}\left(3x^2 + 4\right)$;

(m) $\log_4(\cos 4x)$;   (n) $\log_{10}(\tan 2x)$;

(o) $(x - 2)\log_2(x + 4)$;   (p) e^{7x};

(q) e^{4-3x};   (r) e^{x^4};

(s) $e^{\sin x}$;   (t) $e^{\sec x}$;

(u) $x^2 e^{4x}$;   (v) $x^4 e^{x^3 - 2x + 5}$;

(w) 2^{4x};   (x) $5^{\tan x}$;

(y) $3^{\ln x}$;   (z) $x^3 7^{5x}$.

7. By first expressing the functions in the form $e^{a \ln b}$, find the derivative with respect to x of each of the following:

(a) $x^{\tan x}$;   (b) $x^{\sin x}$;

(c) $(\sin x)^x$;   (d) $(x^2 + 2x + 5)^{x-2}$.

CHAPTER 5
Examples involving Differentiation

Example 1.   Let P be the point $(1,4)$ on the curve defined by the equation $y = x^3 - 4x^2 + x + 6$. Find the equation of the tangent and of the normal to the curve at P, and find the coordinates of the point where the tangent meets the curve again.

Solution.   Since $y = x^3 - 4x^2 + x + 6$, then $\dfrac{dy}{dx} = 3x^2 - 8x + 1$. The gradient of the tangent to the curve at the point with $x = 1$ is found by putting $x = 1$ into this expression for $\dfrac{dy}{dx}$. Hence the gradient of the tangent to the curve at $x = 1$ is $3 - 8 + 1 = -4$. It follows that the equation of the tangent passing through the point $(1,4)$ is

$$y - 4 = -4(x - 1),$$

from which

$$y - 4 = -4x + 4,$$

or

$$y = 8 - 4x.$$

The normal to the curve is the line perpendicular to the tangent. Since it can be shown that two lines are perpendicular precisely when the product of their gradients is -1, and since in this case the tangent has gradient -4, the gradient of the normal will be $(-1)/(-4) = 1/4$. Hence the equation of the normal will be

$$y - 4 = (1/4)(x - 1),$$

which gives

$$4y - 16 = x - 1,$$

or

$$4y = x + 15.$$

The tangent and the curve will meet at those points whose coordinates (x, y) simultaneously satisfy the two equations

$$y = x^3 - 4x^2 + x + 6$$

and

$$y = 8 - 4x.$$

Substituting for y, we need

$$x^3 - 4x^2 + x + 6 = 8 - 4x,$$

which can be expressed as

$$x^3 - 4x^2 + 5x - 2 = 0.$$

In order to solve this cubic equation, we can simply try to factorise it, using the Remainder Theorem to give us one of the roots. However, we can make this much easier for ourselves if we realise that we already know two solutions of this equation. We know that the tangent meets the curve at the point $x = 1$, and indeed we know that $x = 1$ is a point at which the tangent meets the curve in two coincident points. Hence we would expect that $x = 1$ will be a *repeated* root of the equation $x^3 - 4x^2 + 5x - 2 = 0$. Using synthetic division, or long division of polynomials, to find the other factor, we can easily see that

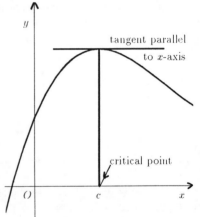

$$x^3 - 4x^2 + 5x - 2 = (x - 1)^2(x - 2).$$

It follows that the other point of intersection of the tangent and the curve is given by $x - 2 = 0$, or $x = 2$. When $x = 2$, $y = 0$ (which is obtained most simply by substituting $x = 2$ in the *equation of the tangent* $y = 8 - 4x$).

A **critical point**, also known as a **turning point**, of a function f is a value of x for which the derivative f' is zero. Hence a critical point of f is a value of x giving a point where the gradient of the tangent to the curve is zero, meaning that the tangent is parallel to the x-axis.

Example 2.   *Find the critical points for the real function*

$$f(x) = \frac{\sin 4x}{\cos^4 x}.$$

List explicitly those critical points that lie in the range $[0, 2\pi]$.

Solution.   We start the solution by calculating the derivative of

$f(x)$, using the Quotient and Chain Rules in the process. We have

$$f'(x) = \frac{\left(\cos^4 x\right) \dfrac{d}{dx}\left(\sin 4x\right) - \left(\sin 4x\right) \dfrac{d}{dx}\left(\cos^4 x\right)}{[\cos^4 x]^2}$$

$$= \frac{\left(\cos^4 x\right)\left(4\cos 4x\right) - \left(\sin 4x\right)\left(-4\cos^3 x \sin x\right)}{\cos^8 x}$$

$$= \frac{4\cos^3 x[\cos x \cos 4x + \sin 4x \sin x]}{\cos^8 x}$$

$$= \frac{4\cos\left(4x - x\right)}{\cos^5 x}$$

$$= \frac{4\cos 3x}{\cos^5 x},$$

on cancelling $\cos^3 x$ from the numerator and denominator of the above expression. Note that we are allowed to do this, because at the x-values that would make $\cos^3 x$ equal to zero, the original function $f(x)$ will be undefined. Note also the simplification of the above expression by using the formula $\cos\left(4x - x\right) = \cos 4x \cos x + \sin 4x \sin x$.

Now $f'(x) = 0$ precisely when $\dfrac{4\cos 3x}{\cos^5 x} = 0$. This happens exactly when $4\cos 3x = 0$. Note that we do *not* want $\cos^5 x = 0$, since if $\cos^5 x = 0$ then $f'(x)$ is *undefined* and does not equal zero. Now

$$4\cos 3x = 0$$

when

$$\cos 3x = 0,$$

which happens when

$$3x = 2k\pi \pm \frac{\pi}{2} \qquad (k \in \mathbb{Z})$$

and therefore when

$$x = \frac{2k\pi}{3} \pm \frac{\pi}{6} \qquad (k \in \mathbb{Z}).$$

The critical points in the interval $[0, 2\pi]$ are found by substituting different values of k into this formula to determine those solutions in the required range. These solutions are $\frac{\pi}{6}, \frac{\pi}{2}, \frac{5\pi}{6}, \frac{7\pi}{6}, \frac{3\pi}{2}$ and $\frac{11\pi}{6}$.

One of the main uses of differentiation in applications is as a way of finding the rate of change of one variable (say y) with respect to another (say x), where y is expressed as a function of x.

To see why this is so, let us consider the problem of trying to find the average velocity of a vehicle. Suppose that the displacement s at time t of the vehicle from its initial position is given by the function $s = f(t)$. Then at time $t = t_0$, the displacement of the vehicle will be $f(t_0)$. At time $t = t_0 + h$, the displacement of the vehicle will be

$f(t_0 + h)$. Hence in the time period of h, the vehicle will have moved $f(t_0 + h) - f(t_0)$. So the average rate of change of the displacement over the time period t_0 to $t_0 + h$ will be

$$\frac{f(t_0 + h) - f(t_0)}{h}.$$

Allowing the length of the time period to tend to zero, we shall obtain the (instantaneous) rate of change of the displacement at the time $t = t_0$, given by

$$\lim_{h \to 0} \frac{f(t_0 + h) - f(t_0)}{h},$$

which is $\dfrac{ds}{dt}$ at $t = t_0$, also denoted by $f'(t_0)$.

Velocity is the name normally given to the rate of change of displacement with respect to t. Equally, **acceleration** is the name for the rate of change of velocity with respect to time.

Example 3.   *An object is moving through a resisting medium. Suppose the displacement s at time t of the object from its initial position is given by*

$$s = 5t + 16t^2 - 6e^{-t/3}.$$

Find the velocity and the acceleration of the object at time $t = 10$.

Solution.   The velocity v at time t is given by

$$\frac{ds}{dt} = 5 + 32t + 2e^{-t/3}.$$

Substituting $t = 10$ in this, we find that $v = 5 + 320 + 2e^{-10/3} \approx 325.07$ (correct to 5 significant figures). The acceleration a is given by the derivative of v with respect to t, and so

$$a = \frac{dv}{dt} = 32 - \frac{2}{3}e^{-t/3}.$$

Hence the acceleration at time $t = 10$ is given by $a = 32 - \frac{2}{3}e^{-\frac{10}{3}} \approx$ 31.976 (correct to 5 significant figures).

Example 4.   *A spherical balloon is being inflated. Find $\dfrac{dA}{dr}$, the rate of change of the surface area A of the balloon with respect to the radius r. In particular, find the value of this rate of change when the balloon has radius 15 cm.*

Solution.   The surface area A of a sphere of radius r is given by $A = 4\pi r^2$. Hence, on differentiating with respect to r, we have $\dfrac{dA}{dr} = 8\pi r$. When $r = 15$, we have $\dfrac{dA}{dr} = 8\pi \times 15 = 120\pi$. Hence the rate of change of A with respect to r is 120π cm.

EXAMPLES 5

1.   Find the point(s) (if any) on the curve $y = x^4 + 2x^2 + 10x + 5$ at which the tangent has gradient 2.

2.   Find the values of x which give the point(s) (if any) on the curve $y = 2\cos 3x$ at which the tangent has gradient 3.

3.   For each of the following curves, find the equations of the tangent and normal to the curve at the given point. Find the point(s) (if any) where the tangent at the given point cuts the curve again:

(a) $y = x^3 - 4x^2 + 4x + 1$ at $(1, 2)$;
(b) $y = x^4 - 3x^3 - 2x^2 + x + 10$ at $(2, -4)$.

4.   For each of the following curves, find the gradient of the tangent to the curve at the point given. Hence find the coordinates of any further point(s) on the curve such that the tangent to the curve at the point found is parallel to the tangent to the curve at the given point:

(a) $y = x^3 - 3x^2 + 4x - 2$ at $(2, 2)$
(b) $y = 3x^4 - 8x^3 - 30x^2 + 40x - 2$ at $(1, 3)$

5.   Let $f(x)$ denote each of the following functions, in turn. Find the derivative $f'(x)$, simplifying as far as possible, and hence find the critical points of f.

(a) $\sin^2 x \cos 2x$,   (b) $\cos^4 x \cos 4x$,

(c) $\dfrac{\sin^3 x}{\cos 3x}$,   (d) $\dfrac{1}{\sin^2 2x \cos 4x}$.

Then find those critical points of f that lie in the interval $[0, 2\pi]$.

6.   Find the velocity and acceleration at time $t = 2$ of a particle whose displacement s from the origin varies with t according to the equation

$$s = t^5 - 2t^3 + 3t^2 - 20t.$$

7.   Find the velocity and acceleration at time $t = 3$ of a particle whose displacement s from the origin varies with t according to the equation

$$s = t^3 - 3t^2 + t - 2\sin t.$$

8.   A manufacturer believes that the cost C of production of an article is related to the number n produced by the formula

$$C = 2n^3 - 5n^2 + 4n - 6.$$

Find the marginal cost $\dfrac{dC}{dn}$, when 50 units are being produced.

9.   The revenue R when n units of a certain commodity are sold is given by

$$R = 24 + 4n - 2n^{\frac{3}{2}}.$$

Find the marginal revenue, $\dfrac{dR}{dn}$, when 100 units are being sold.

10.   The number N of bacteria in a colony at time t days is given by $N = 50t + 2e^{3t}$. At what rate is the colony growing after 2 days?

11.   Find a formula for the area A of a square in terms of its diagonal x. Hence find the value of $\dfrac{dA}{dx}$, the rate of change of the area with respect to x, when $x = 5$.

12.   The formula $V = \frac{4}{3}\pi r^3$ expresses the volume of a sphere in terms of its radius r. Hence find the value of $\dfrac{dV}{dr}$, the rate of change of the volume with respect to r, when $r = 3$.

CHAPTER 6

Higher Derivatives

If y is a function of x (for example, if $y = \sin x$) then we can calculate the derivative of y with respect to x, denoted by $\dfrac{dy}{dx}$. (If $y = \sin x$, then $\dfrac{dy}{dx} = \cos x$, of course.)

Now $\dfrac{dy}{dx}$ is again a function of x, and so there is nothing to stop us differentiating it with respect to x. If we do this, we will obtain the **second derivative** of y with respect to x, which is denoted by $\dfrac{d^2y}{dx^2}$. (In our example, $\dfrac{d^2y}{dx^2} = \dfrac{d}{dx}(\cos x) = -\sin x$.)

We could repeat this process, obtaining the **third derivative** of y with respect to x, which is denoted by $\dfrac{d^3y}{dx^3}$. (Continuing with our example, we have $\dfrac{d^3y}{dx^3} = \dfrac{d}{dx}(-\sin x) = -\cos x$.)

We could continue like this, obtaining successively the fourth, fifth, sixth, ... derivatives of y with respect to x. The derivatives $\dfrac{d^2y}{dx^2}, \dfrac{d^3y}{dx^3}, \dfrac{d^4y}{dx^4}, \ldots$ are known as the **higher derivatives** of y with respect to x.

Please note that it is very important to be careful about notation here. It is quite easy to confuse, for example, $\dfrac{d^2y}{dx^2}$ and $\left(\dfrac{dy}{dx}\right)^2$. However these are two totally separate functions of x. $\dfrac{d^2y}{dx^2}$ is obtained by taking $\dfrac{dy}{dx}$ and differentiating it, while $\left(\dfrac{dy}{dx}\right)^2$ is obtained by taking $\dfrac{dy}{dx}$ and squaring it.

There are various other notations which are quite often used to denote derivatives. For example, if $y = f(x)$, then we can denote the derivative of y with respect to x by y', by $f'(x)$, or by $\dfrac{d}{dx}(f(x))$. We can denote the second derivative by y'', $f''(x)$, or by $\dfrac{d^2}{dx^2}(f(x))$. Similar notations for the third derivative are y''', $f'''(x)$, and $\dfrac{d^3}{dx^3}(f(x))$.

Example 1. If $y = 4x^4 - 7x^3 + 8x^2 + 5x - 11$, find the first, second, third, fourth and fifth derivatives of y with respect to x.

Solution. Since $y = 4x^4 - 7x^3 + 8x^2 + 5x - 11$, we have

$$\frac{dy}{dx} = 16x^3 - 21x^2 + 16x + 5,$$

c

$$\frac{d^2y}{dx^2} = 48x^2 - 42x + 16,$$

$$\frac{d^3y}{dx^3} = 96x - 42,$$

$$\frac{d^4y}{dx^4} = 96,$$

and

$$\frac{d^5y}{dx^5} = 0.$$

Notice that the fifth derivative, and all the subsequent derivatives, will be zero. This is typical behaviour for a **polynomial function**, one that just involves non-negative powers of the independent variable x. If $y = f(x)$, where $f(x)$ is a polynomial function of x of degree n, for $n \in \mathbb{N}$, then the $(n+1)$-th and all subsequent derivatives of y with respect to x will be zero. Here $\mathbb{N}$ denotes the set of *positive* integers.

A **differential equation** (in x, y) is an equation involving the variables x, y and one or more of the derivatives $\dfrac{dy}{dx}, \dfrac{d^2y}{dx^2}$, etc. The study of differential equations, and in particular, finding methods for solving differential equations, forms one of the most important branches of applicable mathematics.

We shall study some of the methods available for solving the simplest types of differential equations later in the book. For now though we shall concentrate on a simple example involving a differential equation.

Example 2.   *Show that*

$$y = x^2 \cos x - 3x \sin x + x \ln x$$

satisfies the differential equation

$$x^2 \frac{d^2y}{dx^2} + y + (x^2 + 2)x^2 \cos x = x \frac{dy}{dx}.$$

Solution.   Since

$$y = x^2 \cos x - 3x \sin x + x \ln x$$

we know that

$$\frac{dy}{dx} = 2x \cos x - x^2 \sin x - 3 \sin x - 3x \cos x + \ln x + x \times \frac{1}{x}$$

$$= \ln x + 1 - x^2 \sin x - 3 \sin x - x \cos x$$

and also

$$\frac{d^2y}{dx^2} = \frac{1}{x} - 2x \sin x - x^2 \cos x - 3 \cos x - \cos x + x \sin x$$

$$= \frac{1}{x} - x \sin x - x^2 \cos x - 4 \cos x.$$

Substituting these into the differential equation, we see that

$$\text{L.H.S.} = x^2 \frac{d^2y}{dx^2} + y + (x^2 + 2)x^2 \cos x$$

$$= x - x^3 \sin x - x^4 \cos x - 4x^2 \cos x + x^2 \cos x$$

$$\qquad\qquad - 3x \sin x + x \ln x + x^4 \cos x + 2x^2 \cos x$$

$$= x - x^3 \sin x - x^2 \cos x - 3x \sin x + x \ln x$$

$$= x(1 - x^2 \sin x - x \cos x - 3 \sin x + \ln x)$$

$$= x \frac{dy}{dx}$$

$$= \text{R.H.S},$$

as required.

Notice that, as with our verification of trigonometric identities earlier, we must not assume that the given equation holds, but rather we must take one side of the equation and show that it equals the other side.

EXAMPLES 6

1. Find $\dfrac{dy}{dx}, \dfrac{d^2y}{dx^2}, \dfrac{d^3y}{dx^3}$ and $\dfrac{d^4y}{dx^4}$ where

    (a) $y = \cos 2x$,   (b) $y = x \sin 3x$,

    (c) $y = x^2 \ln x$,   (d) $y = e^{-3x}$.

2. Prove that $y = x \tan x$ satisfies the differential equation

$$x \frac{d^2y}{dx^2} - 2\frac{dy}{dx} - 2xy \sec^2 x = -2 \tan x.$$

3. Prove that $y = x^3 e^{3x} + 3x \cos 3x - \sin 3x$ satisfies the differential equation

$$x \frac{d^2y}{dx^2} - 2\frac{dy}{dx} + 9xy = 6x^3 (3x + 2) e^{3x}.$$

CHAPTER 7

Implicit Differentiation

An equation such as

$$y = 5\tan^3 x \ln x$$

defines y **explicitly** in terms of x. For every allowed value of x, we have a formula that enables us to calculate the corresponding value of y. We can, in theory at least, plot the graph of the curve, and we can use differentiation to find the gradient of the tangent to the curve at any point on the curve.

Contrast the above situation with the curve defined by the equation

$$3x^2 + 5y^2 - 6x + 20y - 69 = 0.$$

This equation defines y **implicitly** in terms of x, in the sense that if we substitute a value of x then we still have an equation to solve before obtaining the corresponding value(s) of y.

This equation defines an **ellipse**, which looks rather like a squashed circle, and it is reasonable that we should want to find the equation of a tangent to this curve, just as we want to find the tangent to the graph of an explicitly defined function. However we would like to do this without having to resort to solving the equation to find y explicitly in terms of x. There are two reasons for this: one is that such solving will always involve unnecessary extra work; the other is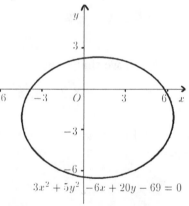
that sometimes it will be impossible to solve a certain equation explicitly, and yet we would still like to obtain the information that differentiation can give us.

The technique we use is known as **implicit differentiation**. More properly, this should be known as the differentiation of implicitly defined functions. In this procedure, we shall assume that an equation we are given defines y as a differentiable function of x, and then we differentiate each term with respect to x, remembering that, by the Chain Rule, to differentiate a term involving y, we first differentiate it with respect to y and then *multiply by* $\dfrac{dy}{dx}$.

Example 1.   *Find y' and y'' at the point $(3,2)$ on the ellipse $3x^2 + 5y^2 - 6x + 20y - 69 = 0$. Hence find the equation of the tangent and normal to the ellipse at $(3,2)$.*

Solution.   On differentiating implicitly with respect to x the equation $3x^2 + 5y^2 - 6x + 20y - 69 = 0$, we obtain

$$6x + 10yy' - 6 + 20y' - 0 = 0.$$

Notice that in carrying out this differentiation, the derivative of $5y^2$ with respect to x is $5 \times 2 \times y \times \dfrac{dy}{dx}$, which is $10yy'$, and the derivative of the constant -69 is 0.

The above relationship gives us the connection between x, y and y' at every point on the curve. To find the gradient of the tangent at a specific point, we need to substitute in the appropriate values for x and y. So we substitute $x = 3$, $y = 2$ into the equation to find the value of y', and we obtain

$$18 + 20y' - 6 + 20y' = 0,$$

from which

$$40y' = -12,$$

or

$$y' = -3/10.$$

It follows that the equation of the tangent to the curve at the point $(3,2)$, having gradient $-3/10$, will be

$$y - 2 = -\frac{3}{10}(x - 3),$$

which is

$$10y - 20 = -3x + 9,$$

or

$$10y + 3x = 29.$$

The normal to the curve will be perpendicular to the tangent and so the normal will have gradient $\frac{-1}{\left(-\frac{3}{10}\right)}$, which is $\frac{10}{3}$. Hence the equation of the normal will be

$$y - 2 = \frac{10}{3}(x - 3),$$

which can be simplified to

$$3y = 10x - 24.$$

To find the value of y'' at the point $(3,2)$, the simplest way is to differentiate the equation $6x + 10yy' - 6 + 20y' = 0$ implicitly with respect to x. We are assuming that y is defined for us as a differentiable function of x, and we shall assume similarly that y' will also be a differentiable function of x, whose derivative we can find by differentiating implicitly using the Chain Rule.

Notice that a term such as yy' involves a product of two functions of x, and so must be differentiated *using the Product Rule*. When we do this differentiation for yy' we will obtain $y \times \dfrac{d}{dx}(y') + y' \times \dfrac{d}{dx}(y)$, which is $y \times \dfrac{d^2y}{dx^2} + y' \times \dfrac{dy}{dx}$, or $yy'' + y'y'$.

On differentiating $6x + 10yy' - 6 + 20y' = 0$ with respect to x we therefore obtain $6 + 10(y'y' + yy'') - 0 + 20y'' = 0$. Substituting in the values for x, y and y', which are $x = 3$, $y = 2$ and $y' = -3/10$, we have $6 + 10(-3/10)^2 + 10 \times 2 \times y'' + 20y'' = 0$, which simplifies to $40y'' = -(69/10)$, or $y'' = -(69/400)$.

Example 2.   *Find* $\dfrac{dy}{dx}$ *in terms of x, y for the variable y defined implicitly in terms of x by the relation*

$$x^3 - 3x^3y + 7xy^4 = 32.$$

Solution.   Differentiating the above equation implicitly with respect to x, we obtain

$$3x^2 - 3\left(3x^2y + x^3y'\right) + 7\left(y^4 + x \times 4y^3y'\right) = 0.$$

Notice here that the terms $3x^2y + x^3y'$ come from differentiating x^3y using the Product Rule, while the terms $y^4 + x \times 4y^3y'$ come about on differentiating xy^4, again using the Product Rule. Notice that the term 32 also has to be differentiated, which leads to the 0 on the right hand side of the equation. *Forgetting to differentiate the constant is a very common source of mistakes in this type of example.*

If we re-arrange the terms in the above equation, we can solve it to find $\dfrac{dy}{dx}$ in terms of x and y. We obtain

$$3x^2 - 9x^2y - 3x^3y' + 7y^4 + 28xy^3y' = 0,$$

from which we have

$$3x^2 - 9x^2y + 7y^4 = 3x^3y' - 28xy^3y',$$

or

$$y' = \frac{3x^2 - 9x^2y + 7y^4}{3x^3 - 28xy^3},$$

provided of course that $3x^3 - 28xy^3 \neq 0$.

EXAMPLES 7

1. If $x^2 + 3y^2 - 2xy + 5x - 4y = 9$, find $\dfrac{dy}{dx}$ in terms of x and y.

2. If $x \sin y - y \sin x = 0$, find $\dfrac{dy}{dx}$ in terms of x and y.

3. Find y' and y'' at the point $(1, -3)$ on the curve
$$x^2 + y^2 + 2xy - 4x + 6y + 18 = 0.$$

4. Find y' and y'' at the point $(2, 1)$ on the curve
$$x^3 + y^3 - 3xy = 3.$$

5. Find the equations of the tangent and normal to the curve
$$4x^3 + 2x^2 y^2 + y^4 = 16$$
at the point $(-2, 2)$.

6. Find the equation of the tangent to the curve
$$\sin(x + 2y) + \cos(2x - y) = 1$$
at the point $\left(\frac{3\pi}{10}, \frac{4\pi}{15}\right)$.

7. Prove that the curves
$$x^2 + y^2 = 10 \quad \text{and} \quad x^2 + 2y^2 - 38x + 19 = 0$$
intersect orthogonally. [Find the points of intersection of the curves and show that the tangents to the two curves at each of the points of intersection are perpendicular.]

CHAPTER 8

Sketching Rational Functions without using Calculus

In this chapter we shall sketch some rational functions, working simply from the form of the function, without using more advanced methods such as Calculus. A **rational function** is one that can be expressed as a ratio of two polynomials. So a rational function has the form

$$f(x) = \frac{n(x)}{d(x)},$$

where $n(x)$ and $d(x)$ are both polynomials in x, which we shall assume to have no factors in common.

Example 1. *Sketch $y = 1/x$.*

Solution. To get an idea of the behaviour of this function, we start by drawing up a table of values of y against x.

x	-100	-10	-1	-0.1	-0.01	0
y	-0.01	-0.1	-1	-10	-100	ND

x	0.01	0.1	1	10	100
y	100	10	1	0.1	0.01

From the table we see that as x becomes very large then y remains positive but becomes very small. We write this as $y \to 0^+$ as $x \to \infty$. [The plus sign here indicates that y remains positive while approaching the value zero.]

Again, if x is large (in modulus) but negative, then y again approaches the value zero, but this time taking on negative values. We write this as $y \to 0^-$ as $x \to -\infty$.

Now we consider what happens as x tends towards zero, taking positive values. When this happens we see that y is positive and that y increases without bound. We write this as $y \to \infty$ as $x \to 0^+$.

Finally we see that $y \to -\infty$ as $x \to 0^-$. This indicates that as x tends to zero, taking negative values, then y becomes very large (in modulus) and negative.

Notice that it is not permissible to divide by zero, and so there is no point on the curve corresponding to $x = 0$. Hence the graph of the function is as shown.

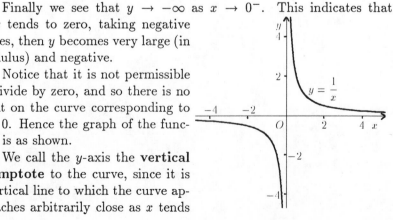

We call the y-axis the **vertical asymptote** to the curve, since it is a vertical line to which the curve approaches arbitrarily close as x tends towards the value zero. For a similar reason, we can say that the x-axis is a **horizontal asymptote** to the curve. We can also describe this latter situation by saying that the curve $y = 1/x$ **behaves asymptotically** like $y = 0$ (written $y \approx 0$ as $x \to \pm\infty$).

Example 2. *Sketch* $y = \dfrac{1}{x-2} - 4.$

Solution. This curve will have the same general shape as the curve $y = 1/x$. As we saw in Chapter 1, the effect of the $(x-2)$-term will be to move the vertical asymptote from the x-axis to the line $x = 2$, while the effect of the (-4)-term will be to move the horizontal asymptote to $y = -4$. Hence $y \approx -4$ as $x \to \pm\infty$.

We can determine some points on the curve by finding where it cuts the axes. Putting $x = 0$, we have $y = \frac{1}{0-2} - 4 = -9/2$. So the curve cuts the y-axis at $(0, -9/2)$.

The curve meets the x-axis when $y = 0$. This happens when

$$0 = \frac{1}{x-2} - 4,$$

so that

$$\frac{1}{x-2} = 4,$$

or

$$x - 2 = 1/4,$$

from which $x = 9/4$. Hence the curve meets the x-axis at the point $(9/4, 0)$.

Example 3. *Sketch* $y = \dfrac{1}{x^2}.$

Solution. We consider the table of values given on the next page. Notice that $y = \dfrac{1}{x^2} = \left(\dfrac{1}{x}\right)^2$, so that every y-value of $y = \dfrac{1}{x^2}$ will be the square of the corresponding y-value for $y = \dfrac{1}{x}$. In particular, all y-values will be positive, so that the curve will lie wholly above the x-axis. Values for $y = \dfrac{1}{x}$ with $y > 1$ will be increased on the curve $y = \dfrac{1}{x^2}$, while those for which $0 < y < 1$ will be decreased on this curve.

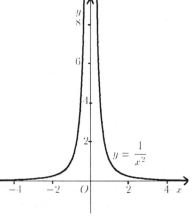

The y-axis is again a vertical asymptote for $y = \dfrac{1}{x^2}$, and equally the x-axis will be a horizontal asymptote to the curve. Notice that this curve is symmetric about the y-axis, whereas the curve $y = \dfrac{1}{x}$ was symmetric about the origin.

x	0	±0.01	±0.2	±0.5	±1	±2	±5	±100
$y = \dfrac{1}{x^2}$	ND	10000	25	4	1	0.25	0.04	0.0001

We shall now develop a systematic way for sketching the rational function

$$f(x) = \frac{n(x)}{d(x)},$$

where $n(x)$ and $d(x)$ are two polynomial functions in the variable x, having no common factor. We follow the procedure outlined below.

1) Factorise the numerator $n(x)$ and find where $n(x) = 0$. This will give the points where the curve meets or crosses the x-axis.

2) Factorise the denominator $d(x)$ and find where $d(x) = 0$. This will give the vertical asymptotes to the curve.

3) Ignore all terms in the numerator and denominator except those involving the highest powers of x. By finding the ratio of these terms, determine the asymptotic behaviour of the curve $y = f(x)$ as $x \to \pm\infty$.

4) By putting $x = 0$, find where the curve cuts the y-axis.

5) Draw up a table of sign for $f(x)$, including in ascending order all the x-values found in 1) and 2) above. This table can be used to decide where the curve lies above the x-axis and where below. From this we can decide how the curve approaches its zeros and how it approaches its vertical asymptotes.

6) Sketch the curve, incorporating all of the information found above. Any inconsistency will indicate that somewhere in the working lies an error.

We shall now carry through an example of this type, in order to demonstrate the method in action.

Example 4.   *Sketch* $y = \dfrac{2x^2 - 8x + 6}{x^2 - 4}$.

Solution.   1)   We can factorise $2x^2 - 8x + 6$ as $2(x - 1)(x - 3)$. Since this is zero when $x = 1$ and $x = 3$, we see that the curve meets or crosses the x-axis where $x = 1$ and where $x = 3$.

2) $x^2 - 4$ is a difference of two squares, and can be readily factorised in the form $(x - 2)(x + 2)$. Hence $x^2 - 4 = 0$ when $x = 2$ and when $x = -2$. It follows that there are vertical asymptotes to the curve at $x = 2$ and at $x = -2$.

3) For x large (in modulus) we know that $2x^2 - 8x + 6 \approx 2x^2$ and that $x^2 - 4 \approx x^2$. Hence it follows that, as $x \to \pm\infty$,

$$y \approx \frac{2x^2}{x^2} = 2.$$

So the curve behaves asymptotically like the straight line $y = 2$. We write this as $y \approx 2$.

4) When $x = 0$, we see that $y = \dfrac{6}{-4} = -\dfrac{3}{2}$. Hence the curve cuts the y-axis at the point $(0, -3/2)$.

5) We now draw up a table of sign for y, including all the x-values we found in 1) and 2) above. This means that we need to include, in order, the x-values $x = -2, 1, 2, 3$.

x	$\to$	-2	$\to$	1	$\to$	2	$\to$	3	$\to$
$2(x-1)$	$-$	$-$	$-$	0	$+$	$+$	$+$	$+$	$+$
$(x-3)$	$-$	$-$	$-$	$-$	$-$	$-$	$-$	0	$+$
$2(x-1)(x-3)$	$+$	$+$	$+$	0	$-$	$-$	$-$	0	$+$
$(x-2)$	$-$	$-$	$-$	$-$	$-$	0	$+$	$+$	$+$
$(x+2)$	$-$	0	$+$	$+$	$+$	$+$	$+$	$+$	$+$
$(x-2)(x+2)$	$+$	0	$-$	$-$	$-$	0	$+$	$+$	$+$
y	$+$	ND	$-$	0	$+$	ND	$-$	0	$+$
Above/Below x-axis	A	VA	B	On	A	VA	B	On	A

In the final row of the above table, we have used A and B to stand for Above and Below respectively, denoting whether the curve lies above or below the x-axis, On to denote when the curve has a point on the x-axis, and VA where there is a vertical asymptote at the point under consideration.

We know that there is a vertical asymptote to the curve at $x = -2$. The table of sign tells us how the curve approaches its vertical asymptote.

To the left of the vertical asymptote at $x = -2$, we know that the y-values on the curve are either getting very large or are becoming very large (in modulus) and negative. From the table of sign we see that to the left of $x = -2$, y is positive. Hence the curve is approaching the top end of the asymptote as $x \to -2$, with $x < -2$.

Similarly, to the right of $x = -2$, the curve is again approaching the vertical asymptote, but this time we see from the table that y is negative, and so this time the curve approaches the asymptote at the bottom end.

Now let us look at how the curve behaves near its zero at $x = 1$.

Consulting the table of sign, we see that the value of y is negative for x close to 1, but with $x < 1$. Hence the curve is below the x-axis for values of x close to $x = 1$, but to the left of $x = 1$. For x slightly to the right of $x = 1$, the table tells us that y is positive. Hence, as shown in the diagram, the curve rises from below the x-axis to above it as x increases from being a little bit smaller than $x = 1$ to being a bit larger than $x = 1$.

The behaviour of the curve near the vertical asymptote at $x = 2$, and near the zero at $x = 3$, is established in a similar way.

It should be clearly realised that we are using the table of sign for y to tell us about the behaviour of the curve. There are three different tables of sign that can give us useful information. These are the tables for y, y' and y''. Each tells us different things about the curve, and so must be given the correct interpretation. This is why I suggest you include the final line shown in the table of sign for y, to help you to remember how to interpret what the table is telling you.

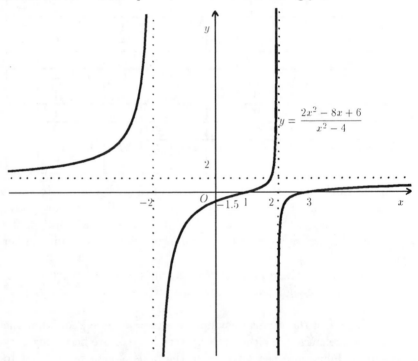

$$y = \frac{2x^2 - 8x + 6}{x^2 - 4}$$

We have completed the diagram in the simplest way possible consistent with the information found above. We can show that this is correct in this case, but the proof of that will have to wait until we have Calculus fully at our disposal.

Example 5.   *Sketch* $y = \dfrac{x^2 - 4}{2x^2 - 8x + 6}$.

Solution.   We are asked here to sketch a function which is the reciprocal of the function we were asked to sketch in Example 4. A few moments thought will convince us that there is the following relationship between the two curves.

1) Zeros on the original curve will correspond to vertical asymptotes to the reciprocal curve.

2) Vertical asymptotes to the original curve will correspond to zeros on the reciprocal curve.

3) Positive values on the original curve will correspond to positive values on the reciprocal curve.

4) Negative values on the original curve will correspond to negative values on the reciprocal curve.

5) Since $y = \dfrac{2x^2 - 8x + 6}{x^2 - 4}$ behaves asymptotically like $y = 2$, the reciprocal curve will behave asymptotically like $y = 1/2$.

6) If there had been any, then non-zero local maxima on the original curve would correspond to non-zero local minima, while non-zero local minima on the original curve would correspond to non-zero local maxima on the reciprocal curve.

It follows that a sketch of the curve we require is as given.

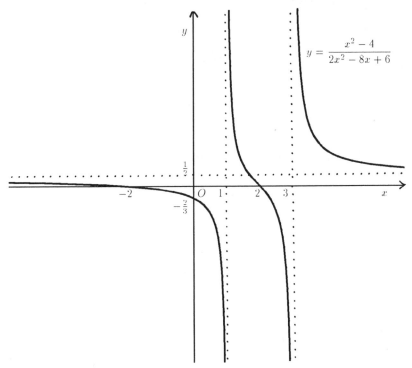

$$y = \frac{x^2 - 4}{2x^2 - 8x + 6}$$

Notice that in this sketch we have drawn the curve so that as x increases past the value $x = 2$ then the curve goes from being above the x-axis to being below it. We have done this because from the above we know that there is a zero at $x = 2$ corresponding to the vertical asymptote to the original curve at $x = 2$, and we know that the original curve lay above the x-axis for $x < 2$ (and so the reciprocal curve does also) while the original curve was below the x-axis for $x > 2$ and so the reciprocal curve is also below the x-axis just to the right of the zero at $x = 2$. A similar argument deals with the behaviour near the two vertical asymptotes and near the other zero on the reciprocal curve.

EXAMPLES 8

1.   Sketch the curves

(a) $y = \dfrac{4}{x}$,

(b) $y = 2 + \dfrac{1}{x+2}$,

(c) $y = \dfrac{3}{x^2}$,

(d) $y = 4 + \dfrac{1}{(x+1)^2}$.

2.   Without using Calculus, sketch the curves

(a) $y = \dfrac{x+1}{(x-3)(x+2)}$,

(b) $y = \dfrac{(x-2)(x-4)(x+2)}{(x+1)(x+4)}$,

(c) $y = \dfrac{(x-3)(x-1)}{(x+2)^2(x+1)}$,

(d) $y = \dfrac{x^2(x-2)}{(x+1)(x-3)}$.

3.   Without using Calculus, sketch the curve

$$y = \frac{x^2 - 4x + 3}{x + 2},$$

and deduce a sketch of the curve

$$y = \frac{x+2}{x^2 - 4x + 3}.$$

4.   Without using Calculus, sketch the curve

$$y = \frac{x-1}{x^2 - 2x - 8},$$

and deduce a sketch of the curve

$$y = \frac{x^2 - 2x - 8}{x - 1}.$$

CHAPTER 9

Concavity and Points of Inflection

We have seen that $f'(c)$ gives the rate of change at $x = c$ of $f(x)$ for increasing x. Put another way, $f'(c)$ gives the slope, at $x = c$, on the curve $y = f(x)$. So $f'(c)$ tells us whether the curve $y = f(x)$ is going upwards or downwards as we look at it from left to right, and also $f'(c)$ tells us how rapidly $f(x)$ is increasing or decreasing.

$f'(c)$	Shape of curve	Typical sketch
Large positive	y increases rapidly as x increases	$(c, f(c))$
Small positive	y increases slowly as x increases	$(c, f(c))$
Small (in modulus) and negative	y decreases slowly as x increases	$(c, f(c))$
Large (in modulus) and negative	y decreases rapidly as x increases	$(c, f(c))$

Just as the derivative of y tells us about the slope of $y = f(x)$, so the derivative of $\dfrac{dy}{dx}$ will tell us about how the gradient $\dfrac{dy}{dx}$ changes as

x changes. For if $f''(c)$ is positive, then we know that the gradient $\dfrac{dy}{dx}$ is increasing as x increases through the value $x = c$. On the other hand, if $f''(c)$ is negative, then we know that the gradient $\dfrac{dy}{dx}$ is decreasing as x increases through the value $x = c$.

The following table indicates the behaviour of $y = f(x)$ for different combinations of the signs of $f'(c)$ and $f''(c)$.

$f'(c)$	$f''(c)$	Description	Sketch	Concavity
+ve	+ve	y increases as x increases, with gradient increasing as x increases		UP
+ve	−ve	y increases as x increases, but with gradient decreasing as x increases		DOWN
−ve	+ve	y decreases as x increases, with steepness of gradient becoming less as x increases		UP
−ve	−ve	y decreases as x increases, but with steepness of gradient becoming greater as x increases		DOWN

We say that $y = f(x)$ is **concave up** at $x = c$ if the curve $y = f(x)$ lies above the tangent to the curve at $x = c$. This means that, as we move from left to right along the curve, the curve is bending to the left.

Similarly, we say that $y = f(x)$ is **concave down** at $x = c$ if the curve $y = f(x)$ lies below the tangent to the curve at $x = c$. This means that, as we move from left to right along the curve, the curve is bending to the right.

From the table given above, we can see that, at $x = c$, $y = f(x)$ is *concave up* if $f''(c) > 0$, and that $y = f(x)$ is *concave down* if $f''(c) < 0$.

A **point of inflection** on $y = f(x)$ is a point at which the concavity changes (whether from up to down, or from down to up). It follows that if $x = c$ gives a point of inflection on the curve $y = f(x)$, and if $f'(x)$ is differentiable at $x = c$, then $f''(c) = 0$. This is because, to one side of the point of inflection, we must have $f''(x) > 0$, with $f''(x) < 0$ on the other side of the point of inflection. Hence, at least if we assume that $f''(x)$ is continuous near $x = c$, then we must have $f''(x) = 0$ at the point of inflection.

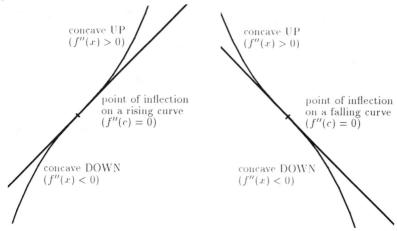

Let us imagine a motor-cyclist who is riding through an S-bend, and who is leaning first to the one side and then to the other as he takes the bends. Then a point of inflection corresponds to the point between the two bends when the motor-cyclist is momentarily upright.

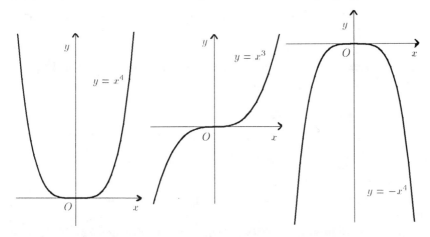

Notice that it is *not* always true that if $x = c$ is such that $f''(c) = 0$ then $x = c$ must give a point of inflection. For, if we consider the three curves given by $y = x^4$, $y = x^3$ and $y = -x^4$, then on each of these curves we can readily see that the second derivative is zero at $x = 0$.

However, if we examine the diagrams given on the previous page, we see that in the case of $y = x^4$ we have a minimum at $x = 0$, on $y = -x^4$ we have a maximum at $x = 0$, and it is only on $y = x^3$ that we actually do have a point of inflection.

To ensure that we do have a point of inflection at a point $x = c$ on $y = f(x)$ for which $f''(c) = 0$, we have to check that the sign of $f''(x)$ does indeed change (whether from positive to negative, or from negative to positive) as x increases through the value $x = c$.

Example 1. *Sketch the curve*

$$y = x^4 - 6x^2 + 3x + 2$$

in a neighbourhood of the points $(0,2)$, $(2,0)$ *and in a neighbourhood of its points of inflection.*

Solution.   We start the solution by finding $\dfrac{dy}{dx}$ and $\dfrac{d^2y}{dx^2}$. Since

$$y = x^4 - 6x^2 + 3x + 2,$$

we have

$$\frac{dy}{dx} = 4x^3 - 12x + 3$$

and

$$\frac{d^2y}{dx^2} = 12x^2 - 12.$$

We need to find the values of y, $\dfrac{dy}{dx}$ and $\dfrac{d^2y}{dx^2}$ at $x = 0$ and at $x = 2$.

Substituting $x = 0$ first, we have $y = 2$, $\dfrac{dy}{dx} = 3$ and $\dfrac{d^2y}{dx^2} = -12$. From these we see that when the curve is in a neighbourhood of the point $(0,2)$, then the curve has a steep positive gradient there (it is sloping at roughly $71°$ to the x-axis) and that the curve is concave down, so that it lies below the tangent to the curve at $(0,2)$.

Now we turn our attention to the point $x = 2$. Substituting $x = 2$, we have $y = 0$, $\dfrac{dy}{dx} = 11$ and $\dfrac{d^2y}{dx^2} = 36$. In this case, the curve has an even steeper positive gradient (this time the curve is at roughly $85°$ to the x-axis), and the curve is concave up. This time therefore the curve lies above its tangent at $x = 2$.

Possible points of inflection on the curve occur when $12x^2 - 12 = 0$. This requires that $12(x - 1)(x + 1) = 0$, or that $x = 1$ or $x = -1$.

We need to check that the concavity does indeed change at both $x = 1$ and at $x = -1$. We do this by drawing up a table of sign for y'' near each of these x-values.

x	$\rightarrow$	-1	$\rightarrow$		$\rightarrow$	1	$\rightarrow$
$x - 1$	$-$	$-$	$-$		$-$	0	$+$
$x + 1$	$-$	0	$+$		$+$	$+$	$+$
$y'' = 12(x-1)(x+1)$	$+$	0	$-$		$-$	0	$+$
Concavity	UP		DOWN	DOWN			UP

Since the concavity does change at both $x = 1$ and $x = -1$, we see that these are both points of inflection on the curve. Substituting these x-values in turn we find that when $x = 1$ we have $y = 0$ and $\dfrac{dy}{dx} = -5$, while when $x = -1$ we see that $y = -6$ and $\dfrac{dy}{dx} = 11$.

Near the point of inflection at $(-1, -6)$, we see that the curve has a steep positive gradient, and that, as x increases from less than -1 to more than -1, the curve changes from being above its tangent to being below its tangent.

Similarly, near the point of inflection at $(1, 0)$, the curve has a fairly steep negative gradient, and this time the curve changes from lying below its tangent to lying above it as x increases through $x = 1$.

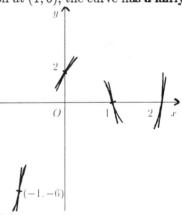

The sketch given is not yet complete because we do not have enough information to be sure how we should join up the sections of the curve. To complete the curve, we need to use Calculus to find where the turning points are. We also need to see what happens to the curve when $x \to \pm\infty$.

EXAMPLES 9

1. Find the set of real numbers for which the function
$$f(x) \equiv x^3 - 12x^2 + 25x + 30$$
is concave down.

2. Express as a union of intervals the set of real numbers for which the function
$$f(x) \equiv x^4 - 2x^3 - 12x^2 + 13x + 20$$
is concave up.

3. Find the points on the curve $y = x^4 + 4x^3 - 18x^2 - 40x + 50$ for which $\dfrac{d^2y}{dx^2} = 0$, and draw up a table of sign for $\dfrac{d^2y}{dx^2}$ near each of these points. Hence determine whether they are points of inflection on the curve.

4.   Find the points on the curve $y = 3x^5 - 5x^4 - 10x^3 + 30x^2 + 3x - 23$ for which $\dfrac{d^2y}{dx^2} = 0$, and draw up a table of sign for $\dfrac{d^2y}{dx^2}$ near each of these points. Hence determine whether they are points of inflection on the curve.

5.   For the curve $y = x^3 - 9x^2 - 21x + 47$, find the gradient of the tangent to the curve at each of the points $(-1, 58)$ and $(3, -70)$, find the concavity of the curve near each of these points, and hence sketch the curve in a neighbourhood of each of these points.

6.   Find any points for which $\dfrac{d^2y}{dx^2} = 0$ on the curve given by the equation $y = x^4 - 8x^3 + 24x^2 - 10x - 2$. Find the gradient of the tangent to the curve at each of the points $(0, -2)$ and $(1, 5)$ and at any points on the curve for which $\dfrac{d^2y}{dx^2} = 0$. Also find the concavity of the curve near each of these points, and hence sketch the curve in a neighbourhood of each of these points.

7.   Find any points of inflection on the curve defined by the equation $y = x^4 - 2x^3 - 36x^2 + 80x + 100$. Find the gradient of the tangent to the curve at each of the points $(-1, -13)$ and $(4, -28)$ and at any points of inflection on the curve. Also find the concavity of the curve near each of these points, and hence sketch the curve in a neighbourhood of each of these points.

CHAPTER 10
Local Maxima and Local Minima

In this chapter we shall see the interpretation of the derivative of a function $f(x)$ in terms of the slope of the graph of the function. We shall assume that $f(x)$ is a function which is differentiable (and therefore continuous) on an interval I.

We say that a function $f(x)$ is **strictly increasing** on an interval I if $f(x_2) > f(x_1)$ for any pair of numbers x_2, x_1 in the interval I for which $x_2 > x_1$. Clearly if the gradient is positive on a graph then the function is increasing, and so, if $f'(x) > 0$ for all points on an open interval I, then $f(x)$ is (strictly) increasing on the open interval I.

Similarly, a function $f(x)$ is said to be **strictly decreasing** on an interval I if $f(x_2) < f(x_1)$ for any pair of numbers x_2, x_1 in the interval I for which $x_2 > x_1$. Clearly if the gradient is negative on a graph then the function is decreasing, and so, if $f'(x) < 0$ for all points on an open interval I, then $f(x)$ is (strictly) decreasing on the interval I.

a strictly increasing function

a strictly decreasing function

A value of x for which $f'(c) = 0$ is called a **critical point**, or **turning point**. As we have already seen, these are the values of x for which the tangent to the curve $y = f(x)$ is parallel to the x-axis.

Providing the gradient $f'(x)$ is continuously changing round about the critical point $x = c$, there are four possibilities that can occur. These are tabulated below.

From the table given below, we can see that there are two possible ways of determining the nature of a point on a curve for which $f'(c) = 0$.

<u>Method 1.</u> Use a table of sign for $f'(x)$ to find the signs of $f'(x)$ on both sides of the value $x = c$. We can classify the point as being a local maximum, local minimum or point of inflection (on a rising or falling curve) according as to which of the four possible arrangements of signs occurs.

Method 2.   Find the value of the second derivative $f''(x)$ at $x = c$. If $f''(c) > 0$ the curve is concave up, and so has a local minimum at $x = c$. On the other hand, if $f''(c) < 0$ the curve is concave down, and so has a local maximum at $x = c$. If $f''(c) = 0$, it is best to use Method 1 to decide on the nature of the turning point.

x	$\rightarrow$	c	$\rightarrow$	$\rightarrow$	c	$\rightarrow$
$f'(x)$	$-$	0	$+$	$+$	0	$-$
Shape of curve						
Name		Local Minimum			Local Maximum	
Concavity		Up			Down	
$f''(x)$	$+$	$+/0$	$+$	$-$	$-/0$	$-$
x	$\rightarrow$	c	$\rightarrow$	$\rightarrow$	c	$\rightarrow$
$f'(x)$	$-$	0	$-$	$+$	0	$+$
Shape of curve						
Name		Horizontal Point of Inflection on a falling curve			Horizontal Point of Inflection on a rising curve	
Concavity	Up		Down	Down		Up
$f''(x)$	$+$	0	$-$	$-$	0	$+$

Method 1 has the advantage that we do not need to find $f''(x)$ in order to apply the method, but it has the draw-back that we have to use a table of sign to determine the nature of the turning point. Method 2 has the advantage that we only need to evaluate $f''(x)$ at the one point $x = c$, but it has the disadvantage that if $f''(c) = 0$ then Method 2 gives us no information about the nature of the point $x = c$.

Usually it is preferable to use Method 2, provided finding $f''(x)$ is not too difficult, retaining Method 1 as a fall-back method.

Example 1.   *Sketch the curve*

$$y = f(x) \equiv x^3 - 5x^2 - 8x + 12,$$

finding where it crosses the coordinate axes, the coordinates and natures of the critical points, and the coordinates of the point of inflection. Find the intervals on which $f(x)$ is strictly increasing, and find the values of x for which $y = f(x)$ is concave up.

Solution.   If we substitute values of x in turn, we readily find that $f(1) = 0$, from which it follows that $x - 1$ is a factor of $f(x)$. Using synthetic division, we see that

$$f(x) = (x - 1)(x^2 - 4x - 12).$$

Continuing to substitute values of x in $g(x) = x^2 - 4x - 12$, we see that $g(1) = -15$, $g(-1) = -7$, while $g(2) = -16$ and $g(-2) = 0$. From this it follows that $x+2$ is a factor of $g(x)$, and so we conclude that $g(x) = (x+2)(x-6)$. Hence

$$f(x) = (x-1)(x+2)(x-6).$$

$$
\begin{array}{c|rrrr}
 & 1 & -5 & -8 & 12 \\
\times 1 & 0 & 1 & -4 & -12 \\
\hline
+ & 1 & -4 & -12 & 0
\end{array}
$$

So the graph of $y = f(x)$ cuts the x-axis at $x = 1$, $x = -2$ and also at $x = 6$. The graph intersects the y-axis at $x = 0$, $y = 12$. Now

$$
\begin{array}{c|rrr}
 & 1 & -4 & -12 \\
\times (-2) & 0 & -2 & 12 \\
\hline
+ & 1 & -6 & 0
\end{array}
$$

$$
\begin{aligned}
f'(x) &= 3x^2 - 10x - 8 \\
&= (x-4)(3x+2),
\end{aligned}
$$

and so $f'(x) = 0$ when $x = 4$ and when $x = -2/3$. Also $f''(x) = 6x - 10$, so that $f''(x) = 0$ when $x = 5/3$.

When $x = 4$, $y = f(4) = 4^3 - 5 \times 4^2 - 8 \times 4 + 12 = -36$, and $f''(4) = 6 \times 4 - 10 = 14$, which is positive. Thus the point $(4, -36)$ is a local minimum on the curve.

When $x = -2/3$,

$$
\begin{aligned}
f(-2/3) &= (-2/3)^3 - 5 \times (-2/3)^2 - 8 \times (-2/3) + 12 \\
&= \frac{-8 - 60 + 144 + 324}{27} \\
&= \frac{400}{27}.
\end{aligned}
$$

Also $f''(-2/3) = 6 \times (-2/3) - 10 = -14$, which is negative. It follows from this that the point $(-2/3, 400/27)$ is a local maximum on the curve.

The only possible point of inflection on the curve occurs where $f''(x) = 0$, which happens when $x = 5/3$. When $x = 5/3$, we find that

$$
\begin{aligned}
y &= f(5/3) \\
&= (5/3)^3 - 5 \times (5/3)^2 - 8 \times (5/3) + 12 \\
&= \frac{125 - 375 - 360 + 324}{27} \\
&= -\frac{286}{27}.
\end{aligned}
$$

To decide whether this point is indeed a point of inflection on the curve, we need to draw up a table of sign for $f''(x)$ in the vicinity of the value $x = 5/3$. Since we are also required to discuss the concavity of the whole curve, we will draw up the table of sign considering all possible values of x at which the concavity could change. However, since the second derivative of $f(x)$ is only zero when $x = 5/3$, the table we require is very simple.

x	$\rightarrow$	5/3	$\rightarrow$
$f''(x) = 6x - 10$	$-$	0	$+$
Concavity	DOWN		UP

Since the concavity of the curve does indeed change at $x = 5/3$, it follows that the point $(5/3, -286/27)$ is a point of inflection on the curve.

To find where the curve is strictly increasing, we need to find the intervals on which the gradient is positive, and so we draw up a table of sign for $f'(x)$, and consider those values of x for which $f'(x) > 0$. Since the sign of $f'(x)$ might change where $f'(x) = 0$, we need to include in our x-values the values $x = 4$ and $x = -2/3$ at which $f'(x) = 0$.

x	$\rightarrow$	$-2/3$	$\rightarrow$	4	$\rightarrow$
$x - 4$	$-$	$-$	$-$	0	$+$
$3x + 2$	$-$	0	$+$	$+$	$+$
$f'(x) = (x - 4)(3x + 2)$	$+$	0	$-$	0	$+$
Inc/Dec	Inc	0	Dec	0	Inc

From this we see that the curve $y = f(x)$ is strictly increasing on the intervals $(-\infty, -2/3)$ and $(4, \infty)$. Notice that although the function is strictly increasing on both of these intervals, it is *not* true that if we choose a point in the first interval, then the value of the function at that point will be less than the value at any point in the second interval. As an example, we easily see that $f(-1) = 14$ while $f(5) = -28$.

The reason for this is of course that the curve decreases in value between the two intervals, and so starts increasing at $x = 4$ from a smaller value than the one it reached near $x = -2/3$.

Finally notice that from the table of sign for the second derivative, we know that the curve is concave up precisely when $x \in (5/3, \infty)$.

We complete the solution of this example with a sketch of the curve.

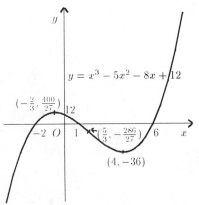

$y = x^3 - 5x^2 - 8x + 12$

$(-\frac{2}{3}, \frac{400}{27})$

$(\frac{5}{3}, -\frac{286}{27})$

$(4, -36)$

Example 2. *Consider the rational function*

$$f(x) = \frac{4(x - 2)^2}{(x + 12)(4x - 15)}.$$

Find the coordinates and nature of the critical point(s) on the curve $y = f(x)$, and also find any point(s) of inflection on the curve. Find also the points where the curve meets the coordinate axes, the asymptotic behaviour of the curve as $x \to \pm\infty$, and the vertical asymptotes on the

curve. Hence sketch the curve. Find also those values of x for which
$y = f(x)$ *is concave down.*

Solution.   In solving problems like this one, we follow the routine we introduced for sketching rational functions, with the addition that we can now use Calculus to determine the precise positions of the maxima, minima and any points of inflection.

$$f(x) = \frac{4(x-2)^2}{(x+12)(4x-15)}$$ meets the x-axis where $x = 2$, and at no other points, since $x = 2$ is the only value of x which makes $f(x) = 0$.

The curve has vertical asymptotes at $x = -12$ and $x = 15/4$, and for no other values of x, since for a vertical asymptote we are looking for the denominator of $f(x)$ to be zero, so that $f(x)$ will be undefined.

As $x \to \pm\infty$, $y \approx \dfrac{4x^2}{4x^2} = 1$. So the curve approaches the line $y = 1$ for positive or negative values of x which are large in modulus.

When $x = 0$, $y = 4(-2)^2/(12)(-15) = -4/45$, giving the point where the curve cuts the y-axis.

We now draw up a table of sign for y against x, including the x-values $x = 2$, $x = -12$ and $x = 15/4$ found above. This table will tell us whether the curve lies above or below the x-axis.

x	$\to$	-12	$\to$	2	$\to$	$15/4$	$\to$
Num=$4(x-2)^2$	$+$	$+$	$+$	0	$+$	$+$	$+$
$x + 12$	$-$	0	$+$	$+$	$+$	$+$	$+$
$4x - 15$	$-$	$-$	$-$	$-$	$-$	0	$+$
Den = $(x+12)(4x-15)$	$+$	0	$-$	$-$	$-$	0	$+$
y	$+$	ND	$-$	0	$-$	ND	$+$
ABOVE/ON/BELOW x-axis	A	VA	B	ON	B	VA	A

We have used A and B in the final line of the table to indicate whether the curve lies Above or Below the x-axis, as well as writing ON to indicate where the curve meets the x-axis and VA to denote a Vertical Asymptote.

From the information gathered above, we could draw a reasonable sketch of the curve. However we shall wait before doing that so that we can use Calculus to determine the precise positions of the critical points on the curve.

We use the Quotient Rule twice in order to calculate $\dfrac{dy}{dx}$ and $\dfrac{d^2y}{dx^2}$. We have

$$\begin{aligned}
\frac{dy}{dx} &= \frac{(x+12)(4x-15)8(x-2) - 4(x-2)^2(8x+33)}{[(x+12)(4x-15)]^2} \\
&= \frac{4(x-2)[2(x+12)(4x-15) - (x-2)(8x+33)]}{(x+12)^2(4x-15)^2} \\
&= \frac{4(x-2)[8x^2 + 66x - 360 - (8x^2 + 17x - 66]}{(x+12)^2(4x-15)^2} \\
&= \frac{4(x-2)[8x^2 + 66x - 360 - 8x^2 - 17x + 66]}{(x+12)^2(4x-15)^2} \\
&= \frac{4(x-2)(49x - 294)}{(x+12)^2(4x-15)^2} \\
&= \frac{196(x-2)(x-6)}{(x+12)^2(4x-15)^2}.
\end{aligned}$$

Notice that in using the Quotient Rule above, we needed to find the derivative of $(x+12)(4x-15)$. We chose to multiply out and express this as $4x^2 + 33x - 180$, which has derivative $8x + 33$, as we stated. An alternative would have been to differentiate $(x+12)(4x-15)$ using the Product Rule, and then simplify the answer. Either method would be acceptable. We chose the method we did because it was slightly easier in this case.

Now we need to use the Quotient Rule again in order to find the second derivative.

In anticipation of this, and to reduce the complexity of the calculations involved, let us start by working out the derivatives of the numerator and denominator, and simplifying these as far as possible. Then

$$\begin{aligned}
\frac{d}{dx}(196(x-2)(x-6)) &= 196\left((x-2) \times 1 + (x-6) \times 1\right) \\
&= 196\left(2x - 8\right).
\end{aligned}$$

Also

$$\begin{aligned}
\frac{d}{dx}\left((x+12)^2(4x-15)^2\right) &= \frac{d}{dx}((x+12)(4x-15))^2 \\
&= 2(x+12)(4x-15)\left[\frac{d}{dx}((x+12)(4x-15))\right] \\
&= 2(x+12)(4x-15)(8x+33),
\end{aligned}$$

quoting the result we found above for the derivative of $(x+12)(4x-15)$.
Then

$$\frac{d^2y}{dx^2} = \frac{(x+12)^2(4x-15)^2 196(2x-8)}{[(x+12)^2(4x-15)^2]^2}$$

$$= \frac{196(x+12)(4x-15)[(x+12)(4x-15)(2x-8)}{(x+12)^4(4x-15)^4}$$

$$= \frac{196\left[(x+12)(8x^2-62x+120)-(x-2)(16x^2-30x-396)\right]}{(x+12)^3(4x-15)^3}$$

$$= \frac{196[8x^3+34x^2-624x+1440-16x^3+62x^2+336x-792]}{(x+12)^3(4x-15)^3}$$

$$= \frac{196[-8x^3+96x^2-288x+648]}{(x+12)^3(4x-15)^3}$$

$$= \frac{(-8)(196)[x^3-12x^2+36x-81]}{(x+12)^3(4x-15)^3}$$

$$= \frac{-1568(x-9)(x^2-3x+9)}{(x+12)^3(4x-15)^3}.$$

It should be noted that we had to do a fair amount of quite difficult algebraic manipulation in this particular example. This is not typical of examples of this type, where usually things will be arranged to work out much more nicely. However it must be pointed out how essential it is that we can perform such algebraic manipulation accurately, if required.

One other point to make is that at the end of the calculation of $\frac{d^2y}{dx^2}$, we needed to be able to factorise $x^3-12x^2+36x-81$. This we did using the Remainder Theorem, although as usual we could have used Synthetic Division as an alternative. Having taken out $x-9$ as a factor, we were then left with x^2-3x+9, which we find cannot be factorised further into real factors since it has a negative discriminant.

We are now able to use the values of $\frac{dy}{dx}$ and $\frac{d^2y}{dx^2}$ found above to determine the coordinates of the turning points on the curve.

Recall that

$$\frac{dy}{dx} = \frac{196(x-2)(x-6)}{(x+12)^2(4x-15)^2},$$

from which we see that turning points on the curve will occur when $196(x-2)(x-6) = 0$, which is when $x = 2$ or $x = 6$.

When $x = 2$, we have $y = 0$ and also $\frac{d^2y}{dx^2} = \frac{-1568(-7)(7)}{14^3(-7)^3}$, which simplifies to the value $-8/98$. Since $\frac{d^2y}{dx^2}$ is negative, we have a local maximum at the point $(2, 0)$.

Substituting $x = 6$, we have $y = 4(4)^2/18 \times 9 = 32/81$ and also $\dfrac{d^2y}{dx^2} = \dfrac{(-1568)(-3)(27)}{18^3(9)^3}$, which simplifies to the value $196/9^4$. Since $\dfrac{d^2y}{dx^2}$ is positive, we have a local minimum at the point $(6, 32/81)$.

The only possible point of inflection on the curve will occur when $\dfrac{d^2y}{dx^2} = 0$, which from the factorised form of $\dfrac{d^2y}{dx^2}$ can only happen when $x = 9$. To decide whether this does indeed give us a point of inflection, we draw up a table of sign for $\dfrac{d^2y}{dx^2}$.

In anticipation of the final part of the question in which we are asked about the concavity of the curve, we will include in our table of sign all those x-values at which $\dfrac{d^2y}{dx^2}$ could possibly change in sign. Since

$$\frac{d^2y}{dx^2} = \frac{-1568(x-9)(x^2-3x+9)}{(x+12)^3(4x-15)^3},$$

the x-values of interest to us are $x = 9$, $x = -12$ and $x = 15/4$. So the required table of sign is

x	$\rightarrow$	-12	$\rightarrow$	$15/4$	$\rightarrow$	9	$\rightarrow$
$-1568(x^2-3x+9)$	$-$	$-$	$-$	$-$	$-$	$-$	$-$
$x-9$	$-$	$-$	$-$	$-$	$-$	0	$+$
NUMERATOR	$+$	$+$	$+$	$+$	$+$	0	$-$
$(x+12)^3$	$-$	0	$+$	$+$	$+$	$+$	$+$
$(4x-15)^3$	$-$	$-$	$-$	0	$+$	$+$	$+$
DENOMINATOR	$+$	0	$-$	0	$+$	$+$	$+$
$\dfrac{d^2y}{dx^2}$	$+$	ND	$-$	ND	$+$	0	$-$
CONCAVITY	UP		DN		UP		DN

$$y = \frac{4(x-2)^2}{(x+12)(4x-15)}$$

Since the curve changes from being concave up to being concave down as x increases through the value $x = 9$, it follows that we do have a point of inflection at $x = 9$, $y = 4/9$.

Finally, we deduce from the above table of sign that

$y = f(x)$ is concave down precisely when $x \in \left(-12, \frac{15}{4}\right) \cup (9, \infty)$.

We complete the solution of the example with the sketch of the curve given earlier, incorporating all the information we have obtained.

Before our final example of this Chapter, we need to consider the relationship between the sizes of the three functions x^n, e^x and $\ln x$ as $x \to \pm\infty$. As $x \to \infty$, we know that x^n (where n is a positive real number), e^x and $\ln x$ all become large and positive. However, if we consider the values of, say, x^3, e^x and $\ln x$ at $x = 1000$ we see that there is a great difference between the values. For $1000^3 = 10^9$, while $e^{1000} \approx 2 \times 10^{434}$, but $\ln 1000 \approx 7$. If we took a larger value of x, then the difference between the values would be even more pronounced.

What this suggests is that, for large values of x, e^x **dominates** x^n, while in turn x^n **dominates** $\ln x$, where n is any positive real number. [The restriction that n should be positive is imposed so that x^n shall tend to ∞ as x increases. If n were negative, then x^n would tend to zero, instead.]

The implication of this domination is that if we were required to calculate, for example, $x^4 / \exp x$, as $x \to \infty$, then we would have

$$\frac{\text{a large positive quantity}}{\text{a far larger positive quantity}}$$

so that the ratio would tend to the value zero, through positive values. In symbols, we would write

$$x^4 / \exp x \to 0^+ \quad \text{as} \quad x \to \infty.$$

Again using the idea of domination, we could see that as $x \to \infty$, $\exp x / \ln x$ would become

$$\frac{\text{a very large positive quantity}}{\text{a much smaller positive quantity}},$$

and so $\exp x / \ln x$ would tend to $+\infty$.

Now let us consider what will happen to $x^m / \exp x$ as $x \to -\infty$, where m is a positive integer. Remember that $1/ \exp x$ can be rewritten as $\exp(-x)$, and so we are considering what happens to $x^m \exp(-x)$ when $x \to -\infty$. Let us put $y = -x$, so that we are finding what happens to $(-y)^m \exp y$ as $y \to +\infty$. As y becomes very large, then $\exp y$ will become extremely large, and also $(-y)^m$ will become large (in modulus) and either positive or negative, depending on whether m is even or odd. So we have

$$x^m / \exp x \to \infty \text{ as } x \to -\infty, \text{ if } m \text{ is even,}$$

and
$$x^m / \exp x \to -\infty \text{ as } x \to -\infty, \text{ if } m \text{ is odd.}$$

Since $\ln x$ is not defined when $x < 0$, it does not make sense to ask what happens to $\ln x$ as $x \to -\infty$. However we can ask what is the situation when we have, for example, a power of x multiplied by $\ln x$, and $x \to 0^+$.

For example, consider what happens to $x^5 \ln x$ as $x \to 0^+$. Notice that in this case, as $x \to 0^+$, $x^5 \to 0$, while $\ln x \to -\infty$. We resolve the problem of finding the limit by putting $y = 1/x$. In this case, we want to find what happens as $y \to \infty$ to the expression $(1/y)^5 \ln(1/y)$, which we can rewrite as $(-\ln y)/(y^5)$. We already know that both $\ln y$ and y^5 will tend to ∞ as $y \to \infty$, and we also know that any positive power of y will dominate $\ln y$. Hence it follows that, as $y \to \infty$, $(-\ln y)/(y^5) \to 0^-$.

After this preliminary discussion, we are ready to tackle the following example, which uses the ideas we met in sketching rational functions, applied to a different situation.

Example 3.   *Sketch the curve $y = (x-2)e^{-x}$, finding the critical point, the point of inflection, and the points where the curve cuts the coordinate axes.*

Solution.   Since e^{-x} is always positive, we can only have $y = 0$ when $x = 2$. Hence the curve meets the x-axis at the point $(2,0)$ and at no other point.

The curve cuts the y-axis where $x = 0$, so that $y = (-2)e^0 = -2$. Hence the curve meets the y-axis at the point with coordinates $(0, -2)$.

As $x \to \infty$, $y \approx x/e^x$, which, by the discussion preceding the example, will tend to zero through positive values.

On the other hand, as $x \to -\infty$, $x - 2$ will tend to $-\infty$ while e^{-x} will tend to ∞. Hence the product of these terms will tend to $-\infty$ as $x \to -\infty$.

Notice that when we are calculating the behaviour of the function for values of x which are large (in modulus), we can ignore the effect of the -2 as this will be swamped by the x-term.

We now need to use Calculus to obtain the coordinates of the critical point and point of inflection on the curve.

Since $y = (x-2)e^{-x}$, we have, on differentiating using the Product Rule,

$$\frac{dy}{dx} = -(x-2)e^{-x} + e^{-x} = (1 - x + 2)e^{-x} = (3 - x)e^{-x}.$$

Differentiating again using the Product Rule, we will find that

$$\frac{d^2y}{dx^2} = -(3 - x)e^{-x} + (-1)e^{-x} = (-1 - 3 + x)e^{-x} = (x - 4)e^{-x}.$$

From these derivatives it follows that the curve can only have a critical point at $x = 3$ (since e^{-x} is always positive), and also that the only possible point of inflection on the curve will lie at the point $x = 4$.

When $x = 3$, we have $y = e^{-3}$ and $\dfrac{d^2y}{dx^2} = -e^{-3}$. It follows that we have a local maximum at the point $(3, e^{-3})$.

When $x = 4$, we know that $y = 2e^{-4}$. To decide whether this is a point of inflection, we need to determine the signs for $\dfrac{d^2y}{dx^2}$ in the vicinity of the x-value $x = 4$.

Since the expression for $\dfrac{d^2y}{dx^2}$ is fairly simple in this case, we shall manage to do this without using a table of sign. For $\dfrac{d^2y}{dx^2} = (x - 4)e^{-x}$, where e^{-x} will always be positive. Therefore the sign of $\dfrac{d^2y}{dx^2}$ will be the same as the sign of $x - 4$. It follows that as x increases through the value $x = 4$, so the sign of $\dfrac{d^2y}{dx^2}$ will change from being negative, to zero, to being positive.

Hence we do indeed have a point of inflection on the curve at the point $(4, 2e^{-4})$.

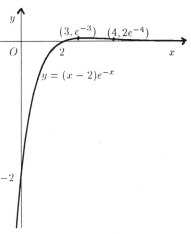

We are now able to complete this example by sketching the curve, using all the information we have found above. Notice that, unlike the rational functions we sketched earlier, there will not be any vertical asymptotes to the curve, since these only occur where we are dividing by an expression that tends to 0. On this curve there is no finite value of x for which that happens.

EXAMPLES 10

1. Let $f(x) \equiv 2x^3 + 3x^2 - 12x - 6$. Express as a union of intervals the set of real numbers for which $f'(x) > 0$.

2. Let $f(x) \equiv x^4 + 4x^3 - 8x^2 - 48x + 50$. Express as a union of intervals the set of real numbers for which $f'(x) < 0$.

3. Let $f(x) \equiv (x^2 - 6x + 7) e^{2x}$. Express as a union of intervals the set of real numbers for which $f(x)$ is strictly increasing.

4. Let $f(x) \equiv \sin^2 x \cos 2x$. Express as a union of intervals the set of real numbers x with $0 \le x \le \pi$ for which $f(x)$ is strictly decreasing.

5.   For each of the following curves, find where it meets the axes, find the x-coordinates and nature of each critical point, and the coordinates of any points of inflection, and hence sketch the curve:

$$\text{(a)} \quad y = x^3 - 3x^2 - x + 3;$$
$$\text{(b)} \quad y = x^3 - 6x^2 + 9x - 4.$$

6.   (a)   Find the critical points on the curve

$$y = \frac{(x-6)(x+2)}{(x-7)}.$$

Determine the nature of each critical point, the intersections of the curve with the coordinate axes, and the vertical asymptote to the curve. Find the asymptotic behaviour of the curve as $x \to \pm\infty$. Draw up a table of sign for y, and hence sketch the curve.

(b)   Deduce from (a) a sketch of the curve

$$y = \frac{(x-7)}{(x-6)(x+2)}.$$

7.   (a)   Find the critical points on the curve

$$y = \frac{2(x-1)(x+7)}{(x-2)}.$$

Determine the nature of each critical point, the intersections of the curve with the coordinate axes, and the vertical asymptote to the curve. Find the asymptotic behaviour of the curve as $x \to \pm\infty$. Draw up a table of sign for y, and hence sketch the curve.

(b)   Deduce from (a) a sketch of the curve

$$y = \frac{(x-2)}{2(x-1)(x+7)}.$$

8.   (a)   Find the critical point and the point of inflection on the curve

$$y = \frac{(x-3)}{(x-1)^2}.$$

Determine the nature of the critical point, the intersections of the curve with the coordinate axes, and the vertical asymptote to the curve. Find the asymptotic behaviour of the curve as $x \to \pm\infty$. Draw up a table of sign for y, and hence sketch the curve.

(b)   Deduce from (a) a sketch of the curve

$$y = \frac{(x-1)^2}{(x-3)}.$$

9. (a) Find the critical point and the point of inflection on the curve

$$y = \frac{(x+3)}{(x+2)^2}.$$

Determine the nature of the critical point, the intersections of the curve with the coordinate axes, and the vertical asymptote to the curve. Find the asymptotic behaviour of the curve as $x \to \pm\infty$. Draw up a table of sign for y, and hence sketch the curve.

(b) Deduce from (a) a sketch of the curve

$$y = \frac{(x+2)^2}{(x+3)}.$$

10. (a) Find the critical point on the curve

$$y = \frac{(x+4)(x-4)}{(x+2)(x-2)}.$$

Determine the nature of the critical point, the intersections of the curve with the coordinate axes, and the vertical asymptotes to the curve. Show that the curve has no point of inflection. Find the asymptotic behaviour of the curve as $x \to \pm\infty$. Draw up a table of sign for y, and hence sketch the curve.

(b) Deduce from (a) a sketch of the curve

$$y = \frac{(x+2)(x-2)}{(x+4)(x-4)}.$$

11. (a) Find the critical point on the curve

$$y = \frac{(x+5)(x-11)}{(x-5)(x-1)}.$$

Determine the nature of the critical point, the intersections of the curve with the coordinate axes, and the vertical asymptotes to the curve. Show that the curve has no point of inflection. Find the asymptotic behaviour of the curve as $x \to \pm\infty$. Draw up a table of sign for y, and hence sketch the curve.

(b) Deduce from (a) a sketch of the curve

$$y = \frac{(x-5)(x-1)}{(x+5)(x-11)}.$$

D

12.   Do each of the following (1) become very large, (2) become very large (in modulus) and negative, or (3) tend to zero?

(a) $x^2 e^{2x}$ as x becomes very large.

(b) $x^3 e^{-3x}$ as x becomes very large.

(c) $x e^{-x}$ as x becomes very large (in modulus) and negative.

(d) $x^2 e^{3x}$ as x becomes very large (in modulus) and negative.

(e) $x^{-3} e^x$ as x becomes very large.

(f) $x^4 e^{2x}$ as x tends to zero.

(g) $x^{-2} \ln x$ as x tends to zero $(x > 0)$.

(h) $x^3 \ln x$ as x tends to zero $(x > 0)$.

13.   Sketch each of the following curves, after finding any critical points, any points of inflection, those points where the curve meets the coordinate axes, and after considering also the behaviour of the curve as $x \to \pm\infty$:

(a) $y = (x - 3) e^{-x}$;

(b) $y = (x + 2) e^x$;

(c) $y = (x - 1)^2 e^{2x}$;

(d) $y = (x + 2)^2 e^{-x}$.

CHAPTER 11

Absolute Maxima and Absolute Minima

In this chapter, and in examples based on the ideas developed here, we shall find it useful to have at our disposal certain formulae, which are all quite well known. We shall prove them all later in the chapters on applications of integration.

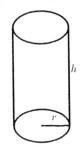

For a right circular cylinder, of height h, base radius r, the volume is πr^2, while the curved surface area (not including the base and the top) is $2\pi rh$.

For a sphere of radius r, the volume is $\frac{4}{3}\pi r^3$, and the surface area is $4\pi r^2$.

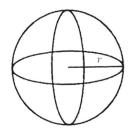

For a right circular cone having height h, base radius r and with slant height l $\left(\text{so that } l = \sqrt{h^2 + r^2}\right)$, the volume is $\frac{1}{3}\pi r^2 h$, while the curved surface area (not including the base) is πrl. (Note that the slant height of a right circular cone is the distance from the vertex of the cone to any point on the circumference of the base of the cone.)

In some circumstances, particularly when tackling problems having a 'practical' basis, we sometimes need to find the greatest or the least value that a function $f(x)$ can take when the variable x is restricted to lie in a certain range of values.

We call $f(c)$ the **absolute maximum** of $f(x)$ for $x \in S$ if we have $f(c) \geq f(x)$ for all $x \in S$ (with of course $c \in S$). From this definition, the absolute maximum that $f(x)$ takes on the set S is precisely what it says, that is, it is the greatest possible value the function takes while x varies throughout the set S.

We define $f(c)$ to be the **absolute minimum** of $f(x)$ for $x \in S$ if $f(c) \leq f(x)$ for all $x \in S$ (with of course $c \in S$). Again, the absolute minimum on a set S is precisely the least value the function takes as x is allowed to vary throughout the set S.

From the diagram, which shows a typical situation, you can see that an absolute maximum and an absolute minimum need not occur at local maxima and minima on the curve.

It can be shown though that *if S is a closed interval then the absolute maximum and absolute minimum of f(x) on S must occur either at end-points of S or at local maxima or local minima of f(x) on S.*

Suppose we are given a closed set S, and asked to find the absolute maximum and absolute minimum of $f(x)$ on S. Our routine is to find the values of $f(x)$ at any turning points on the curve in the set S, and to find the values of the function at the end-points of S, and then choose the greatest of these to be the absolute maximum and the least to be the absolute minimum.

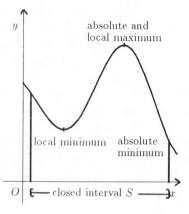

Example 1. *Find the absolute maximum and absolute minimum values of the function $f(x) \equiv 2x^3 - 3x^2 - 36x + 70$ for $0 \le x \le 4$.*

Solution.   We start by finding the turning points on the curve. Now

$$f'(x) = 6x^2 - 6x - 36$$
$$= 6(x^2 - x - 6)$$
$$= 6(x - 3)(x + 2).$$

Hence the turning points on the curve will occur at the points $x = 3$ (which satisfies the condition $0 \le x \le 4$) and $x = -2$ (which does not satisfy the condition and so can be ignored).

Now we evaluate the function at the end-points of the interval $[0, 4]$ and at the turning point that lies in the interval. We have $f(0) = 70$, $f(4) = 6$ and $f(3) = -11$. Hence the absolute maximum for $f(x)$ on the interval $[0, 4]$ is 70 which occurs when $x = 0$, while the absolute minimum is -11 at $x = 3$.

In more practical problems, we will sometimes not be given the restriction on the variable, but instead we will be expected to work this out from the implications of the practical situation involved. One frequent condition that is useful is that measurements of many physical quantities, for example lengths, have to be positive. This condition is used in the next example.

Example 2. *A farmer wishes to enclose a field with a length of fencing. Because of the use he wishes to put the field to, the farmer wants to have a rectangular field, one side of which should have a gap of 10 m without a fence. Furthermore, the farmer wishes to have a fence down the centre of the field, not completely dividing the field into two* pieces, *but leaving a gap of* 10 m *at the edge of the field near to the gap in the perimeter fence. Given that the farmer has a length of* 196 m *of fencing to use, find the dimensions of the field having the largest possible area.*

Solution.   Let x m be the length of the side of the field that contains the gap, and let y m be the length of the sides of the field perpendicular to that one. Then let A denote the area of the field so that $A = xy$. We need to find the abolute maximum value that A can have.

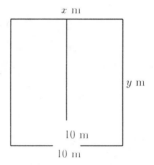

We have a restriction imposed on x and y by the fact that the farmer has a finite length of fence at his disposal. The total length of fence he will use in the set-up we have described is $x + (x - 10) + y + y + (y - 10) = 2x + 3y - 20$. We require $2x + 3y - 20 = 196$, from which we find that $x = \frac{1}{2}(216 - 3y)$ or that $y = \frac{1}{3}(216 - 2x)$.

From practical considerations, we need to have $x \geq 10$, since we require a gap of 10 m in the fence on one of the sides of the field of length x, and also we need $x \leq 93$. This requirement arises because we need to have $y \geq 10$, so that, using $x = \frac{1}{2}(216 - 3y)$, we obtain the given restriction on x.

Hence, substituting for y in $A = xy$, we have $A = \frac{1}{3}x(216 - 2x)$. So we want to find the absolute maximum of the function $A = \frac{1}{3}x(216 - 2x)$ subject to $10 \leq x \leq 93$. Now

$$\frac{dA}{dx} = \frac{1}{3}(216 - 4x)$$
$$= \frac{4}{3}(54 - x),$$

so that the turning point on the curve occurs at $x = 54$. We evaluate A at each of the values $x = 10$, $x = 54$ and $x = 93$. We find that $A(10) = 1960/3$, $A(93) = 930$ and $A(54) = 1944$. Hence the absolute maximum value occurs at the local maximum of the function, with the field having dimensions 54 m by 36 m.

Example 3.   *It has been suggested that there is a relationship $N = 200x(108 - x^2)$ between the number N of birds that can survive in a breeding colony of sea-birds and the density x of the nests in the colony. It is also believed that the values $x = 2$ and $x = 8$ represent extreme values for x beyond which the colony would not be viable. Find the absolute maximum and absolute minimum values for N.*

Solution.   We simply need to find the absolute maximum and absolute minimum values for N with x restricted to the range $[2, 8]$.

Now

$$N = 200 \left(108x - x^3\right)$$

so that

$$\frac{dN}{dx} = 200 \left(108 - 3x^2\right)$$

or

$$\frac{dN}{dx} = 600 \left(36 - x^2\right) = 600(6 - x)(6 + x).$$

From this we see that the turning points on the curve will occur at $x = 6$ and at $x = -6$. However, notice that we are not interested in the value $x = -6$ since this lies outside the range of values we are to consider. Now we evaluate the function at the three points $x = 2$, $x = 6$ and $x = 8$, since these are the end-points of the interval together with the turning point.

We have $N(2) = 41600$, $N(6) = 86400$ and $N(8) = 70400$. Hence the absolute maximum for N is 86400 which occurs when $x = 6$, while the absolute minimum is $N = 41600$ which happens when $x = 2$.

When we are considering the case of a function defined on an interval S which is not a closed interval, we have to treat the problem of finding the absolute maximum and absolute minimum slightly differently. In this case, we again consider all the values of the function at any turning points that lie within S, and the values of the function at any end-points of S that lie within S. However in this case we also need to consider the value that the function approaches as x approaches any end-points of S that do not lie within S. The greatest of these values gives the absolute maximum for the function, provided it occurs for a value of x lying within S. Otherwise we say that the absolute maximum does not exist. We deal in a similar manner with the absolute minimum.

Example 4.   *Two positive numbers are such that their sum is 100. Find the numbers if the product of the square of the one with the cube of the other is to be a maximum.*

Solution.   Let the two numbers be x and y. Then we have $x + y = 100$. We need to find the maximum value of $T = x^2 y^3$, subject to the requirement that x, y are positive. We can put these conditions on x in the form $x > 0$ and $x < 100$, since if $y > 0$ and $x + y = 100$ then $x < 100$ follows.

We need to find the maximum value of T subject to $0 < x < 100$. We use the equation $x + y = 100$ in the form $y = 100 - x$ to eliminate y from the formula for T, so that we can use differentiation to find the maximum.

Now $T = x^2(100 - x)^3$, and so, using the Product and Chain Rules to find $\dfrac{dT}{dx}$, we find that

$$\frac{dT}{dx} = 2x(100-x)^3 + x^2 \times 3(100-x)^2 \times (-1)$$

$$= x(100-x)^2 \left(2(100-x) - 3x\right)$$

$$= x(100-x)^2 \left(200 - 2x - 3x\right)$$

$$= x(100-x)^2 \left(200 - 5x\right).$$

The turning points occur where $\dfrac{dT}{dx} = 0$, from which we require that $x(100-x)^2(200-5x) = 0$. This happens when $x = 0$, or $x = 100$, or $200 - 5x = 0$ from which we deduce that $x = 40$.

Recalling that we are only interested in those values of x for which $0 < x < 100$, we see that the only turning point satisfying this condition is the turning point at $x = 40$. At $x = 40$, $T = 40^2.60^3$.

We also have to consider what happens to T as x tends to the ends of the open interval to which it belongs. Now as $x \to 0$, $T \to 0$, while as $x \to 100$, $T \to 0$ again.

It follows that the (absolute) maximum value of T occurs at the turning point, and is given when the two numbers are 40 and 60.

Example 5. *It has been suggested that in an underwater cable with a core of radius r and an insulating sheath of radius R, the rate of signalling is given by $S = -kx^2 \ln x$, where k is a positive constant, and $x = r/R$. Find the value of x which gives the most rapid rate of transmission.*

Solution.   We need to find the maximum value of S, subject to the conditions $0 < x \le 1$. (There clearly must be a core to the cable, and so we must have $r > 0$ and so $x > 0$. On the other hand, it would be feasible, though rather impracticable, to have a cable consisting entirely of an uninsulated sheath, which would mean that $r = R$, or $x = 1$.)

Now,

$$\frac{dS}{dx} = -2kx \ln x - kx^2(1/x)$$

$$= -2kx \ln x - kx$$

$$= -kx(2\ln x + 1).$$

So $\dfrac{dS}{dx} = 0$ when $x = 0$ and when $\ln x = -1/2$. This happens when $x = 0$ and when $x = \exp(-1/2)$. The turning point which belongs to the interval $(0, 1]$ is $x = \exp(-1/2)$. When this happens we have

$$S = -k(e^{-(1/2)})^2 \ln\left(e^{-1/2}\right)$$

$$= -k(e^{-1})(-1/2)$$

$$= k/2e.$$

We also have to consider what happens at the end-point $x = 1$ and as $x \to 0$.

Now, at $x = 1$, we have $S = -k(1)^2 \ln 1 = 0$, since $\ln 1 = 0$. Finally as $x \to 0^+$, then since, by the methods we used in the last chapter, $x^2 \ln x \to 0^-$, it follows that $S \to 0^+$.

Hence the maximum rate of transmission will occur for the value $x = \exp(-1/2) \approx 0.607$. (Although we were not required to find it, notice that the minimum will occur here at $x = 1$.)

EXAMPLES 11

1.   Find the absolute maximum and absolute minimum values for the function
$$f(x) \equiv x^3 - 3x^2 - 9x + 24$$
for x in the interval $[1, 4]$.

2.   Find the absolute maximum and absolute minimum values for the function
$$f(x) \equiv x + \frac{432}{x^3}$$
for x in the interval $[4, 8]$.

3.   A rectangle has a perimeter of 100 cm. What is the maximum possible area of the rectangle?

4.   An isosceles triangle has a perimeter of 60 cm. What is the maximum possible area of the triangle?

5.   The sum of two positive numbers is 24. Find the numbers if the product of the one with the square of the other is to have its maximum value.

6.   A rectangular sheet of paper has an area 294 cm². The margins at the top and bottom are 3 cm while those at the sides are 2 cm. What is the maximum possible area of printing on the sheet?

7.   A cylindrical mug is to hold 54π cm³ of liquid. The cost of production of 1 cm² of the base is twice the cost of 1 cm² for the side. Find the dimensions of the mug that will hold the required volume for which the cost is a minimum.

8.   A lens of focal length 75 cm forms the image of an object on a screen. If the distance u cm between the object and the lens is related to the distance v cm between the image and the lens by the equation
$$\frac{1}{u} + \frac{1}{v} = \frac{1}{75},$$
express the distance d $(= u + v)$ between the object and the image as a function of u alone, and hence find the minimum possible distance between the object and the image.

9. A ray of light from the point A is reflected by a plane mirror to the point B. Let X and Y be the perpendicular projections from the points A and B to the mirror. Let $|AX| = a$, $|BY| = b$ and $|XY| = c$. Suppose the ray of light strikes the mirror at the point P between X and Y, and that $|XP| = x$. Express the distance travelled by the ray of light in terms of x, and show that this distance is a minimum when $\sin \alpha = \sin \beta$, where α

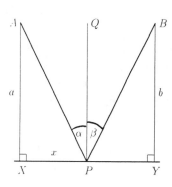

and β are the angles APQ and BPQ respectively, where PQ is the line perpendicular to the mirror through P.

10. Suppose that A and B are points with parameters a and b respectively on the parabola $y^2 = 4cx$. Suppose that we are to find the point T with parameter t on the parabola such that the area of triangle ABT inscribed in the parabola is a maximum, where T is assumed to lie between A and B. It can be shown that the area of the triangle is

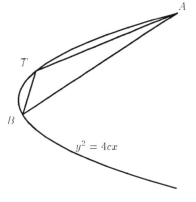

$$c^2 (t - a)(b - t)(b - a).$$

Find the value of t in terms of a and b which gives the maximum for the above expression, subject to the condition $a \le t \le b$.

CHAPTER 12
Introduction to Integration

Calculus consists of two important techniques—differentiation and integration—and the application of these techniques to different types of problems. We have already seen how to differentiate, and some of the applications that can be made of differentiation. Now we shall follow through the same procedure for integration.

Differentiation is concerned with the problem of finding the rate of change of a variable y with respect to x, when we are given y as a function of x.

Integration is concerned with the reverse problem. If we know that y is a function of x, and we are given $\dfrac{dy}{dx}$, the rate of change of y with respect to x, can we find the function which expresses y in terms of x?

We shall start by considering the following simple example.

Example 1. *A stone is thrown vertically upwards with an initial velocity of 50 ft/sec. Assuming that the stone is subject to a steady downward acceleration, due to gravity, of 32 ft/sec^2, find how high the stone is, and its velocity, 3 sec after it is thrown.*

Solution. Let t denote the time (measured in seconds) from the moment the stone is thrown, and let y denote the height (in feet) of the stone above its starting position at time t. Also, we shall let v (in feet per second) be the velocity of the stone at time t. Notice that v will be given by $\dfrac{dy}{dt}$, and that v will be positive if the stone is travelling upwards, and that v will be negative if y is decreasing.

By assumption, as the stone moves through space, it is subjected to a downward acceleration of 32 ft/sec^2. Since acceleration is given by the rate of change of velocity, it follows that we have

$$\frac{dv}{dt} = -32.$$

Notice that we have a negative sign here because the velocity is positive in an upward direction, and so the rate of change of velocity would be positive if the upward velocity were increasing. Clearly this is not the case, since the upward velocity is decreasing as time increases.

We want to find what v is, knowing that $\dfrac{dv}{dt} = -32$. One possible value for v is that $v = -32t$ (since then $\dfrac{dv}{dt} = -32$). Another possibility is that we could have

$$v = -32t + \text{ any constant}$$

and in fact it can be shown that if $\dfrac{dv}{dt} = -32$ then

$$v = -32t + c,$$

for some value of the constant c. Furthermore it can be shown that this is the only possible form of the solution.

From the conditions of the problem, we know that, when $t = 0$, then $v = 50$. Substituting these values into the equation for v, we see that

$$50 = -32 \times 0 + c,$$

from which we have

$$c = 50.$$

Notice that we could have also obtained this result graphically, by plotting the graph of v against t, which must be a straight line of slope -32, passing through the point $v = 50$, $t = 0$.

Next we know that

$$\frac{dx}{dt} = v = 50 - 32t.$$

We now need to find what x could be. One possibility is that

$$x = 50t - 16t^2,$$

(because if $x = 50t - 16t^2$ then $\dfrac{dx}{dt} = 50 - 32t$). Again it can be shown that all possible solutions for x will have the form

$$x = 50t - 16t^2 + d,$$

for some suitably chosen value of the constant d.

Now under the conditions of this particular example, we have $x = 0$ when $t = 0$. We substitute these values into the formula for x and we obtain

$$0 = 50 \times 0 - 16 \times 0^2 + d,$$

from which we have $d = 0$. Hence we have obtained

$$x = 50t - 16t^2.$$

Finally, we need to find the values of x and v when $t = 3$. Substituting $t = 3$ into the equations for v and x, we have

$$v = 50 - 32 \times 3 = -46$$

and

$$x = 50 \times 3 - 16 \times 3^2 = 150 - 144 = 6.$$

From these we see that after 3 seconds the stone is 6 feet above the point from which it was thrown, and that it is *falling* at 46 feet per second. (We obtain the information that the stone is falling from the fact that the velocity (measured in an upward direction) is negative.)

Given a function $f(x)$ of x, the **indefinite integral of** $f(x)$, which is denoted by

$$\int f(x)\, dx,$$

is the collection of functions of the form

$$F(x) + c,$$

where the derivative with respect to x of $F(x) + c$ is $f(x)$.

We call $\int$ the **integral sign**, $f(x)$ the **integrand**, x the **variable of integration**, and c the **constant of integration**, or **arbitrary constant**.

Notice that

$$\int f(x)\, dx = F(x) + c \quad \text{precisely when} \quad \frac{d}{dx}\left(F(x)\right) = f(x).$$

It follows from this that differentiation and integration are inverses of one another, in the sense that

$$\int \frac{d}{dx}\left(F(x)\right) dx = F(x) + c,$$

and

$$\frac{d}{dx}\left(\int f(x)\, dx\right) = f(x).$$

Since differentiation and integration are inverses of one another, it follows that the rules concerning differentiation will have analogues for integration. We shall later see the rules for integration that correspond to the Product and Chain Rules. In the meantime we simply state the following rules which apply for any functions f and g and for any constant c:

$$\int cf(x)\, dx = c \int f(x)\, dx,$$

$$\int (f(x) + g(x))\, dx = \int f(x)\, dx + \int g(x)\, dx.$$

The following table enables us to integrate many of the standard functions. In each case the result is checked by showing that the derivative of the entry given as the integral in the table is the integrand. It is important to memorise this table of standard integrals. This should not be difficult since it is basically our earlier table of standard derivatives of standard functions read back-to-front.

$f(x)$	$\int f(x)\,dx$	Note
k	$kx + c$	k constant
x^n	$\dfrac{x^{n+1}}{n+1} + c$	$n \neq 0,\ n \neq -1$
$\dfrac{1}{x}$	$\ln|x| + c$	$x \neq 0$
e^x	$e^x + c$	
a^x	$\dfrac{1}{\ln a} a^x + c$	a constant, $a \neq 1,\ a > 0$
$\cos x$	$\sin x + c$	
$\sin x$	$-\cos x + c$	
$\sec^2 x$	$\tan x + c$	
$\operatorname{cosec}^2 x$	$-\cot x + c$	
$\sec x \tan x$	$\sec x + c$	
$\operatorname{cosec} x \cot x$	$-\operatorname{cosec} x + c$	
$\dfrac{1}{\sqrt{1 - x^2}}$	$\sin^{-1} x + c$ or $-\cos^{-1} x + c$	$x \in (-1, 1)$
$\dfrac{1}{1 + x^2}$	$\tan^{-1} x + c$	

Only one of the above results is not quite straightforward, and that is the one concerning $\displaystyle\int \frac{1}{x}\,dx$. For $x > 0$ then certainly

$$\frac{d}{dx}\left(\ln|x| + c\right) = \frac{d}{dx}\left(\ln x + c\right) = \frac{1}{x}.$$

If $x < 0$, then we let $u = -x$, so that $u > 0$. Also $|x| = (-x) = u$, so that

$$\ln|x| = \ln u.$$

By the Chain Rule, differentiating with respect to x, we have

$$\frac{d}{dx}\left(\ln|x| + c\right) = \frac{d}{du}(\ln u + c) \times \frac{du}{dx}$$

$$= \frac{1}{u} \times (-1)$$

$$= \frac{1}{(-x)} \times (-1)$$

$$= \frac{1}{x}.$$

Hence, provided $x \neq 0$,

$$\frac{d}{dx}\left(\ln|x| + c\right) = \frac{1}{x}.$$

From this it follows that

$$\int \frac{1}{x}\,dx = \ln|x| + c,$$

provided that $x \neq 0$, as required.

In a number of integration examples, the main difficulty lies in trying to reduce the integrand to the forms of the standard integrals given in the above table.

Example 2. Find $\int \left(x^5 - 8x^3 + 7x^2 - 7 + \dfrac{3}{x^2} - \dfrac{8}{x^4} \right) dx.$

Solution.   Using the rules for integration, we have

$$\int \left(x^5 - 8x^3 + 7x^2 - 7 + \frac{3}{x^2} - \frac{8}{x^4} \right) dx$$

$$= \int \left(x^5 - 8x^3 + 7x^2 - 7 + 3x^{-2} - 8x^{-4} \right) dx$$

$$= \frac{1}{6}x^6 - \frac{8}{4}x^4 + \frac{7}{3}x^3 - 7x + \frac{3}{-1}x^{-1} - \frac{8}{-3}x^{-3} + c$$

$$= \frac{x^6}{6} - 2x^4 + \frac{7x^3}{3} - 7x - \frac{3}{x} + \frac{8}{3x^3} + c.$$

Note that the routine for integrating powers of x, other than x^{-1}, is to *increase the power by 1 and divide by the new power*.

Notice also that when, as in the above example, we have a number of arbitrary constants arising from integrating the sum of a number of terms, then we lump them all together as one arbitrary constant.

Finally notice that it is a good idea to check the result of finding an indefinite integral. The easiest way to do this is to differentiate the answer you have obtained, and see whether this reduces to the integrand you started from.

Example 3. Find $\int \cot^2 x \, dx.$

Solution.   Using the trigonometric formula $\operatorname{cosec}^2 x = 1 + \cot^2 x$, we have

$$\int \cot^2 x \, dx = \int (\operatorname{cosec}^2 x - 1) \, dx$$

$$= -\cot x - x + c.$$

Example 4. Find $\int \left(x^{\frac{5}{3}} + \dfrac{2}{x^2} \right)^2 dx.$

Solution.   We start the solution by expanding the bracket. We have

$$\int \left(x^{\frac{5}{3}} + \frac{2}{x^2} \right)^2 dx = \int \left(x^{\frac{10}{3}} + 4x^{-\frac{1}{3}} + 4x^{-4} \right) dx$$

$$= \frac{x^{\frac{13}{3}}}{\frac{13}{3}} + \frac{4x^{\frac{2}{3}}}{\frac{2}{3}} + \frac{4x^{-3}}{-3} + c$$

$$= \frac{3x^{\frac{13}{3}}}{13} + 6x^{\frac{2}{3}} - \frac{4}{3x^3} + c.$$

Example 5. *A curve passes through the point* $(0, 3)$, *and is such that its gradient at the typical point* (x, y) *is* $3x^2 - 4 + \sin x$. *Find the equation of the curve.*

Solution. At the point (x, y), the gradient of the curve is $\dfrac{dy}{dx}$, which is given to be $3x^2 - 4 + \sin x$. Hence

$$\frac{dy}{dx} = 3x^2 - 4 + \sin x.$$

Therefore, on integrating this with respect to x, we have

$$y = \int \left(3x^2 - 4 + \sin x \right) dx,$$

from which we see that

$$y = x^3 - 4x - \cos x + c,$$

where c is the arbitrary constant of integration. We know that the curve must pass through the point $(0, 3)$, and this enables us to determine the value of the constant c. For, on substituting $x = 0$ and $y = 3$, we have

$$3 = 0^3 - 4 \times 0 - \cos 0 + c,$$

from which $c = 4$. It follows that the equation of the curve is

$$y = x^3 - 4x - \cos x + 4.$$

One way of looking at the above solution is that for different values of the arbitrary constant c we have a family of curves, all parallel to each other, and each having the required gradient $3x^2 - 4 + \sin x$. From our earlier considerations of curve-sketching, we know that different values of the arbitrary constant c will have the effect of moving the curve up or down. So we require to choose the appropriate value of c such that the curve passes through the point $(0, 3)$.

Integration is a subject which developed as a means of solving problems which arose in practical situations. Before examining some of these applications, we would like to extend the range of functions that we can integrate. We shall do this by introducing two important methods of integration, namely Integration by Change of Variable and Integration by Parts.

EXAMPLES 12

1. A variable y is expressed in terms of x in such a way that

$$\frac{dy}{dx} = 4x^3 + 2x^{-2}.$$

Given that $y = 2$ when $x = 1$, find y in terms of x and find the value of y when $x = 2$.

2.   A particle passes the origin at time $t = 0$ with velocity 5 units. The acceleration of the particle at time t is given by

$$\frac{dv}{dt} = 2t - \sin t,$$

where v gives the velocity of the particle at time t. Find v and x, the displacement of the particle from the origin, in terms of t, and find the velocity and acceleration of the particle when $t = \pi$, and also the distance of the particle from the origin at that time.

3.   Find each of the following:

(a) $\int \left(3x^5 + 8x - 2 + 3x^{-4}\right) dx;$

(b) $\int \left(4x^3 - 3x^{-2} - 8x^{-5}\right) dx;$

(c) $\int (x - 2)(x + 4) \, dx;$

(d) $\int \left(x^2 - 1\right)^2 dx;$

(e) $\int \tan^2 x \, dx;$

(f) $\int (\sec x + \tan x)^2 \, dx;$

(g) $\int \operatorname{cosec} x \, (\operatorname{cosec} x - \cot x) \, dx;$

(h) $\int 5^x \, dx.$

4.   A curve has gradient $3x^2 + \cos x$ at the point (x, y) and passes through the point $(0, 1)$. Find the equation of the curve.

5.   A curve has gradient $2 \sin x - 3 \cos x$ at the point (x, y) and passes through the point $\left(\frac{\pi}{2}, 2\right)$. Find the equation of the curve.

CHAPTER 13

Integration by Change of Variable

The technique of Change of Variable enables us to reverse the results obtained by differentiating using the Chain Rule.

For example, if we wish to differentiate $(x^3 - 5x^2 + 7x - 3)^3$, we put $u = x^3 - 5x^2 + 7x - 3$, so that on differentiating with respect to x using the Chain Rule we obtain

$$\underbrace{3(x^3 - 5x^2 + 7x - 3)^2}_{\text{from diff. } u^3 \text{ w.r.t. } u} \times \underbrace{(3x^2 - 10x + 7)}_{\frac{du}{dx}}.$$

Again, if we wish to differentiate $\sin(5x+4)$ then we set $u = 5x+4$, so that the derivative is

$$\underbrace{\cos(5x + 4)}_{\text{from diff. } \sin u \text{ w.r.t. } u} \times \underbrace{5}_{\frac{du}{dx}}.$$

As another example, if we wish to differentiate e^{4x^2-3x} with respect to x, the derivative is (if we let $u = 4x^2 - 3x$),

$$\underbrace{e^{4x^2-3x}}_{\text{from diff. } e^u \text{ w.r.t. } u} \times \underbrace{(8x - 3)}_{\frac{du}{dx}}.$$

Integration being the reverse process to differentiation, it follows that

$$\int 3(x^3 - 5x^2 + 7x - 3)^2 \times (3x^2 - 10x + 7)\, dx = (x^3 - 5x^2 + 7x - 3)^3 + c,$$

$$\int \cos(5x + 4) \times 5\, dx = \sin(5x + 4) + c,$$

$$\int e^{4x^2-3x} \times (8x - 3)\, dx = e^{4x^2-3x} + c,$$

c being the arbitrary constant of integration in each case.

In each of the above examples, the integrand has the form

$$\text{(function of } u) \times \text{(derivative of } u \text{ w.r.t. } x),$$

where u is a suitably chosen function of x. In each case we determine the indefinite integral by integrating the function of u with respect to u, and then expressing u back in terms of x.

For example, if we put $u = x^3 - 5x^2 + 7x - 3$, then $\dfrac{du}{dx} = 3x^2 - 10x + 7$, and so

$$\int 3(x^3 - 5x^2 + 7x - 3)^2 \times (3x^2 - 10x + 7)\, dx = \int 3u^2 \times \frac{du}{dx}\, dx$$

$$= u^3 + c$$

$$= (x^3 - 5x^2 + 7x - 3)^3 + c.$$

Similarly, taking $u = 4x^2 - 3x$, so that $\dfrac{du}{dx} = 8x - 3$, we have

$$\int e^{4x^2 - 3x} \times (8x - 3)\, dx = \int e^u \times \frac{du}{dx}\, dx$$
$$= e^u + c$$
$$= e^{4x^2 - 3x} + c.$$

In both of the above, the connection is obtained by differentiating the third expression with respect to x, using the Chain Rule. However this does suggest a possible technique for integration.

Given an integral, try to express the integrand in the form

$$f(u) \times \frac{du}{dx},$$

where u is a function of x which is to be chosen from the form of the integrand we are given. Then we find the integrand of $f(u)$ with respect to u, and finally we substitute for u in terms of x.

This procedure is known as **integration by change of variable**, or **integration by substitution**.

There are a number of standard types of integrand for which there are specific changes of variable. However, before tackling these standard types, we shall look first at some non-standard integrands.

Example 1. Find $\displaystyle\int \left(3x^4 - 7x^2 + 20\right)^5 \left(12x^3 - 14x\right) dx.$

Solution.   In this example, we notice that the integrand is in two parts, and that the derivative of $3x^4 - 7x^2 + 20$ is $12x^3 - 14x$, which is also part of the integrand. This suggests that we should put $u = 3x^4 - 7x^2 + 20$, so that $\dfrac{du}{dx} = 12x^3 - 14x$. Hence

$$\int \left(3x^4 - 7x^2 + 20\right)^5 \left(12x^3 - 14x\right) dx = \int u^5 \times \frac{du}{dx}\, dx$$
$$= \frac{1}{6} u^6 + c$$
$$= \frac{1}{6}(3x^4 - 7x^2 + 20)^6 + c.$$

When making a change of variable in an integral, it is normal to write du instead of $\dfrac{du}{dx}\, dx$, to denote that we are integrating a function of u with respect to u.

Notice that after a change of variable in an indefinite integral, we must always present our answer in terms of the original variable x, rather than in terms of a variable u that we have chosen to introduce in order to solve the problem.

Example 2. *Find* $\displaystyle\int \left(5x^3 - 8\right)^{\frac{1}{3}} x^2 \, dx.$

Solution.   In this example, we shall put $u = 5x^3 - 8$, since we notice that the derivative of $5x^3 - 8$ is (except for being multiplied by a constant) also a term appearing in the integrand. So we have $\dfrac{du}{dx} = 15x^2$, which we rewrite as $x^2 dx = \frac{1}{15} du$.

$$\int \left(5x^3 - 8\right)^{\frac{1}{3}} x^2 \, dx = \int u^{\frac{1}{3}} \times \frac{1}{15} \, du$$

$$= \frac{1}{15} \cdot \frac{3}{4} u^{\frac{4}{3}} + c$$

$$= \frac{1}{20} \left(5x^3 - 8\right)^{\frac{4}{3}} + c.$$

Example 3. *Find* $\displaystyle\int \left(\cos(\sec x)\right) \sec x \tan x \, dx.$

Solution.   Here we notice that $\sec x$ appears in the integrand, and also that $\sec x \tan x$ (which is the derivative of $\sec x$) is part of the integrand. So we let $u = \sec x$, from which $\dfrac{du}{dx} = \sec x \tan x$, which we can think of as $du = \sec x \tan x \, dx$.

$$\int \left(\cos(\sec x)\right) \sec x \tan x \, dx = \int \cos u \, du$$

$$= \sin u + c$$

$$= \sin(\sec x) + c.$$

From these examples, you can see how important it is that we can recognise that an integrand can be written in the form

$$\text{(function of } u) \times \text{(derivative of } u),$$

where u denotes a suitable function of x. In order to be able to recognise possible substitutions, it is very important to have the table of standard derivatives firmly fixed in the memory.

Example 4. *Find* $\displaystyle\int \frac{x}{3x^2 + 7} \, dx.$

Solution.   In this example, we will put $u = 3x^2 + 7$, because then $\dfrac{du}{dx} = 6x$, and so we can replace $x \, dx$ by $\frac{1}{6} du$. So

$$\int \frac{x}{3x^2 + 7} \, dx = \int \frac{\frac{1}{6} du}{u}$$

$$= \frac{1}{6} \int \frac{du}{u}$$

$$= \frac{1}{6} \ln |u| + c$$

$$= \frac{1}{6} \ln |3x^2 + 7| + c.$$

Example 5. *Find* $\int e^{\tan x} \sec^2 x \, dx$.

Solution.   In this example, the key is to notice that the derivative of $\tan x$ is $\sec^2 x$. This suggests that we should put $u = \tan x$, from which we have $du = \sec^2 x \, dx$.

$$\int e^{\tan x} \sec^2 x \, dx = \int e^u du$$
$$= e^u + c$$
$$= e^{\tan x} + c.$$

One very common type of change of variable is the *linear change of variable*

$$u = ax + b,$$

where a, b are constants with $a \neq 0$. We can use linear changes of variable in order to extend our earlier table of standard integrals.

Integrand $= f(x)$	Integral $= \int f(x)\,dx$	Notes
$\cos mx$	$\frac{1}{m} \sin mx + c$	m a non-zero constant
$\sin mx$	$-\frac{1}{m} \cos mx + c$	m a non-zero constant
$\dfrac{1}{\sqrt{a^2 - x^2}}$	$\sin^{-1} \dfrac{x}{a} + c$	a a positive constant $x \in (-a, a)$
$\dfrac{1}{a^2 + x^2}$	$\dfrac{1}{a} \tan^{-1} \dfrac{x}{a} + c$	a a non-zero constant
e^{mx}	$\frac{1}{m} e^{mx} + c$	m a non-zero constant
$\dfrac{1}{x + a}$	$\ln |x + a| + c$	a a constant, $x \neq -a$

Each of the above can easily be checked by differentiating the integral we have quoted and showing that we obtain the integrand given. Instead, however, we prefer to establish some of these integrals by means of change of variable.

Let m be a non-zero constant. Then, if we let $u = mx$, we have $du = m \, dx$, and so

$$\int \sin mx \, dx = \int \sin u \times \frac{1}{m} \, du$$
$$= \frac{1}{m} \int \sin u \, du$$
$$= \frac{1}{m} (-\cos u) + c$$
$$= -\frac{1}{m} \cos mx + c,$$

while similarly

$$\int \cos mx \, dx = \int \cos u \times \frac{1}{m} \, du$$

$$= \frac{1}{m} \int \cos u \, du$$

$$= \frac{1}{m} \sin u + c$$

$$= \frac{1}{m} \sin mx + c.$$

Now suppose that a is a positive constant. Then this time we shall take $u = \dfrac{x}{a}$, so that $du = \dfrac{1}{a} \, dx$, or $dx = a \, du$. Hence, we have

$$\int \frac{1}{\sqrt{a^2 - x^2}} \, dx = \int \frac{a \, du}{\sqrt{a^2 - a^2 u^2}}$$

$$= \int \frac{a \, du}{\sqrt{a^2 \left(1 - u^2\right)}}$$

$$= \int \frac{a \, du}{a\sqrt{1 - u^2}}$$

$$= \int \frac{du}{\sqrt{1 - u^2}}$$

$$= \sin^{-1} u + c$$

$$= \sin^{-1} \frac{x}{a} + c.$$

Making the same substitution, but this time taking a to be any non-zero constant, we have

$$\int \frac{dx}{a^2 + x^2} = \int \frac{a \, du}{a^2 + a^2 u^2}$$

$$= \int \frac{a \, du}{a^2 \left(1 + u^2\right)}$$

$$= \frac{1}{a} \int \frac{du}{1 + u^2}$$

$$= \frac{1}{a} \tan^{-1} u + c$$

$$= \frac{1}{a} \tan^{-1} \frac{x}{a} + c.$$

Now we assume that m is a non-zero constant. We shall let $u = mx$, from which we have $du = m \, dx$, so that

$$\int e^{mx} \, dx = \int e^u \times \frac{1}{m} \, du$$

$$= \frac{1}{m} \int e^u \, du$$

$$= \frac{1}{m} e^u + c$$

$$= \frac{1}{m} e^{mx} + c.$$

For our final verification, we take a to be any constant. Then putting $u = x + a$, we have $du = dx$, and so

$$\int \frac{dx}{x+a} = \int \frac{du}{u}$$

$$= \ln |u| + c$$

$$= \ln |x + a| + c.$$

We shall use the above results in the following straightforward examples.

Example 6. *Find* $\int (2 \sin 2x - 6 \cos 3x) \, dx$.

Solution.

$$\int (2 \sin 2x - 6 \cos 3x) \, dx = 2 \int \sin 2x \, dx - 6 \int \cos 3x \, dx$$

$$= 2 \left(-\frac{1}{2} \right) \cos 2x - 6 \left(\frac{1}{3} \right) \sin 3x + c$$

$$= -\cos 2x - 2 \sin 3x + c.$$

Example 7. *Find* $\int \frac{dx}{9 + x^2}$.

Solution.

$$\int \frac{dx}{9 + x^2} = \frac{1}{3} \tan^{-1} \frac{x}{3} + c.$$

Sometimes we are given an integrand of the form $\dfrac{1}{\sqrt{\text{quadratic}}}$ or $\dfrac{1}{\text{quadratic}}$. In order to deal with such integrands, we often need to complete the square and then make a linear change of variable in order to convert the integrand to one of the standard forms we have listed in the table above.

Example 8. *Find* $\displaystyle\int \frac{dx}{\sqrt{7 - 6x - x^2}}$.

Solution. We start by completing the square in the expression $7 - 6x - x^2$. Now

$$
\begin{aligned}
7 - 6x - x^2 &= 7 - (x^2 + 6x) \\
&= 7 - [(x + 3)^2 - 9] \\
&= 16 - (x + 3)^2 \\
&= 4^2 - (x + 3)^2.
\end{aligned}
$$

Hence, if we put $u = x + 3$ so that $du = dx$, we have

$$
\begin{aligned}
\int \frac{dx}{\sqrt{7 - 6x - x^2}} &= \int \frac{dx}{\sqrt{4^2 - (x + 3)^2}} \\
&= \int \frac{du}{\sqrt{4^2 - u^2}} \\
&= \sin^{-1} \frac{u}{4} + c \\
&= \sin^{-1}\left(\frac{x + 3}{4}\right) + c.
\end{aligned}
$$

Example 9. *Find* $\displaystyle\int \frac{dx}{x^2 + 8x + 41}$.

Solution. Again we start by completing the square, this time in the expression $x^2 + 8x + 41$. Now

$$
\begin{aligned}
x^2 + 8x + 41 &= (x + 4)^2 - 16 + 41 \\
&= (x + 4)^2 + 25 \\
&= (x + 4)^2 + 5^2.
\end{aligned}
$$

. Hence, taking $u = x + 4$, so that $du = dx$, we have

$$
\begin{aligned}
\int \frac{dx}{x^2 + 8x + 41} &= \int \frac{dx}{(x + 4)^2 + 5^2} \\
&= \int \frac{du}{u^2 + 5^2} \\
&= \frac{1}{5} \tan^{-1} \frac{u}{5} + c \\
&= \frac{1}{5} \tan^{-1}\left(\frac{x + 4}{5}\right) + c.
\end{aligned}
$$

EXAMPLES 13

1.   By making a suitable change of variable, find each of the following:

(a) $\displaystyle\int x\sqrt{x^2+5}\,dx;$ (b) $\displaystyle\int x^2\left(3x^3-4\right)^5\,dx;$

(c) $\displaystyle\int \frac{x}{\left(x^2+4\right)^5}\,dx;$ (d) $\displaystyle\int \frac{x^3}{x^4+9}\,dx;$

(e) $\displaystyle\int \left(2x^3+3x^2-5\right)^9\left(x^2+x\right)\,dx;$

(f) $\displaystyle\int \left(x^4-2x^2+7\right)^6\left(x^3-x\right)\,dx;$

(g) $\displaystyle\int \left(\sin\left(\tan x\right)\right)\sec^2 x\,dx;$

(h) $\displaystyle\int \left(\tan^5 x-\tan^2 x\right)\sec^2 x\,dx;$

(i) $\displaystyle\int e^{\sin x}\cos x\,dx;$ (j) $\displaystyle\int 3^{\tan x}\sec^2 x\,dx.$

2.   Write down the integral with respect to x of each of the following:

(a) $\sin 5x+\cos 3x;$ (b) $\cos 4x-\sin 2x;$

(c) $\dfrac{1}{\sqrt{9-x^2}};$ (d) $\dfrac{1}{\sqrt{25-x^2}};$

(e) $\dfrac{1}{16+x^2};$ (f) $\dfrac{1}{100+x^2};$

(g) $e^{4x};$ (h) $e^{-5x};$

(i) $\dfrac{1}{x+12};$ (j) $\dfrac{1}{x-5}.$

3.   By making a suitable linear change of variable, find each of the following:

(a) $\displaystyle\int \left[(3x+5)^{74}+(3x+5)^{50}\right]dx;$

(b) $\displaystyle\int \left[(2x-3)^{45}+(2x-3)^{53}\right]dx;$

(c) $\displaystyle\int (x+7)^{\frac{4}{3}}\,dx;$ (d) $\displaystyle\int (4x-5)^{\frac{7}{2}}\,dx;$

(e) $\displaystyle\int \frac{dx}{\sqrt{4x+3}};$ (f) $\displaystyle\int \frac{dx}{\sqrt{5x-4}};$

(g) $\displaystyle\int \cos(3x-2)dx;$ (h) $\displaystyle\int \sin(5x+2)dx;$

(i) $\displaystyle\int \sec^2 7x\, dx$;   (j) $\displaystyle\int \csc^2 4x\, dx$;

(k) $\displaystyle\int \sec(3x+4)\tan(3x+4)dx$;

(l) $\displaystyle\int \csc(2x+5)\cot(2x+5)dx$;

(m) $\displaystyle\int \dfrac{dx}{4+3x}$;   (n) $\displaystyle\int \dfrac{dx}{5-2x}$;

(o) $\displaystyle\int e^{4-3x}dx$;   (p) $\displaystyle\int e^{3x+4}dx$;

(q) $\displaystyle\int 2^{4-x}dx$;   (r) $\displaystyle\int 5^{3x+1}dx$.

4. By completing the square, find each of the following:

(a) $\displaystyle\int \dfrac{dx}{x^2+8x+25}$;   (b) $\displaystyle\int \dfrac{dx}{x^2-2x+10}$;

(c) $\displaystyle\int \dfrac{dx}{\sqrt{15-2x-x^2}}$;   (d) $\displaystyle\int \dfrac{dx}{\sqrt{21+4x-x^2}}$;

(e) $\displaystyle\int \dfrac{dx}{\sqrt{4x-x^2}}$;   (f) $\displaystyle\int \dfrac{dx}{\sqrt{45-8x-4x^2}}$.

CHAPTER 14

Integration By Parts

The method of Integration by Parts corresponds to the Product Rule for differentiation. Recall that, if $f(x)$ and $g(x)$ are two functions that can be differentiated, then by the Product Rule, we have

$$\frac{d}{dx}\left(f(x) \times g(x)\right) = f(x) \times \frac{d}{dx}\left(g(x)\right) + g(x) \times \frac{d}{dx}\left(f(x)\right).$$

From this it follows, since integration is the reverse of differentiation, that

$$f(x) \times g(x) = \int f(x) \times \frac{d}{dx}\left(g(x)\right)dx + \int g(x) \times \frac{d}{dx}\left(f(x)\right)dx.$$

Writing f', g' rather than $\frac{d}{dx}\left(f(x)\right)$, $\frac{d}{dx}\left(g(x)\right)$, respectively, and rearranging the terms, we see that

$$fg = \int fg'\,dx + \int gf'\,dx,$$

or

$$\int fg'\,dx = fg - \int gf'\,dx.$$

This last version should be memorized, and is the rule for **Integration by Parts**.

In order to use the method of Integration by Parts successfully, we need to be able to recognise an integrand as a product of two terms (f and g'), one of which (g') we will need to integrate, the other (f) we will need to differentiate.

Be warned that not all integrands which are products of two terms need to be integrated by parts. In fact the majority of examples from the last chapter were integrands which were products. However the examples in that chapter had the feature that where there were two parts to the integrand, one part was the derivative of the other. This was what led us in those examples to use a Change of Variable.

It is a good idea to consider Change of Variable as the preferred option, reserving Integration by Parts as an alternative when Change of Variable methods are unsuccessful.

Having decided to apply the technique of Integration by Parts to a particular example, the hardest part of the solution is frequently to decide which part of the integrand is to be f and which is to be g'. Notice that g' has to be a function that can be integrated, and that f must be a function that we can differentiate, and which preferably becomes simpler when we differentiate it. Although there are exceptions, one good candidate for f is a positive integral power of x.

Example 1. *Find* $\int (5x-4)\sin 4x\, dx$.

Solution.   In this example, we put $f = 5x-4$, from which we have $f' = 5$, and we put $g' = \sin 4x$, leading to $g = \int \sin 4x\, dx = -\frac{1}{4}\cos 4x$. The reason for this choice is that $5x-4$ becomes simpler when differentiated, while $\sin 4x$ does not become much more complicated when integrated. Had we chosen to take f and g' the other way round, then when we integrated $5x-4$ we would have obtained $\frac{5}{2}x^2 - 4x$, a polynomial of higher degree than we started with.

$$\int (5x-4)\sin 4x\, dx = (5x-4)\left(-\frac{1}{4}\cos 4x\right) - \int -\frac{1}{4}\cos 4x \times 5\, dx$$

$$= -\frac{1}{4}(5x-4)\cos 4x + \frac{5}{4}\int \cos 4x\, dx$$

$$= -\frac{1}{4}(5x-4)\cos 4x + \frac{5}{4} \times \frac{1}{4}\sin 4x + c$$

$$= -\frac{1}{4}(5x-4)\cos 4x + \frac{5}{16}\sin 4x + c.$$

You will notice that in the above example, and in all examples involving Integration by Parts, we do not include an arbitrary constant when finding g from g' by integration. The reason for this is that if we did include such an arbitrary constant then we would find that it would cancel out from the final answer.

However we do need to include an arbitrary constant when we have completed the integration. Notice that in the final lines of the above example we wrote the solution as

$$-\frac{1}{4}(5x-4)\cos 4x + \frac{5}{4} \times \frac{1}{4}\sin 4x + c$$

rather than as

$$-\frac{1}{4}(5x-4)\cos 4x + \frac{5}{4} \times \left(\frac{1}{4}\sin 4x + c^*\right),$$

which equals

$$-\frac{1}{4}(5x-4)\cos 4x + \frac{5}{4} \times \frac{1}{4}\sin 4x + \frac{5}{4} \times c^*.$$

These are equivalent, since c and c^* are both arbitrary constants, and $\frac{5}{4} \times$ (an arbitrary number) is equal to another arbitrary number. We chose the form we did simply because it looks slightly neater.

Example 2. *Find* $\int x^2 \cos 3x\, dx$.

Solution.   In this example, it will be convenient to let

$$I = \int x^2 \cos 3x\, dx.$$

For the same reason as in the last example, we put $f = x^2$, giving $f' = 2x$, and we put $g' = \cos 3x$, from which $g = \int \cos 3x \, dx = \frac{1}{3} \sin 3x$.

$$I = \int x^2 \cos 3x \, dx$$

$$= x^2 \left(\frac{1}{3} \sin 3x \right) - \int \frac{1}{3} \sin 3x \times 2x \, dx$$

$$= \frac{x^2}{3} \sin 3x - \frac{2}{3} \int x \sin 3x \, dx.$$

In order to integrate $x \sin 3x$ we use integration by parts again. We must take $f = x$, leading to $f' = 1$, and $g' = \sin 3x$, from which we have $g = \int \sin 3x \, dx = -\frac{1}{3} \cos 3x$. If we took $f = \sin 3x$ and $g' = x$ then after integrating by parts again we would return to the original integral and need to start the solution all over again.

$$I = \frac{x^2}{3} \sin 3x - \frac{2}{3} \int x \sin 3x \, dx$$

$$= \frac{x^2}{3} \sin 3x - \frac{2}{3} \left(x \times \left(-\frac{1}{3} \cos 3x \right) - \int -\frac{1}{3} \cos 3x \times 1 \, dx \right)$$

$$= \frac{x^2}{3} \sin 3x + \frac{2}{9} x \cos 3x - \frac{2}{9} \int \cos 3x \, dx$$

$$= \frac{x^2}{3} \sin 3x + \frac{2}{9} x \cos 3x - \frac{2}{27} \sin 3x + c.$$

In the next example, the natural thing to do would be to take $f = x^3 + 6x$ and $g' = \ln x$. That would be no good however since we do not yet have a way of integrating $\ln x$. Since we can differentiate $\ln x$ and integrate $x^3 + 6x$, we choose to put $f = \ln x$ and $g' = x^3 + 6x$. This at least enables us to start on the solution of the problem.

Example 3. *Find* $\int (x^3 + 6x) \ln x \, dx$.

Solution.   Taking $f = \ln x$ and $g' = x^3 + 6x$, for the reasons given in the introduction to this example, we will have $f' = \dfrac{1}{x}$ while $g = \int (x^3 + 6x) \, dx = \frac{1}{4} x^4 + 3x^2$. Hence, we have

$$\int (x^3 + 6x) \ln x \, dx = \left(\frac{1}{4} x^4 + 3x^2 \right) \ln x - \int \left(\frac{1}{4} x^4 + 3x^2 \right) \frac{1}{x} \, dx$$

$$= \left(\frac{1}{4} x^4 + 3x^2 \right) \ln x - \int \left(\frac{1}{4} x^3 + 3x \right) dx$$

$$= \left(\frac{1}{4} x^4 + 3x^2 \right) \ln x - \left(\frac{1}{16} x^4 + \frac{3}{2} x^2 \right) + c$$

$$= \left(\frac{1}{4} x^4 + 3x^2 \right) \ln x - \frac{1}{16} x^4 - \frac{3}{2} x^2 + c.$$

Example 4. Find $\int (2x - 3) e^{3x} \, dx$.

Solution.   The choice of f and g' is made here for exactly the reasons we used in the earlier examples. We put $f = 2x - 3$ so that $f' = 2$ and we put $g' = e^{3x}$ from which we have $g = \frac{1}{3}e^{3x}$.

$$\int (2x - 3) e^{3x} \, dx = (2x - 3) \left(\frac{1}{3}e^{3x} \right) - \int \frac{1}{3}e^{3x} \times 2 \, dx$$

$$= \frac{1}{3}(2x - 3)e^{3x} - \frac{2}{3} \int e^{3x} \, dx$$

$$= \frac{1}{3}(2x - 3)e^{3x} - \frac{2}{9}e^{3x} + c.$$

In the following example, we use a trick which sometimes works and which enables us to use Integration by Parts on integrands which do not appear to be products. The trick consists of writing the integrand as 1 times itself.

Example 5. Find $\int \ln x \, dx$.

Solution.   Having written $\ln x$ as $1 \times \ln x$, we put $f = \ln x$, so that $f' = \dfrac{1}{x}$, and $g' = 1$ from which $g = x$. There would be no sense in taking $f = 1$ which would just lead to $f' = 0$, and leave us no further forward. Then

$$\int \ln x \, dx = \int 1 \times \ln x \, dx$$

$$= x \ln x - \int x \left(\frac{1}{x} \right) dx$$

$$= x \ln x - \int 1 \, dx$$

$$= x \ln x - x + c.$$

A similar method works for $\int \sin^{-1} x \, dx$ and for $\int \tan^{-1} x \, dx$.

Example 6. Find $\int \sin^{-1} x \, dx$.

Solution.   Here we shall let $f = \sin^{-1} x$, so that $f' = \dfrac{1}{\sqrt{1 - x^2}}$, and we shall let $g' = 1$ from which $g = x$. Then we have

$$\int \sin^{-1} x \, dx = \int 1 \times \sin^{-1} x \, dx$$

$$= x \times \sin^{-1} x - \int x \times \frac{1}{\sqrt{1 - x^2}} \, dx$$

$$= x \sin^{-1} x - \int \frac{x}{\sqrt{1 - x^2}} \, dx.$$

In order to find $\displaystyle\int \frac{x}{\sqrt{1-x^2}}\,dx$, we notice that the denominator involves $1-x^2$ and that the numerator is x, which is a constant multiple of $-2x$. So we make the substitution $u = 1 - x^2$, so that $du = -2x\,dx$, and $-\frac{1}{2}\,du = x\,dx$. Hence we see that

$$\int \sin^{-1} x\,dx = x \sin^{-1} x - \int \frac{x}{\sqrt{1-x^2}}\,dx$$

$$= x \sin^{-1} x - \int \frac{-\frac{1}{2}\,du}{\sqrt{u}}$$

$$= x \sin^{-1} x + \frac{1}{2}\int \frac{du}{u^{\frac{1}{2}}}$$

$$= x \sin^{-1} x + \frac{1}{2}\int u^{-\frac{1}{2}}\,du$$

$$= x \sin^{-1} x + \frac{1}{2}\left(2u^{\frac{1}{2}}\right) + c$$

$$= x \sin^{-1} x + \left(1-x^2\right)^{\frac{1}{2}} + c$$

$$= x \sin^{-1} x + \sqrt{1-x^2} + c.$$

EXAMPLES 14

1.   Use Integration by Parts to find each of the following:

(a) $\displaystyle\int x e^{3x}\,dx;$

(b) $\displaystyle\int x \sin 3x\,dx;$

(c) $\displaystyle\int x^3 \ln x\,dx;$

(d) $\displaystyle\int x \cos 5x\,dx;$

(e) $\displaystyle\int x^2 \sin 4x\,dx;$

(f) $\displaystyle\int \left(x^2 - x\right) e^{3x}\,dx;$

(g) $\displaystyle\int \left(x^2 + 4x - 5\right) \sin 2x\,dx;$

(h) $\displaystyle\int \left(x^2 + 2\right) \cos 5x\,dx;$

(i) $\displaystyle\int x^{-2} \ln x\,dx;$

(j) $\displaystyle\int \sin^{-1} 2x\,dx.$

CHAPTER 15
Trigonometric Integrals

In this chapter we shall develop methods by which a number of integrals involving the trigonometric functions can be found. Later on, we shall be concerned to find methods for integrals involving powers of $\sec x$ and $\tan x$, and for integrals involving powers of $\operatorname{cosec} x$ and $\cot x$.

Firstly though we deal with the simplest case, which is integrals of the form

$$\int \sin^n x \cos^m x \, dx, \quad \text{where} \quad m, n \geq 0.$$

There are different methods for various different cases. These are as follows:

(1)   if m is an *odd* positive integer, and n is not, substitute $u = \sin x$;

(2)   if n is an *odd* positive integer, and m is not, substitute $u = \cos x$;

(3)   if m, n are both *odd* positive integers, put u equal to the one of $\sin x$ and $\cos x$ which occurs to the larger power (noticing that if the powers of $\sin x$ and $\cos x$ are equal, then it is slightly easier to put $u = \sin x$, but it really does not make much difference in this case);

(4)   if m, n are both *even* positive integers, use the double angle formulae

$$\cos^2 x = \frac{1}{2}(1 + \cos 2x), \qquad \sin^2 x = \frac{1}{2}(1 - \cos 2x)$$

to reduce the integrand to a form which can be integrated by the methods of (1)–(3) above.

In each of the cases (1)–(3) above, it may also be necessary to use the formula $\cos^2 x + \sin^2 x = 1$ in either of the forms

$$\cos^2 x = 1 - \sin^2 x$$

or

$$\sin^2 x = 1 - \cos^2 x$$

in order to reduce the integrand to a suitable form.

Example 1.   *Find* $\displaystyle\int \sin^4 x \cos x \, dx$.

Solution.   Since this integral involves an odd power of $\cos x$ and an even power of $\sin x$, it is of type (1). So we will substitute $u = \sin x$, so that $du = \cos x \, dx$.

$$\int \sin^4 x \cos x \, dx = \int u^4 \, du$$

$$= \frac{1}{5} u^5 + c$$

$$= \frac{1}{5} \sin^5 x + c.$$

Example 2. *Find* $\int \sin^2 x \cos^3 x \, dx$.

Solution.   Again, this integral involves an odd power of $\cos x$, and so we will put $u = \sin x$, and $du = \cos x \, dx$. This time though, we will need to use the formula $\cos^2 x = 1 - \sin^2 x$ in order to express the integrand in terms of $\sin x$ and hence in terms of u.

$$\int \sin^2 x \cos^3 x \, dx = \int \sin^2 x \left(1 - \sin^2 x\right) \cos x \, dx$$

$$= \int u^2 \left(1 - u^2\right) du$$

$$= \int \left(u^2 - u^4\right) du$$

$$= \frac{1}{3} u^3 - \frac{1}{5} u^5 + c$$

$$= \frac{1}{3} \sin^3 x - \frac{1}{5} \sin^5 x + c.$$

Example 3. *Find* $\int \sin^5 x \, dx$.

Solution.   This time the power of $\cos x$ in the integrand is the power zero. The expression $\sin x$ occurs to an odd power. This means that this integral is of type (2), and so the appropriate substitution is $u = \cos x$, with $du = -\sin x \, dx$. Again we will need to use the formula $\sin^2 x = 1 - \cos^2 x$ in order to put the integrand in terms of $\cos x$ before we can integrate it.

$$\int \sin^5 x \, dx = \int \sin^4 x \sin x \, dx$$

$$= \int \left(\sin^2 x\right)^2 \sin x \, dx$$

$$= \int \left(1 - \cos^2 x\right)^2 \sin x \, dx$$

$$= \int \left(1 - 2\cos^2 x + \cos^4 x\right) \sin x \, dx$$

$$= \int \left(1 - 2u^2 + u^4\right) (-du)$$

(substituting $u = \cos x$)

$$= -\left(u - \frac{2}{3} u^3 + \frac{1}{5} u^5\right) + c$$

$$= -\cos x + \frac{2}{3} \cos^3 x - \frac{1}{5} \cos^5 x + c.$$

Example 4. *Find* $\int \sin^{\frac{1}{2}} x \cos x \, dx.$

Solution.   In this integral we have a fractional power of $\sin x$. This does not affect the difficulty of the problem, since we have an odd power of $\cos x$, so that method (1) will apply.

$$\int \sin^{\frac{1}{2}} x \cos x \, dx = \int u^{\frac{1}{2}} du$$

$$= \frac{2}{3} u^{\frac{3}{2}} + c$$

$$= \frac{2}{3} \sin^{\frac{3}{2}} x + c.$$

Example 5. *Find* $\int \sin^2 x \cos^2 x \, dx.$

Solution.   In this integral we have both $\sin x$ and $\cos x$ to even powers. Therefore we have to use method (4), which involves using the double angle formulae to try to reduce the integrand to a more amenable form.

$$\sin^2 x \cos^2 x = \left[\frac{1}{2}(1 - \cos 2x) \right] \times \left[\frac{1}{2}(1 + \cos 2x) \right]$$

$$= \frac{1}{4}(1 - \cos^2 2x)$$

$$= \frac{1}{4}\left(1 - \left(\frac{1}{2}(1 + \cos 4x) \right) \right)$$

$$= \frac{1}{4}\left(1 - \frac{1}{2} - \frac{1}{2} \cos 4x \right)$$

$$= \frac{1}{4}\left(\frac{1}{2} - \frac{1}{2} \cos 4x \right)$$

$$= \frac{1}{8} - \frac{1}{8} \cos 4x.$$

Notice the second use of the double angle formula above in order to write $\cos^2 2x = \frac{1}{2}(1 + \cos 4x)$. As a result of the above trigonometric manipulation, we have

$$\int \sin^2 x \cos^2 x \, dx = \int \left(\frac{1}{8} - \frac{1}{8} \cos 4x \right) dx$$

$$= \frac{1}{8}x - \frac{1}{8} \cdot \frac{1}{4} \sin 4x + c$$

$$= \frac{1}{8}x - \frac{1}{32} \sin 4x + c.$$

Before seeing how to tackle integrals involving $\sec x$ and $\tan x$, we must consider how to deal with the simplest integrals of this type. Both of the following results are standard integrals, *which should be learnt.*

E

$$\int \tan x \, dx = \ln|\sec x| + c$$

and

$$\int \sec x \, dx = \ln|\sec x + \tan x| + c.$$

In both of these, the simplest proof involves using the fact that we know the correct answer. For

$$\int \tan x \, dx = \int \frac{\sec x \tan x}{\sec x} \, dx$$

$$= \int \frac{du}{u}$$

(if we let $u = \sec x$ so that $du = \sec x \tan x \, dx$)

$$= \ln|u| + c$$

$$= \ln|\sec x| + c.$$

Similarly, we have

$$\int \sec x \, dx = \int \frac{(\sec x + \tan x)\sec x}{\sec x + \tan x} \, dx$$

$$= \int \frac{(\sec^2 x + \sec x \tan x)}{\sec x + \tan x} \, dx$$

$$= \int \frac{du}{u}$$

(on putting $u = \sec x + \tan x$ and $du = (\sec x \tan x + \sec^2 x) \, dx$)

$$= \ln|u| + c$$

$$= \ln|\sec x + \tan x| + c.$$

The methods for dealing with integrands of the form $\sec^m x \tan^n x$, where m, n are integers (m, $n \geq 0$, of course) are as follows:

(1)   if there is an *even* positive power of $\sec x$ then put $u = \tan x$;

(2)   if there are *odd* positive powers of *both* $\sec x$ and $\tan x$ then put $u = \sec x$;

(3)   if there is an *odd* positive power of $\sec x$ and an *even* power of $\tan x$ then express the integral purely in terms of $\sec x$, and use Integration by Parts.

This final case is usually a very unpleasant one to deal with, involving quite difficult manipulations.

In all of the above cases, the formula $\sec^2 x = 1 + \tan^2 x$ can be very important.

Example 6. *Find* $\int \sec^2 x \tan^3 x \, dx$.

Solution.   In this example we have an even power of $\sec x$ and so method (1) applies. We shall therefore put $u = \tan x$ from which we have $du = \sec^2 x \, dx$.

$$\int \sec^2 x \tan^3 x \, dx = \int u^3 \, du$$

$$= \frac{1}{4} u^4 + c$$

$$= \frac{1}{4} \tan^4 x + c.$$

Example 7. *Find* $\int \sec^5 x \tan^3 x \, dx$.

Solution.   In this example we have an odd power of $\sec x$ and an odd power of $\tan x$, and hence method (2) applies. We shall therefore put $u = \sec x$ so that $du = \sec x \tan x \, dx$.

$$\int \sec^5 x \tan^3 x \, dx = \int \sec^4 x \tan^2 x \, (\sec x \tan x) \, dx$$

$$= \int \sec^4 x \, (\sec^2 x - 1)(\sec x \tan x) \, dx$$

$$= \int u^4 (u^2 - 1) \, du$$

$$= \int (u^6 - u^4) \, du$$

$$= \frac{1}{7} u^7 - \frac{1}{5} u^5 + c$$

$$= \frac{1}{7} \sec^7 x - \frac{1}{5} \sec^5 x + c.$$

As suggested earlier the hardest type of example is that for which we have an odd power of $\sec x$ combined with an even power of $\tan x$.

Example 8. *Find* $\int \sec^3 x \, dx$.

Solution.   It will be helpful in this example to let

$$I = \int \sec^3 x \, dx.$$

We begin the solution of the example by writing the integrand in the form $\sec x \times \sec^2 x$, and we shall use Integration by Parts to find an expression for I. In the Integration by Parts we shall let $f = \sec x$, which leads to $f' = \sec x \tan x$, and we shall take $g' = \sec^2 x$, from which we have $g = \int g' \, dx = \int \sec^2 x \, dx = \tan x$. Any alternative choices for f and g' would have led to a more complicated situation after the first Integration by Parts.

$$\int \sec^3 x \, dx = \int \sec x \sec^2 x \, dx$$

$$= \sec x \tan x - \int \tan x \, (\sec x \tan x) \, dx$$

$$= \sec x \tan x - \int \sec x \tan^2 x \, dx$$

$$= \sec x \tan x - \int \sec x \left(\sec^2 x - 1\right) \, dx$$

(from the formula $\sec^2 x = 1 + \tan^2 x$)

$$= \sec x \tan x - \int \left(\sec^3 x - \sec x\right) \, dx$$

$$= \sec x \tan x - \int \sec^3 x \, dx + \int \sec x \, dx$$

$$= \sec x \tan x - I + \ln |\sec x + \tan x| + 2c.$$

Hence we have

$$I = \sec x \tan x - I + \ln |\sec x + \tan x| + 2c$$

so that

$$2I = \sec x \tan x + \ln |\sec x + \tan x| + 2c$$

or

$$I = \frac{1}{2} \sec x \tan x + \frac{1}{2} \ln |\sec x + \tan x| + c.$$

You will have noticed that in the above example, we arrived back at our original integral after Integrating by Parts, so that we were then able to obtain an equation involving I which we could solve to find I.

You will also have noticed that when we introduced an arbitrary constant we called it $2c$ rather than c. The reason for this was simply that we knew what was coming, and by taking the arbitrary constant as $2c$ we obtained a slightly neater-looking answer. However it would *not* have been wrong to have taken·the constant as c.

Finally, notice the point at which we did introduce the arbitrary constant. This was the point at which we were equating the two versions of $\int \sec^3 x \, dx$. The reason for bringing in an arbitrary constant at that point is that any two indefinite integrals for $\sec^3 x$ will both equal the same function of x, but they could differ by a constant. So we introduced the constant at the point we did in order to compensate for this possible difference.

The rules involved in integrating functions involving $\operatorname{cosec} x$ and $\cot x$ are very similar to those involving $\sec x$ and $\tan x$, with the obvious changes that $\tan x$ is replaced by $\cot x$ and $\sec x$ is replaced by $\operatorname{cosec} x$. There are also some changes of plus signs to minus signs.

Before tackling some integrals involving $\operatorname{cosec} x$ and $\cot x$, we must consider how to deal with integrating these functions themselves. Both of the following results are standard integrals, *which should be learnt.*

$$\int \cot x \, dx = \ln|\sin x| + c$$

and

$$\int \operatorname{cosec} x \, dx = \ln|\operatorname{cosec} x - \cot x| + c.$$

In the second of these, the simplest proof involves using the fact that we know the correct answer. For the first, we shall write $\cot x = \dfrac{\cos x}{\sin x}$, and use a Change of Variable. We shall put $u = \sin x$, so that $du = \cos x \, dx$. Then

$$\int \cot x \, dx = \int \frac{\cos x}{\sin x} \, dx$$
$$= \int \frac{du}{u}$$
$$= \ln|u| + c$$
$$= \ln|\sin x| + c.$$

We also have

$$\int \operatorname{cosec} x \, dx = \int \frac{(\operatorname{cosec} x - \cot x)\operatorname{cosec} x}{\operatorname{cosec} x - \cot x} \, dx$$
$$= \int \frac{(\operatorname{cosec}^2 x - \operatorname{cosec} x \cot x)}{\operatorname{cosec} x - \cot x} \, dx$$
$$= \int \frac{du}{u}$$

(if we let $u = \operatorname{cosec} x - \cot x$ giving $du = (\operatorname{cosec}^2 x - \operatorname{cosec} x \cot x) \, dx$)
$$= \ln|u| + c$$
$$= \ln|\operatorname{cosec} x - \cot x| + c.$$

Example 9. *Find* $\displaystyle\int \operatorname{cosec}^4 x \cot^2 x \, dx$.

Solution.   In this example, we will need to make the change of variable $u = \cot x$, from which $du = -\operatorname{cosec}^2 x \, dx$. We need to use the formula $\operatorname{cosec}^2 x = 1 + \cot^2 x$ to express one of the $\operatorname{cosec}^2 x$ terms in terms of $\cot x$. Then

$$\int \operatorname{cosec}^4 x \cot^2 x \, dx = \int (1 + \cot^2 x)\cot^2 x \operatorname{cosec}^2 x \, dx$$
$$= -\int (1 + u^2) u^2 \, du$$

$$= -\int \left(u^2 + u^4 \right) du$$

$$= -\frac{1}{3}u^3 - \frac{1}{5}u^5 + c$$

$$= -\frac{1}{3}\cot^3 x - \frac{1}{5}\cot^5 x + c.$$

Example 10.   *Find* $\int \csc^5 x \cot x \, dx$.

Solution.   In this example, we shall substitute $u = \csc x$, since we have an odd power of both $\csc x$ and $\cot x$. Then we know that $du = -\csc x \cot x \, dx$.

$$\int \csc^5 x \cot x \, dx = -\int \csc^4 x \left(-\csc x \cot x \, dx \right)$$

$$= -\int u^4 \, du$$

$$= -\frac{1}{5}u^5 + c$$

$$= -\frac{1}{5}\csc^5 x + c.$$

EXAMPLES 15

1.   By putting $u = \sin x$ or $u = \cos x$, find each of the following:

(a) $\int \sin^7 x \cos x \, dx$;   (b) $\int \sin^6 x \cos x \, dx$;

(c) $\int \sin^{\frac{5}{2}} x \cos x \, dx$;   (d) $\int \sin^4 x \cos^3 x \, dx$;

(e) $\int \sin^3 x \cos^2 x \, dx$;   (f) $\int \sin x \cos^6 x \, dx$;

(g) $\int \sin^3 x \cos^{\frac{5}{3}} x \, dx$;   (h) $\int \sin^5 x \cos^2 x \, dx$.

2.   By using the formulae

$$\sin^2 x = \frac{1}{2}(1 - \cos 2x) \quad \text{and} \quad \cos^2 x = \frac{1}{2}(1 + \cos 2x),$$

find each of the following:

(a) $\int \sin^2 x \, dx$;   (b) $\int \cos^2 x \, dx$;

(c) $\int \sin^4 x \, dx$;   (d) $\int \cos^4 x \, dx$;

(e) $\int \sin^4 x \cos^2 x \, dx$;   (f) $\int \sin^6 x \, dx$.

3.   Find each of the following:

(a) $\int \sec^2 x \tan^5 x \, dx;$

(b) $\int \sec^2 x \tan^{\frac{5}{2}} x \, dx;$

(c) $\int \sec^4 x \tan^2 x \, dx;$

(d) $\int \tan^4 x \, dx;$

(e) $\int \sec^3 x \tan^3 x \, dx;$

(f) $\int \sec x \tan^5 x \, dx;$

(g) $\int \sec^3 x \tan^5 x \, dx;$

(h) $\int \sec^3 x \tan^7 x \, dx;$

(i) $\int \sec x \tan^2 x \, dx;$

(j) $\int \operatorname{cosec}^2 x \cot x \, dx;$

(k) $\int \operatorname{cosec}^2 x \cot^4 x \, dx;$

(l) $\int \cot^4 x \, dx;$

(m) $\int \operatorname{cosec} x \cot^3 x \, dx;$

(n) $\int \operatorname{cosec}^3 x \cot^3 x \, dx.$

CHAPTER 16
Trigonometric Substitutions

There are certain types of integrals which have substitutions which lead to the trigonometric integrals we studied in the last chapter. These integrals are those which involve either $\sqrt{a^2 - x^2}$, $\sqrt{a^2 + x^2}$ or $\sqrt{x^2 - a^2}$.

For integrands which involve $\sqrt{a^2 - x^2}$, where a is a positive constant, we put $x = a \sin \theta$.

For integrands which involve $\sqrt{a^2 + x^2}$, where a is a positive constant, we put $x = a \tan \theta$.

For integrands which involve $\sqrt{x^2 - a^2}$, where a is a positive constant, we put $x = a \sec \theta$.

In each case, we assume that the form of the integrand does not lead us to make a straightforward substitution of the form $u = a^2 - x^2$, for example.

In some cases, it may be necessary to complete the square in x and make a linear change of variable before we are able to reduce the integrand to one of the above forms.

Example 1. *Find* $\displaystyle\int \frac{dx}{x\sqrt{1 - x^2}}.$

Solution. Since this integrand involves $\sqrt{1 - x^2}$, and there is no obvious change of variable, we put $x = \sin \theta$ so that $dx = \cos \theta \, d\theta$. Notice also that then $1 - x^2 = 1 - \sin^2 \theta = \cos^2 \theta$, so that $\sqrt{1 - x^2} = \cos \theta$.

$$\int \frac{dx}{x\sqrt{1 - x^2}} = \int \frac{\cos \theta \, d\theta}{\sin \theta \times \cos \theta}$$

$$= \int \frac{d\theta}{\sin \theta}$$

$$= \int \operatorname{cosec} \theta \, d\theta$$

$$= \ln |\operatorname{cosec} \theta - \cot \theta| + c$$

$$= \ln \left| \frac{1}{x} - \frac{\sqrt{1 - x^2}}{x} \right| + c$$

$$= \ln \left| \frac{1 - \sqrt{1 - x^2}}{x} \right| + c.$$

Notice how in this example we use a right-angled triangle in order to express our answer in terms of the original variable x instead of the θ we have introduced. If θ is the angle shown then we may take the side

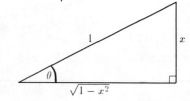

opposite θ to have length x while the hypoteneuse has length 1. By Pythagoras' theorem, the third side of the triangle has length $\sqrt{1 - x^2}$.

Example 2. Find $\displaystyle\int \frac{dx}{\sqrt{x^2 - 6x + 25}}$.

Solution. In this example, we start by completing the square in $x^2 - 6x + 25$, so as to reduce the integrand to one of the above types. We have

$$x^2 - 6x + 25 = (x - 3)^2 + 16 = (x - 3)^2 + 4^2,$$

so that

$$\int \frac{dx}{\sqrt{x^2 - 6x + 25}} = \int \frac{dx}{\sqrt{(x - 3)^2 + 4^2}}$$

(putting $u = x - 3$, so that $du = dx$)

$$= \int \frac{du}{\sqrt{u^2 + 4^2}}.$$

To deal with this integral, we put $u = 4 \tan \theta$, so that $du = 4 \sec^2 \theta \, d\theta$. We also see that

$$\begin{aligned}
u^2 + 4^2 &= 16 \tan^2 \theta + 16 \\
&= 16 \left(\tan^2 \theta + 1 \right) \\
&= 16 \sec^2 \theta.
\end{aligned}$$

From this, we see that

$$\begin{aligned}
\int \frac{du}{\sqrt{u^2 + 4^2}} &= \int \frac{4 \sec^2 \theta \, d\theta}{\sqrt{16 \sec^2 \theta}} \\
&= \int \frac{4 \sec^2 \theta \, d\theta}{4 \sec \theta} \\
&= \int \sec \theta \, d\theta \\
&= \ln |\sec \theta + \tan \theta| + c^* \\
&= \ln \left| \frac{\sqrt{u^2 + 4^2}}{4} + \frac{u}{4} \right| + c^*
\end{aligned}$$

(using a suitable right-angled triangle to find $\sec \theta$ in terms of u)

$$= \ln \left| \frac{\sqrt{(x - 3)^2 + 4^2}}{4} + \frac{x - 3}{4} \right| + c^*$$

(replacing u by $x - 3$)

$$= \ln \left| \frac{\sqrt{(x - 3)^2 + 4^2} + x - 3}{4} \right| + c^*$$

$$= \ln \left| \sqrt{x^2 - 6x + 25} + x - 3 \right| - \ln 4 + c^*$$

(using one of the laws of logarithms)

$$= \ln \left| \sqrt{x^2 - 6x + 25} + x - 3 \right| + c,$$

where at the end we are combining the arbitrary constant c^* and the number $-\ln 4$ to give a new arbitrary constant c.

Notice again in this example, we use a right-angled triangle to enable us to express our answer in terms of the original variable x. In this triangle, one of the angles is θ, and we may assume that since $u = 4 \tan \theta$ the sides of the triangle are u and 4. The hypotenuse of the triangle will have length $\sqrt{u^2 + 4^2}$, by Pythagoras' theorem. Since we took $u = x - 3$, we may therefore find $\sec \theta$ and $\tan \theta$ in terms of x, as we did.

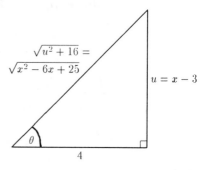

Example 3. *Find* $\int \sqrt{12 - 4x - x^2}\, dx.$

Solution. As in the last example, we start the solution by completing the square and obtain

$$12 - 4x - x^2 = 4^2 - (x + 2)^2.$$

We will therefore make the linear change of variable $x + 2 = 4 \sin \theta$, so that $dx = 4 \cos \theta\, d\theta$. Also

$$4^2 - (x + 2)^2 = 4^2 - 4^2 \sin^2 \theta$$
$$= 4^2 \left(1 - \sin^2 \theta\right)$$
$$= 4^2 \cos^2 \theta.$$

It follows therefore that

$$\int \sqrt{12 - 4x - x^2}\, dx = \int \sqrt{4^2 - (x + 2)^2}\, dx$$
$$= \int \sqrt{4^2 \cos^2 \theta} \times 4 \cos \theta\, d\theta$$
$$= 8 \int 2 \cos^2 \theta\, d\theta$$
$$= 8 \int (1 + \cos 2\theta)\, d\theta$$

(on using the double angle formula $2 \cos^2 x = \cos 2x + 1$)

$$= 8 \left(\theta + \frac{1}{2} \sin 2\theta \right) + c$$

$$= 8 \left(\theta + \sin \theta \cos \theta \right) + c$$

(on using $\sin 2\theta = 2 \sin \theta \cos \theta$)

$$= 8 \sin^{-1} \left(\frac{x+2}{4} \right) + 8 \frac{x+2}{4} \sqrt{1 - \left(\frac{x+2}{4} \right)^2} + c$$

(on substituting for θ in terms of x)

$$= 8 \sin^{-1} \left(\frac{x+2}{4} \right) + 2 (x+2) \sqrt{\frac{12 - 4x - x^2}{16}} + c$$

$$= 8 \sin^{-1} \left(\frac{x+2}{4} \right) + \frac{1}{2} (x+2) \sqrt{12 - 4x - x^2} + c.$$

This example is again a rather complicated one, involving as it does the use of trigonometric formulae to convert the integrand to a convenient form, and again to turn the answer back in terms of x. There is also some manipulation of fractions inside a square-root sign, and finally the use of

$$\sin^{-1} \left(\frac{x+2}{4} \right) = \theta.$$

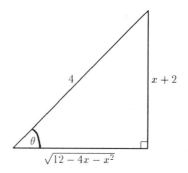

4

$x+2$

θ

$\sqrt{12 - 4x - x^2}$

This of course arises from the fact that we have put $x + 2 = 4 \sin \theta$, from which we have $\sin \theta = \dfrac{x+2}{4}$, so that the above formula gives θ. (We are assuming implicitly here that the value of θ is chosen to lie in the first or second quadrants, to make this conclusion correct. Since there is sufficient difficulty in examples of the above type, we have chosen to sacrifice strict accuracy in favour of a slightly simplified approach, which will not lead to incorrect conclusions.)

The above example does bring out one important fact about Mathematics, and that is that it is better to tackle problems by doing a large number of small steps accurately, rather than by trying to do a small number of large steps, which almost certainly lead to mistakes.

EXAMPLES 16

1.   By making an appropriate trigonometric substitution, find each of the following:

(a) $\displaystyle\int \frac{dx}{(9-x^2)^{\frac{3}{2}}}$;

(b) $\displaystyle\int \frac{x^2}{(4-x^2)^{\frac{3}{2}}}\,dx$;

(c) $\displaystyle\int \sqrt{25-x^2}\,dx$;

(d) $\displaystyle\int \sqrt{36-x^2}\,dx$;

(e) $\displaystyle\int \frac{dx}{(9+8x-x^2)^{\frac{3}{2}}}$;

(f) $\displaystyle\int \frac{x^2}{(5-4x-x^2)^{\frac{3}{2}}}\,dx$;

(g) $\displaystyle\int \frac{dx}{(x^2+9)^2}$;

(h) $\displaystyle\int \frac{dx}{(x^2-2x+5)^{\frac{1}{2}}}$.

2.   If $y = \ln\left|x + \sqrt{x^2+k}\right|$, where $k \neq 0$ is a constant, show that $\dfrac{dy}{dx} = \dfrac{1}{\sqrt{x^2+k}}$. Deduce that

$$\int \frac{dx}{\sqrt{x^2+k}} = \ln\left|x + \sqrt{x^2+k}\right| + c,$$

where k is any non-zero constant, and c is the constant of integration.

Hence find

(a) $\displaystyle\int \frac{dx}{\sqrt{x^2+5}}$;

(b) $\displaystyle\int \frac{dx}{\sqrt{x^2-7}}$;

(c) $\displaystyle\int \frac{dx}{(x^2-4x+5)^{\frac{1}{2}}}$;

(d) $\displaystyle\int \frac{dx}{(x^2-6x+3)^{\frac{1}{2}}}$.

Also use the above result to obtain a shorter solution for Example 1 in the text, and for 1(h) above.

CHAPTER 17

Partial Fractions

Given a **rational function**—that is, a quotient of two polynomials having no common factor—such as

$$\frac{2x^4 + x^3 - x^2 - 15x + 62}{x^3 + 2x^2 - 3x - 10},$$

where there is no obvious relationship between the denominator and the numerator, then the usual way to proceed, if asked to integrate such an expression, is to use the method of Partial Fractions.

We can think of Partial Fractions as providing a technique for reversing the results of expressing a sum of fractions over a common denominator, as for example in

$$\frac{5}{x - 3} - \frac{2}{x + 2} = \frac{5(x + 2) - 2(x - 3)}{(x - 3)(x + 2)} = \frac{3x + 16}{(x - 3)(x + 2)}.$$

The method of Partial Fractions only applies to **proper fractions**—that is, those for which the degree of the numerator is less than the degree of the denominator. If this is not the case, then we need to use **long division of polynomials** in order to express the rational function as a quotient term together with a term which is a proper fraction.

The technique of long division of polynomials is explained in detail in the chapter on basic techniques. Here, we shall content ourselves with an example to practise the technique. Recall that at all stages the important thing is to keep the highest power of x correct.

Example 1. *Find the quotient and remainder when the expression $x^4 - 3x^3 - 7x + 6$ is divided by $x^2 - 5x + 4$.*

Solution. In setting up the traditional long division format, notice that we keep terms involving the same power of x under one another, and notice that we insert a term $+ 0x^2$ in the dividend, in order to create a column for the x^2-terms. We always do this if there is a term missing from the dividend.

$$
\begin{array}{r}
x^2 + 2x + 6 \\
x^2 - 5x + 4 \overline{\smash{\big)}\ x^4 - 3x^3 + 0x^2 - 7x + 6} \\
\underline{x^4 - 5x^3 + 4x^2} \\
2x^3 - 4x^2 - 7x \\
\underline{2x^3 - 10x^2 + 8x} \\
6x^2 - 15x + 6 \\
\underline{6x^2 - 30x + 24} \\
15x - 18
\end{array}
$$

Hence the quotient is $x^2 + 2x + 6$, while the remainder is $15x - 18$. It follows that

$$x^4 - 3x^3 - 7x + 6 = \left(x^2 - 5x + 4\right)\left(x^2 + 2x + 6\right) + (15x - 18),$$

and so, on dividing by $x^2 - 5x + 4$, we have

$$\frac{x^4 - 3x^3 - 7x + 6}{x^2 - 5x + 4} = x^2 + 2x + 6 + \frac{15x - 18}{x^2 - 5x + 4}.$$

Using the above method, we can express an **improper fraction**—that is, one where the degree of the numerator is at least as large as the degree of the denominator—as a sum of a polynomial together with a proper fraction.

The next step in the method of Partial Fractions is to *factorise the denominator* completely, as a product of linear factors and quadratic factors, having real numbers as coefficients, such that the quadratic terms cannot be factorised further using real numbers as coefficients. In doing this, the Remainder Theorem can help us to determine a linear factor, and synthetic division (or long division of polynomials) can then help us to determine the remaining term which still needs to be factorised.

The methods of the following example should all be familiar from the earlier examples we did in the chapters on Curve Sketching, and are included here purely for revision purposes.

Example 2. *Factorise* $x^4 + 4x^3 - 8x^2 - 48x + 80$ *as a product of linear and quadratic factors.*

Solution.   Let $f(x) \equiv x^4 + 4x^3 - 8x^2 - 48x + 80$. Then

$$f(0) = 80 \neq 0,$$
$$f(1) = 1 + 4 - 8 - 48 + 80 = 29 \neq 0,$$
$$f(-1) = 1 - 4 - 8 + 48 + 80 = 117 \neq 0,$$
$$f(2) = 16 + 32 - 32 - 96 + 80 = 0.$$

Hence $x = 2$ is a root of $f(x) = 0$ and so $x - 2$ is a factor of $f(x)$. We shall use long division to obtain the other factor, although we could equally well use synthetic division.

$$
\begin{array}{r}
x^3 + 6x^2 + 4x - 40 \\
x - 2 \, \overline{\big)\, x^4 + 4x^3 - 8x^2 - 48x + 80} \\
\underline{x^4 - 2x^3} \\
6x^3 - 8x^2 \\
\underline{6x^3 - 12x^2} \\
4x^2 - 48x \\
\underline{4x^2 - 8x} \\
-40x + 80 \\
\underline{-40x + 80} \\
0
\end{array}
$$

Hence we have $f(x) = (x - 2)\left(x^3 + 6x^2 + 4x - 40\right)$. We shall let $g(x) \equiv x^3 + 6x^2 + 4x - 40$.

There is no point in trying $x = 0$, $x = 1$ or $x = -1$ as roots of $g(x) = 0$, since these values of x were not roots of $f(x) = 0$. So the first value of x that we try is $x = 2$ again. Now

$$g(2) = 8 + 24 + 8 - 40 = 0.$$

Hence $x - 2$ is a factor of $g(x)$. We use long division again to find the other factor.

$$
\begin{array}{r}
x^2 \quad + \quad 8x \quad + \quad 20 \\
x - 2 \enclose{longdiv}{x^3 \; + \; 6x^2 \; + \quad 4x \; - \; 40} \\
\underline{x^3 \; - \; 2x^2} \\
8x^2 \; + \quad 4x \\
\underline{8x^2 \; - \; 16x} \\
20x \; - \; 40 \\
\underline{20x \; - \; 40} \\
0
\end{array}
$$

It follows that $g(x) = (x-2)\left(x^2 + 8x + 20\right)$. Since $x^2 + 8x + 20$ cannot be factorised any further, (its discriminant is $-16 < 0$), we see that

$$x^4 + 4x^3 - 8x^2 - 48x + 80 = (x-2)^2\left(x^2 + 8x + 20\right).$$

We now wish to try to break proper fractions of polynomials into a sum of terms, each having a single term in its denominator. There are a number of different cases to consider.

(1)   The denominator has *distinct linear factors*.

In this case the fraction can be expressed as a sum of terms, each of which is a constant divided by one of the terms from the denominator. The values of the constants can most readily be found by using the **cover up rule**, as in the following example.

Example 3.   *Find partial fractions for*

$$\frac{x^2 + 8x - 5}{(x-2)(x+1)(x+3)}.$$

Solution.   We assume that we can write

$$\frac{x^2 + 8x - 5}{(x-2)(x+1)(x+3)} = \frac{A}{x-2} + \frac{B}{x+1} + \frac{C}{x+3}.$$

To find the value of A, we put $x = 2$ in the left-hand side of the equation, 'covering up' the $(x-2)$-factor. So we have to find the value at $x = 2$ of

$$\frac{x^2 + 8x - 5}{\rule{1.2cm}{0.35cm}(x+1)(x+3)}.$$

Then

$$A = \frac{2^2 + 8 \times 2 - 5}{(2+1)(2+3)} = \frac{15}{3 \times 5} = 1.$$

Similarly, we 'cover up' the term $x + 1$ on the left-hand side of the equation, and put $x = -1$ in the remainder. This will give us the value of B. We have

$$B = \frac{-12}{-3 \times 2} = 2.$$

We can find C in a corresponding manner. This time we obtain

$$C = \frac{-20}{(-5) \times (-2)} = -2.$$

From this we conclude that

$$\frac{x^2 + 8x - 5}{(x - 2)(x + 1)(x + 3)} = \frac{1}{x - 2} + \frac{2}{x + 1} - \frac{2}{x + 3}.$$

You might be interested to express the right-hand side of this equation over a common denominator, and show that it is indeed equal to the left-hand side.

(2)   The denominator has a *repeated linear factor*.

In this case we can express the rational function as a sum of terms, each of the form of a constant over each non-repeating linear factor, together with a sum of terms of the form of a constant divided by each power in turn of the repeated factor in the denominator from 1 up to the highest power occurring in the denominator.

We determine the constants which are divided by the *highest* powers of the linear terms as in (1) above. To find the other terms, we have to cross-multiply by the denominator, and then either equate the various coefficients of x involved, or substitute different values of x into the equation we obtain. The method will become clear once the following example has been studied.

Example 4.   *Find partial fractions for*

$$\frac{x^3 + 6x^2 + 11}{(x - 1)^3 (x + 2)}.$$

Solution.   We assume that the above expression has a partial fraction decomposition

$$\frac{x^3 + 6x^2 + 11}{(x - 1)^3 (x + 2)} = \frac{A}{(x - 1)^3} + \frac{B}{(x - 1)^2} + \frac{C}{x - 1} + \frac{D}{x + 2}.$$

Using the cover up rule, taking $x = 1$ and covering up the $(x - 1)^3$ term on the left hand side, we can find that

$$A = \frac{18}{3} = 6.$$

We can also use the cover up rule to find D, as we did in the previous example. We find

$$D = \frac{27}{(-3)^3} = \frac{27}{-27} = -1.$$

We now multiply both sides of the above equation by the denominator of the left-hand side, as we do so substituting the values for A and D that we have just found. We have

$$\frac{\left(x^3 + 6x^2 + 11\right)(x-1)^3 (x+2)}{(x-1)^3 (x+2)} = \frac{6(x-1)^3 (x+2)}{(x-1)^3}$$
$$+ \frac{B(x-1)^3 (x+2)}{(x-1)^2} + \frac{C(x-1)^3 (x+2)}{x-1} - \frac{(x-1)^3 (x+2)}{x+2},$$

and, on cancelling terms from the numerator and denominator,

$$x^3 + 6x^2 + 11 = 6(x+2) + B(x-1)(x+2)$$
$$+ C(x-1)^2 (x+2) - (x-1)^3.$$

There are two possible ways of finding the remaining constants, B and C. We could multiply out each of the terms and collect up the terms in each power of x. Then we could equate the powers of x on both sides of the equation. This is the method we shall use in the next example. Here, we shall substitute values for x and obtain a pair of equations from which we can find B and C. The values $x = 1$ and $x = -2$ have already been used in the cover up rule, so we shall try different values.

We shall take $x = 0$. Then we have

$$11 = 12 - 2B + 2C + 1,$$

and, taking $x = -1$, we have

$$16 = 6 - 2B + 4C + 8.$$

Rearranging these equations, we have

$$-B + C = -1,$$
$$-B + 2C = 1,$$

from which we see that $C = 2$ and $B = 3$.

We therefore conclude that

$$\frac{x^3 + 6x^2 + 11}{(x-1)^3 (x+2)} = \frac{6}{(x-1)^3} + \frac{3}{(x-1)^2} + \frac{2}{x-1} - \frac{1}{x+2}.$$

As with the last example, you may like to check that this is correct by putting the right-hand side of the above equation over its common denominator.

You may be wondering why we chose the values $x = 0$ and $x = -1$ to substitute. The answer was simply to make the calculations simple. $x = 0$ is usually a good value to substitute, and after that we wish to choose the smallest values of x that we can. However the answers we obtain would not have altered had we chosen alternative values for x.

(3)   The denominator has an *irreducible quadratic factor*.

In this case we deal with any linear terms as in (1) and (2) above. All (non-repeating) irreducible quadratic factors in the denominator contribute terms of the form

$$\frac{\text{linear term}}{\text{irreducible quadratic}}$$

to the sum, where the linear terms will have the form $Ax + B$, with A and B being constants which we are to find by the methods described in (2) above.

Example 5.   *Find partial fractions for*

$$\frac{2x^2 - 10x + 3}{(x^2 + 5)(x - 2)}.$$

Solution.   We notice that $x^2 + 5$ is an irreducible quadratic term, and so we have to use the method described above. Hence we assume that

$$\frac{2x^2 - 10x + 3}{(x^2 + 5)(x - 2)} = \frac{Ax + B}{x^2 + 5} + \frac{C}{x - 2}.$$

We can find C by putting $x = 2$ and using the cover up rule. So we obtain

$$C = \frac{8 - 20 + 3}{4 + 5} = \frac{-9}{9} = -1.$$

Proceeding as in the previous example, we multiply both sides by the expression $(x^2 + 5)(x - 2)$, and substitute $C = -1$. So we have

$$2x^2 - 10x + 3 = (Ax + B) \times (x - 2) + (-1) \times (x^2 + 5)$$

or

$$2x^2 - 10x + 3 = Ax^2 + Bx - 2Ax - 2B - x^2 - 5,$$

which reduces to

$$2x^2 - 10x + 3 = (A - 1)x^2 + (B - 2A)x - (2B + 5).$$

If now we compare the coefficients of the various powers of x in the above identity, we can see that we must have $2 = A - 1$, $-10 = B - 2A$ and $3 = -(2B + 5)$. From this we can obtain, on solving the equations, $A = 3$ and $B = -4$.

Notice that we only needed to compare the coefficients of two of the powers of x in order to find the two constants, A and B.

We conclude from the above that

$$\frac{2x^2 - 10x + 3}{(x^2 + 5)(x - 2)} = \frac{3x - 4}{x^2 + 5} - \frac{1}{x - 2}.$$

The reason that we are allowed to equate the coefficients in the above solution is that we are trying to find values of A, B and C for which the equation holds **identically**. In other words we want the equation to be valid whatever value we care to substitute for x. If this is to be the case, then it can be shown that all corresponding coefficients on the two sides of the equation have to be equal.

(4)   The denominator has a *repeated irreducible quadratic factor*.

A term in the denominator such as $(x^2 + 2)^3$ would contribute terms of the form

$$\frac{Ax + B}{(x^2 + 2)^3} + \frac{Cx + D}{(x^2 + 2)^2} + \frac{Ex + F}{x^2 + 2}$$

to the partial fraction decomposition. All other terms are dealt with as described in (1)–(3) above. The constants, A down to F, are then found using the methods of cross-multiplication and either equating coefficients or substituting values of x, as in (1)–(3) above.

Since there is no real extension of our knowledge to be gained by going through the (usually) complicated details of examples of this type, we shall not do such an example.

Our main use for the method of Partial Fractions is as a way of breaking up a rational function into a sum of terms each of which we can integrate. Most of the terms we have obtained in the above can be integrated quite easily. However, there is one slightly more difficult case. This is the case involving a term such as

$$\frac{5x + 8}{x^2 + 4x + 8}.$$

The method for integrating terms such as this one is as follows.

Example 6.   *Find*

$$\int \frac{5x + 8}{x^2 + 4x + 8}\, dx.$$

Solution.   Let

$$I = \int \frac{5x + 8}{x^2 + 4x + 8}\, dx.$$

We start the solution by completing the square in the denominator, and then making a suitable linear change of variable. We easily see that

$$x^2 + 4x + 8 = (x + 2)^2 + 4,$$

and so we put $u = x + 2$, from which $du = dx$ and also $x = u - 2$. Hence our integral becomes

$$I = \int \frac{5(u - 2) + 8}{u^2 + 4}\, du = \int \frac{5u - 2}{u^2 + 4}\, du.$$

To deal with this integral, we break it into two parts, by dividing each of the two terms from the numerator by the denominator. So we have

$$I = \int \frac{5u - 2}{u^2 + 4} \, du = \int \frac{5u}{u^2 + 4} \, du - 2 \int \frac{du}{u^2 + 4}.$$

The final one of these integrals is of a standard type leading to a $\tan^{-1}$ term. To deal with the first integral, we shall make a second change of variable. We notice that the numerator is a constant multiple of the derivative of the denominator, which suggests that we should put $v = u^2 + 4$, which means that $dv = 2u \, du$, or $u \, du = \frac{1}{2} \, dv$. We have

$$I = \frac{5}{2} \int \frac{dv}{v} - 2 \int \frac{du}{u^2 + 4}$$

$$= \frac{5}{2} \ln |v| - 2.\frac{1}{2} \tan^{-1} \frac{u}{2} + c$$

$$= \frac{5}{2} \ln |u^2 + 4| - \tan^{-1} \frac{u}{2} + c$$

$$= \frac{5}{2} \ln |x^2 + 4x + 8| - \tan^{-1} \frac{x + 2}{2} + c.$$

We now combine together most of the results of this section in the following quite complicated example. As we have seen with earlier examples, however, it is not difficult to do such examples if we concentrate on doing one small step at a time.

Example 7. *Find*

$$\int \frac{x^4 - 4x^3 + 14x + 4}{x^3 - 7x^2 + 16x - 10} \, dx.$$

Solution.   Since the degree 4 of the numerator is greater than the degree 3 of the denominator, we must start by long division to reduce the rational function to the format to which we can apply the Partial Fraction method.

$$
\begin{array}{r}
x + 3 \\
x^3 - 7x^2 + 16x - 10 \overline{\smash{\big)}\, x^4 - 4x^3 + 0x^2 + 14x + 4} \\
x^4 - 7x^3 + 16x^2 - 10x \\
\hline
3x^3 - 16x^2 + 24x + 4 \\
3x^3 - 21x^2 + 48x - 30 \\
\hline
5x^2 - 24x + 34
\end{array}
$$

It follows from this that

$$\frac{x^4 - 4x^3 + 14x + 4}{x^3 - 7x^2 + 16x - 10} = x + 3 + \frac{5x^2 - 24x + 34}{x^3 - 7x^2 + 16x - 10}.$$

Our first priority is therefore to find partial fractions for

$$\frac{5x^2 - 24x + 34}{x^3 - 7x^2 + 16x - 10}.$$

Before we can do this, we need to factorise the denominator. So we let $f(x) \equiv x^3 - 7x^2 + 16x - 10$. Now

$$f(0) = -10 \neq 0,$$
$$f(1) = 0.$$

It follows that $x - 1$ is a factor of $x^3 - 7x^2 + 16x - 10$.

We shall use synthetic division to find the other factor. (Note that there is no deep significance in this choice—we merely chose to do this to add a bit of variety to the proceedings.)

$$
\begin{array}{c|rrrr}
 & 1 & -7 & 16 & -10 \\
1 & 0 & 1 & -6 & 10 \\
\hline
 & 1 & -6 & 10 & 0
\end{array}
$$

Then, from the synthetic division, we have

$$f(x) = (x - 1)\left(x^2 - 6x + 10\right).$$

Since $x^2 - 6x + 10$ has a negative discriminant, it follows that it cannot be factorised further into real factors.

We are now ready to find the partial fractions. We shall assume that

$$\frac{5x^2 - 24x + 34}{(x - 1)(x^2 - 6x + 10)} = \frac{A}{x - 1} + \frac{Bx + C}{x^2 - 6x + 10}.$$

By the cover up rule, we see that

$$A = \frac{5 - 24 + 34}{1 - 6 + 10} = \frac{15}{5} = 3.$$

Multiplying the above equation by $(x - 1)\left(x^2 - 6x + 10\right)$, and substituting $A = 3$, we see that

$$5x^2 - 24x + 34 = 3\left(x^2 - 6x + 10\right) + (Bx + C)(x - 1).$$

On multiplying out the right-hand side of this equation, and equating coefficients, we deduce that

$$5 = 3 + B,$$
$$-24 = -18 - B + C,$$
$$34 = 30 - C.$$

From the first and third of these equations, we see that $B = 2$ and $C = -4$.

We now need to find

$$\int \left(x + 3 + \frac{3}{x - 1} + \frac{2x - 4}{x^2 - 6x + 10} \right) dx$$

$$= \frac{1}{2}x^2 + 3x + 3\ln|x - 1| + \int \frac{2x - 4}{x^2 - 6x + 10}\, dx.$$

Let

$$I = \int \frac{2x - 4}{x^2 - 6x + 10}\, dx.$$

We shall use the method of Example 6 to find I. Notice firstly that $x^2 - 6x + 10 = (x - 3)^2 + 1$. We therefore put $u = x - 3$, so that $du = dx$ and also $x = u + 3$. On substituting, we have

$$\begin{aligned}
I &= \int \frac{2x - 4}{x^2 - 6x + 10}\, dx \\
&= \int \frac{2(u + 3) - 4}{u^2 + 1}\, du \\
&= \int \frac{2u + 2}{u^2 + 1}\, du \\
&= \int \frac{2u}{u^2 + 1}\, du + 2\int \frac{du}{u^2 + 1} \\
&= \int \frac{dv}{v} + 2\int \frac{du}{u^2 + 1}
\end{aligned}$$

(on taking $v = u^2 + 1$, so that $dv = 2u\, du$, in the first integral)

$$\begin{aligned}
&= \ln|v| + 2\tan^{-1} u + c \\
&= \ln|u^2 + 1| + 2\tan^{-1} u + c \\
&= \ln|x^2 - 6x + 10| + 2\tan^{-1}(x - 3) + c.
\end{aligned}$$

From this we can finally deduce that

$$\int \frac{x^4 - 4x^3 + 14x + 4}{x^3 - 7x^2 + 16x - 10}\, dx = \frac{1}{2}x^2 + 3x + 3\ln|x - 1|$$

$$+ \ln|x^2 - 6x + 10| + 2\tan^{-1}(x - 3) + c.$$

As a far simpler example of the method of Partial Fractions in action, consider the following, where a is any non-zero constant.

Example 8. *Find*

$$\int \frac{dx}{x^2 - a^2}.$$

Solution.   We can factorise $x^2 - a^2$ as $(x - a)(x + a)$, and so we have, on using partial fractions,

$$\begin{aligned}
\int \frac{dx}{x^2 - a^2} &= \int \frac{dx}{(x - a)(x + a)} \\
&= \int \frac{A}{x - a}\, dx + \int \frac{B}{x + a}\, dx \\
&= \frac{1}{2a}\int \frac{dx}{x - a} - \frac{1}{2a}\int \frac{dx}{x + a}
\end{aligned}$$

(using the cover up rule to determine the constants A and B)

$$= \frac{1}{2a} \ln|x - a| - \frac{1}{2a} \ln|x + a| + c$$

$$= \frac{1}{2a} \left[\ln|x - a| - \ln|x + a|\right] + c$$

$$= \frac{1}{2a} \ln\left|\frac{x - a}{x + a}\right| + c.$$

The above result is sometimes very useful, and so should be added to the list of standard integrals to be learnt.

EXAMPLES 17

1. Find the quotient and remainder when:
   (a) $x^3 + 5x^2 + 7x - 3$ is divided by $x^2 + 3x - 1$;
   (b) $x^4 + 4x^3 + 4x^2 + x - 5$ is divided by $x^2 + 3x + 4$;
   (c) $x^4 - x^3 + 5x$ is divided by $x^2 + 2x + 2$.

2. Express each of the following as a product of real linear and irreducible real quadratic factors:
   (a) $x^4 - 3x^3 - 7x^2 + 27x - 18$;
   (b) $x^4 - 8x^2 + 8x + 15$;
   (c) $x^4 - 5x^3 + 9x^2 - 8x + 4$.

3. Find partial fractions for each of the following:

   (a) $\dfrac{3x + 9}{(x - 1)(x + 1)(x + 2)}$;   (b) $\dfrac{12x^2 - 18}{(x - 2)(x + 1)(x + 3)}$;

   (c) $\dfrac{x^2 + 2x + 4}{(x + 1)^2 \, x}$;   (d) $\dfrac{2x^2 - 6x - 4}{(x - 1)^2 \, (x + 1)}$;

   (e) $\dfrac{x^3 - x^2 - 10x - 6}{(x + 1)^3 \, (x - 1)}$;   (f) $\dfrac{4x^3 - 16x^2 + 16x + 4}{(x - 1)^2 \, (x - 3)^2}$;

   (g) $\dfrac{24 - x}{(x + 2)(x^2 + 9)}$;   (h) $\dfrac{4x^2 + 7x}{(x - 2)(x^2 + 6)}$;

   (i) $\dfrac{2x^3 - x^2 - 3x - 1}{(x - 1)^2 \, (x^2 + 2)}$;   (j) $\dfrac{13x + 16}{(x + 2)^2 \, (x^2 + 1)}$.

4. By completing the square in the denominator, and making a suitable linear change of variable, find each of:

   (a) $\displaystyle \int \frac{2x + 3}{x^2 + 4x + 5} \, dx$;   (b) $\displaystyle \int \frac{x + 1}{x^2 - 6x + 13} \, dx$.

5.   Use partial fractions to find each of the following:

(a) $\displaystyle\int \frac{x-4}{(x+2)(x-1)}\,dx;$

(b) $\displaystyle\int \frac{x}{(x+3)(x+2)}\,dx;$

(c) $\displaystyle\int \frac{5-7x}{x^3-2x^2-x+2}\,dx;$

(d) $\displaystyle\int \frac{7x-8}{x^3-x^2-2x}\,dx;$

(e) $\displaystyle\int \frac{8}{x(x-2)^2}\,dx;$

(f) $\displaystyle\int \frac{12x^2}{(x-1)(x+1)^2}\,dx;$

(g) $\displaystyle\int \frac{2x+12}{(x+1)(x^2+4)}\,dx;$

(h) $\displaystyle\int \frac{15x-x^2}{(x+3)(x^2+9)}\,dx;$

(i) $\displaystyle\int \frac{20}{(x-2)(x^2+4x+8)}\,dx;$

(j) $\displaystyle\int \frac{3x^2+14x+5}{(x-3)(x^2+6x+10)}\,dx.$

6.   By first dividing the numerator by the denominator, and then using partial fractions, find each of the following:

(a) $\displaystyle\int \frac{2x^2+x}{(x+2)(x-1)}\,dx;$

(b) $\displaystyle\int \frac{3x^3-27x-4}{(x-3)(x+1)}\,dx;$

(c) $\displaystyle\int \frac{x^4-x^3-8x^2+15}{(x-2)^2(x+1)}\,dx;$

(d) $\displaystyle\int \frac{x^4+x^3+3}{(x-1)^2(x^2+4)}\,dx.$

CHAPTER 18

Two Methods using Complex Numbers

In Chapter 15 we learnt a method which enabled us to integrate a function, such as $\cos^4 x$ or $\sin^2 x \cos^2 x$, which involves only even powers of $\sin x$ and $\cos x$. We used the formulae

$$\sin^2 x = \frac{1}{2}(1 - \cos 2x)$$

and

$$\cos^2 x = \frac{1}{2}(1 + \cos 2x)$$

to express the integrand in terms of sines and cosines of multiples of the number x, which we could then integrate.

An alternative method is to use complex numbers as in the following example.

Example 1. *Use complex numbers to show that*

$$\sin^2 x \cos^4 x = -\frac{1}{32}\cos 6x - \frac{1}{16}\cos 4x + \frac{1}{32}\cos 2x + \frac{1}{16},$$

and hence find $\displaystyle\int \sin^2 x \cos^4 x \, dx$.

Solution. Let

$$z = e^{ix} = \cos x + i \sin x,$$

so that

$$\frac{1}{z} = e^{-ix} = \cos x - i \sin x.$$

Adding these two equations, we see that

$$z + \frac{1}{z} = 2 \cos x,$$

while, on subtracting, we have

$$z - \frac{1}{z} = 2i \sin x.$$

Furthermore, we have, for any integer n,

$$z^n = e^{inx} = \cos nx + i \sin nx,$$

so that

$$\frac{1}{z^n} = \frac{1}{e^{inx}} = e^{-inx} = \cos nx - i \sin nx.$$

Adding these two equations, we see that

$$z^n + \frac{1}{z^n} = 2 \cos nx,$$

while, on subtracting, we have

$$z^n - \frac{1}{z^n} = 2i \sin nx.$$

To avoid having a solution that is littered with fractions, we shall consider first the expression $(2i \sin x)^2 (2 \cos x)^4$, from which we can find $\sin^2 x \cos^4 x$ by division. We have

$$(2i \sin x)^2 (2 \cos x)^4 = \left(z - \frac{1}{z}\right)^2 \left(z + \frac{1}{z}\right)^4$$

$$= \left(z - \frac{1}{z}\right)^2 \left(z + \frac{1}{z}\right)^2 \left(z + \frac{1}{z}\right)^2$$

$$= \left[\left(z - \frac{1}{z}\right)\left(z + \frac{1}{z}\right)\right]^2 \left(z + \frac{1}{z}\right)^2$$

$$= \left[z^2 - \frac{1}{z^2}\right]^2 \left(z + \frac{1}{z}\right)^2$$

$$= \left[z^4 - 2 + \frac{1}{z^4}\right]\left(z^2 + 2 + \frac{1}{z^2}\right)$$

$$= z^6 - 2z^2 + \frac{1}{z^2} + 2z^4 - 4 + \frac{2}{z^4} + z^2 - \frac{2}{z^2} + \frac{1}{z^6}$$

$$= z^6 + 2z^4 - z^2 - 4 - \frac{1}{z^2} + \frac{2}{z^4} + \frac{1}{z^6}$$

$$= \left(z^6 + \frac{1}{z^6}\right) + 2\left(z^4 + \frac{1}{z^4}\right) - \left(z^2 + \frac{1}{z^2}\right) - 4$$

$$= 2\cos 6x + 4\cos 4x - 2\cos 2x - 4.$$

It follows that

$$(2i)^2 2^4 \sin^2 x \cos^4 x = 2\cos 6x + 4\cos 4x - 2\cos 2x - 4,$$

so that, on dividing by -2^6, we have

$$\sin^2 x \cos^4 x = -\frac{1}{2^5} \cos 6x - \frac{1}{2^4} \cos 4x + \frac{1}{2^5} \cos 2x + \frac{1}{2^4}$$

$$= -\frac{1}{32} \cos 6x - \frac{1}{16} \cos 4x + \frac{1}{32} \cos 2x + \frac{1}{16},$$

as we had to show. It follows therefore that

$$\int \sin^2 x \cos^4 x \, dx = \int \left(-\frac{1}{32} \cos 6x - \frac{1}{16} \cos 4x + \frac{1}{32} \cos 2x + \frac{1}{16}\right) dx$$

$$= -\frac{1}{192} \sin 6x - \frac{1}{64} \sin 4x + \frac{1}{64} \sin 2x + \frac{1}{16} x + c.$$

As a second example using complex numbers, consider the problem of finding $\int e^{5x} \sin 3x \, dx$. One possible way of finding this integral is to use integration by parts twice over, thereby retrieving the original integral, and obtaining an equation which can be solved to find the integral. We shall use this method in Chapter 28.

As an alternative approach, we can use complex numbers. In particular, we use the fact that

$$\int e^{mx} dx = \frac{1}{m} e^{mx} + c$$

for any non-zero constant m, whether m is real or complex.

Example 2.   *Find*

$$\int e^{5x} \sin 3x \, dx.$$

Solution.   Consider

$$\int e^{5x} \cos 3x \, dx + i \int e^{5x} \sin 3x \, dx$$

$$= \int e^{5x}(\cos 3x + i \sin 3x) dx$$

$$= \int e^{5x} e^{3ix} \, dx$$

$$= \int e^{(5+3i)x} \, dx$$

$$= \frac{1}{5+3i} e^{(5+3i)x} + c$$

$$= \frac{1}{5+3i} e^{5x} e^{3ix} + c$$

$$= \frac{5-3i}{(5+3i)(5-3i)} e^{5x}(\cos 3x + i \sin 3x) + c$$

(multiplying top and bottom by $5 - 3i$)

$$= \frac{5-3i}{25+9} e^{5x}(\cos 3x + i \sin 3x) + c$$

$$= \frac{e^{5x}}{34}(5-3i)(\cos 3x + i \sin 3x) + c$$

$$= \frac{e^{5x}}{34}(5\cos 3x - 3i \cos 3x + 5i \sin 3x$$

$$+ 3 \sin 3x) + c_1 + ic_2$$

(writing the arbitrary constant in the form $c_1 + ic_2$)

$$= \frac{e^{5x}}{34}(5\cos 3x + 3\sin 3x) + c_1$$

$$+ i\left(\frac{e^{5x}}{34}(5\sin 3x - 3\cos 3x) + c_2\right).$$

Hence, on equating real and imaginary parts of the above equation, we have

$$\int e^{5x} \cos 3x \, dx = \frac{e^{5x}}{34}(5\cos 3x + 3\sin 3x) + c_1$$

and

$$\int e^{5x} \sin 3x \, dx = \frac{e^{5x}}{34}(5\sin 3x - 3\cos 3x) + c_2.$$

As you see, we obtain two results for the amount of work required to obtain the one integral, and also the work involved in integrating using this method is less than that involved in the method involving integrating by parts twice. The difficulty comes from manipulating the complex numbers involved.

EXAMPLES 18

1.   Use complex numbers to find constants a, b, c such that

$$\sin^4 x = a \cos 4x + b \cos 2x + c,$$

and hence find

$$\int \sin^4 x \, dx.$$

2.   Use complex numbers to find constants a, b, c such that

$$\cos^4 x = a \cos 4x + b \cos 2x + c,$$

and hence find

$$\int \cos^4 x \, dx.$$

3.   Use complex numbers to find constants a, b, c, d such that

$$\sin^4 x \cos^2 x = a \cos 6x + b \cos 4x + c \cos 2x + d,$$

and hence find

$$\int \sin^4 x \cos^2 x \, dx.$$

4.   Use complex numbers to find each of:

(a) $\int e^{3x} \cos 4x \, dx;$ (b) $\int e^{2x} \cos 2x \, dx;$

(c) $\int e^{-x} \sin 3x \, dx;$ (d) $\int e^{4x} \sin x \, dx.$

CHAPTER 19

Tables of Integrals

We have so far dealt with a number of ways of tackling different types of integrand. However we have not been able to give a method which will enable us to tackle any integral which is set to us. One reason for this is that there are integrals which cannot be solved.

One idea that we have so far not discussed is the idea of using a formula which gives us the result of integrals of particular types. Lists of such formulae are known as Tables of Integrals. The formulae are obtained in various ways, frequently using Integration by Parts, or sometimes more advanced techniques which we have not discussed.

Many Calculus text books give extensive tables of integrals. Here we shall content ourselves with using some of the better known of these formulae. Such formulae can be readily checked by showing that the derivative of the answer to the integral problem is equal to the given integrand.

Consider firstly the formula

$$\int \frac{dx}{(a^2 - x^2)^n}$$

$$= \frac{1}{2(n-1)a^2} \left[\frac{x}{(a^2 - x^2)^{n-1}} + (2n - 3) \int \frac{dx}{(a^2 - x^2)^{n-1}} \right],$$

which holds provided $a \neq 0$ and $n \neq 0, 1$. We can use this formula in the following example.

Example 1. *Find*

$$\int \frac{dx}{(a^2 - x^2)^3},$$

where a is a non-zero constant.

Solution. We apply the formula given above, firstly with $n = 3$ and then with $n = 2$. We are then left with an integral of the same form, but we cannot use the formula with $n = 1$ since this is a value of n for which the formula is not valid.

$$\int \frac{dx}{(a^2 - x^2)^3} = \frac{1}{2 \times 2 \times a^2} \left[\frac{x}{(a^2 - x^2)^2} + 3 \int \frac{dx}{(a^2 - x^2)^2} \right]$$

$$= \frac{1}{4a^2} \left[\frac{x}{(a^2 - x^2)^2} \right] + \frac{3}{4a^2} \left[\int \frac{dx}{(a^2 - x^2)^2} \right]$$

$$= \frac{1}{4a^2} \left[\frac{x}{(a^2 - x^2)^2} \right] + \frac{3}{4a^2} \left[\frac{1}{2a^2} \left[\frac{x}{a^2 - x^2} + \int \frac{dx}{a^2 - x^2} \right] \right]$$

$$= \frac{1}{4a^2}\left[\frac{x}{(a^2-x^2)^2}\right] + \frac{3}{8a^4}\left[\frac{x}{a^2-x^2}\right] + \frac{3}{8a^4}\int \frac{dx}{a^2-x^2}$$

$$= \frac{1}{4a^2}\left[\frac{x}{(a^2-x^2)^2}\right] + \frac{3}{8a^4}\left[\frac{x}{a^2-x^2}\right] - \frac{3}{8a^4}\cdot\frac{1}{2a}\ln\left|\frac{x-a}{x+a}\right| + c$$

$$= \frac{1}{4a^2}\left[\frac{x}{(a^2-x^2)^2}\right] + \frac{3}{8a^4}\left[\frac{x}{a^2-x^2}\right] - \frac{3}{16a^5}\ln\left|\frac{x-a}{x+a}\right| + c.$$

The final integral here was obtained using the method of Partial Fractions as we did in Example 8 in Chapter 17, for the almost identical integral.

Now we consider the formula

$$\int \sin^n x\, dx = -\frac{1}{n}\sin^{n-1} x \cos x + \frac{n-1}{n}\int \sin^{n-2} x\, dx,$$

which holds provided $n \neq 0$. (Of course if $n = 0$ the integral reduces to $\int 1\, dx$, for which no complicated formula is necessary.)

We use the above formula in the following example.

Example 2.   Find $\int \sin^6 x\, dx$.

Solution.   We apply the formula given above, in the cases $n = 6$, 4, and 2.

$$\int \sin^6 x\, dx$$

$$= -\frac{1}{6}\sin^5 x \cos x + \frac{5}{6}\int \sin^4 x\, dx$$

$$= -\frac{1}{6}\sin^5 x \cos x + \frac{5}{6}\left[-\frac{1}{4}\sin^3 x \cos x + \frac{3}{4}\int \sin^2 x\, dx\right]$$

$$= -\frac{1}{6}\sin^5 x \cos x - \frac{5}{24}\sin^3 x \cos x + \frac{15}{24}\int \sin^2 x\, dx$$

$$= -\frac{1}{6}\sin^5 x \cos x - \frac{5}{24}\sin^3 x \cos x + \frac{15}{24}\left[-\frac{1}{2}\sin x \cos x + \frac{1}{2}\int \sin^0 x\, dx\right]$$

$$= -\frac{1}{6}\sin^5 x \cos x - \frac{5}{24}\sin^3 x \cos x - \frac{15}{48}\sin x \cos x + \frac{15}{48}\int 1\, dx$$

$$= -\frac{1}{6}\sin^5 x \cos x - \frac{5}{24}\sin^3 x \cos x - \frac{5}{16}\sin \cos x + \frac{5}{16}x + c.$$

In this example we have obtained an answer in terms of powers of $\sin x$. We have earlier seen methods we could use by which we could solve the same problem by expressing the integrand in terms of cosines of multiples of x, which we could then integrate. This method of solution would yield an answer that would look different to the answer we have obtained above. In fact though, by using our trigonometric formulae, we could show that these two answers would be equivalent to one another.

The following formula is obtained from the standard trigonometric formulae. It uses the formulae in a form that we have not encountered them, although it is readily deduced from the addition formulae we have met. We have

$$\int \sin mx \sin nx \, dx = -\frac{\sin(m+n)x}{2(m+n)} + \frac{\sin(m-n)x}{2(m-n)} + c,$$

provided that $m^2 \neq n^2$.

Example 3. *Find*

$$\int \sin 6x \sin 3x \, dx.$$

Solution. Using the formula given above with $m = 6$ and $n = 3$, we have

$$\int \sin 6x \sin 3x \, dx = -\frac{\sin 9x}{18} + \frac{\sin 3x}{6} + c.$$

Our final formula is valid provided $m \neq -1$ and $n \neq 0$. It is established by integration by parts. The formula is

$$\int x^m (\ln x)^n dx = \frac{x^{m+1}(\ln x)^n}{m+1} - \frac{n}{m+1} \int x^m (\ln x)^{n-1} dx.$$

Example 4. *Find*

$$\int x^{\frac{3}{2}} (\ln x)^2 dx.$$

Solution. Using the above formula with $m = \frac{3}{2}$ and with $n = 2$, and then with $n = 1$, we have

$$\int x^{\frac{3}{2}} (\ln x)^2 dx = \frac{x^{\frac{5}{2}}(\ln x)^2}{\frac{5}{2}} - \frac{2}{\frac{5}{2}} \int x^{\frac{3}{2}} (\ln x)^1 dx$$

$$= \frac{2}{5} x^{\frac{5}{2}} (\ln x)^2 - \frac{4}{5} \int x^{\frac{3}{2}} \ln x \, dx$$

$$= \frac{2}{5} x^{\frac{5}{2}} (\ln x)^2 - \frac{4}{5} \left[\frac{x^{\frac{5}{2}}(\ln x)^1}{\frac{5}{2}} - \frac{1}{\frac{5}{2}} \int x^{\frac{3}{2}} (\ln x)^0 \, dx \right]$$

$$= \frac{2}{5} x^{\frac{5}{2}} (\ln x)^2 - \frac{4}{5} \left[\frac{2}{5} x^{\frac{5}{2}} \ln x - \frac{2}{5} \int x^{\frac{3}{2}} \, dx \right]$$

$$= \frac{2}{5} x^{\frac{5}{2}} (\ln x)^2 - \frac{4}{5} \left[\frac{2}{5} x^{\frac{5}{2}} \ln x - \frac{4}{25} x^{\frac{5}{2}} \right] + c$$

$$= \frac{2}{5} x^{\frac{5}{2}} (\ln x)^2 - \frac{8}{25} x^{\frac{5}{2}} \ln x + \frac{16}{125} x^{\frac{5}{2}} + c.$$

Several of the formulae we met above expressed an integral in terms of a simpler integral of the same type. Such formulae are known as **reduction formulae** or **recurrence relations**.

EXAMPLES 19

1.   Use the table of integrals given below to find the following:

(a) $\displaystyle\int \frac{\sqrt{9+4x^2}}{x}\,dx;$ (b) $\displaystyle\int \frac{1}{x\sqrt{4+x^2}}\,dx;$

(c) $\displaystyle\int \left(25-x^2\right)^{\frac{3}{2}}\,dx;$ (d) $\displaystyle\int \sin^4 2x\,dx;$

(e) $\displaystyle\int \cos^6 3x\,dx;$ (f) $\displaystyle\int \sec^5 2x\,dx;$

(g) $\displaystyle\int \sin 7x \cos 3x\,dx;$ (h) $\displaystyle\int x^4 \ln x\,dx;$

(i) $\displaystyle\int \frac{\sqrt{4-x^2}}{x^2}\,dx;$ (j) $\displaystyle\int e^{5x} \sin 2x\,dx;$

(k) $\displaystyle\int x^4 \sin 2x\,dx;$ (l) $\displaystyle\int \cot^3 3x\,dx;$

(m) $\displaystyle\int \frac{dx}{x^2\sqrt{4x+3}};$ (n) $\displaystyle\int x^3 \sqrt{3x+5}\,dx.$

TABLE OF INTEGRALS

In this table, it is assumed that a is a non-zero constant, and that b is also a constant.

$$\int \sin^n ax\,dx = -\frac{\sin^{n-1}ax \cos ax}{na} + \frac{n-1}{n}\int \sin^{n-2}ax\,dx \quad (n>1)$$

$$\int \cos^n ax\,dx = \frac{\cos^{n-1}ax \sin ax}{na} + \frac{n-1}{n}\int \cos^{n-2}ax\,dx \quad (n>1)$$

$$\int \sec^n ax\,dx = \frac{\sec^{n-2}ax \tan ax}{a(n-1)} + \frac{n-2}{n-1}\int \sec^{n-2}ax\,dx \quad (n>1)$$

$$\int \cot^n ax\,dx = -\frac{\cot^{n-1}ax}{a(n-1)} - \int \cot^{n-2}ax\,dx \quad (n>1)$$

$$\int x^n \sin ax\,dx = -\frac{x^n}{a}\cos ax + \frac{n}{a}\int x^{n-1}\cos ax\,dx \quad (n\neq 0)$$

$$\int x^n \cos ax\,dx = \frac{x^n}{a}\sin ax - \frac{n}{a}\int x^{n-1}\sin ax\,dx \quad (n\neq 0)$$

$$\int \sin ax \cos bx \, dx = -\frac{\cos (a+b)x}{2(a+b)} - \frac{\cos (a-b)x}{2(a-b)} + c \quad (a^2 \neq b^2)$$

$$\int e^{ax} \sin bx \, dx = \frac{e^{ax}}{a^2+b^2} (a \sin bx - b \cos bx) + c$$

$$\int x^n \ln ax \, dx = \frac{x^{n+1}}{n+1} \ln ax - \frac{x^{n+1}}{(n+1)^2} + c \quad (n \neq -1)$$

$$\int \frac{\sqrt{a^2-x^2}}{x^2} \, dx = -\sin^{-1} \frac{x}{a} - \frac{\sqrt{a^2-x^2}}{x} + c \quad (a > 0)$$

$$\int \frac{1}{x\sqrt{a^2+x^2}} \, dx = -\frac{1}{a} \ln \left| \frac{a+\sqrt{a^2+x^2}}{x} \right| + c$$

$$\int \frac{\sqrt{a^2+x^2}}{x} \, dx = \sqrt{a^2+x^2} - a \ln \left| \frac{a+\sqrt{a^2+x^2}}{x} \right| + c$$

$$\int x^n \sqrt{ax+b} \, dx = \frac{2x^n(ax+b)^{\frac{3}{2}}}{a(2n+3)}$$
$$- \frac{2nb}{a(2n+3)} \int x^{n-1} \sqrt{ax+b} \, dx \quad (n > 0)$$

$$\int \frac{x^n}{\sqrt{ax+b}} \, dx = \frac{2x^n\sqrt{ax+b}}{a(2n+1)} - \frac{2nb}{a(2n+1)} \int \frac{x^{n-1}}{\sqrt{ax+b}} \, dx \quad (n > 0)$$

$$\int \frac{dx}{x^n\sqrt{ax+b}} = -\frac{\sqrt{ax+b}}{b(n-1)x^{n-1}}$$
$$- \frac{a(2n-3)}{2b(n-1)} \int \frac{dx}{x^{n-1}\sqrt{ax+b}} \quad (n > 0, n \neq 1, b \neq 0)$$

$$\int \frac{dx}{x\sqrt{ax+b}} = \begin{cases} \dfrac{2}{\sqrt{-b}} \tan^{-1} \sqrt{\dfrac{ax+b}{-b}} + c, & b < 0 \\[3mm] \dfrac{1}{\sqrt{b}} \ln \left| \dfrac{\sqrt{ax+b}-\sqrt{b}}{\sqrt{ax+b}+\sqrt{b}} \right| + c, & b > 0 \end{cases}$$

$$\int (a^2-x^2)^{\frac{3}{2}} \, dx = -\frac{x}{8} (2x^2 - 5a^2) \sqrt{a^2-x^2} + \frac{3a^4}{8} \sin^{-1} \frac{x}{a} + c \quad (a > 0)$$

F

CHAPTER 20

The Definite Integral

So far we have concentrated on developing methods for tackling different types of integral. Before seeing how to apply our knowledge of integration to various practical problems, we need to introduce a further piece of notation—we need to define the definite integral.

If $f(x)$ is any real function of x, having $F(x)$ as an indefinite integral, we define the **definite integral of $f(x)$ from $x = a$ to $x = b$**, which is denoted by

$$\int_a^b f(x)\,dx,$$

to be

$$\int_a^b f(x)\,dx = F(b) - F(a).$$

It is convenient to denote $F(b) - F(a)$ by $[F(x)]_a^b$, so that

$$\int_a^b f(x)dx = [F(x)]_a^b = F(b) - F(a).$$

We call a and b the limits of integration, where a is the **lower limit** and b is the **upper limit**.

We only make the definition given above when $f(x)$ is a continuous function for all x between $x = a$ and $x = b$. For example, we do not define

$$\int_{-1}^1 \frac{1}{x^2}\,dx,$$

since the function $\dfrac{1}{x^2}$ becomes infinite at $x = 0$, which lies in the interval $[-1, 1]$, which is the **range of integration**.

Similarly, we would not define

$$\int_0^{\frac{\pi}{2}} \sec^2 x\,dx,$$

since

$$\sec^2 x = \frac{1}{\cos^2 x},$$

and so $\sec^2 x$ tends to infinity as x tends to $\pi/2$, since $\cos x$ is zero at $x = \pi/2$.

$F(x)$ can be any indefinite integral of $f(x)$, and so we may choose $F(x)$ to have 0 as its arbitrary constant. If we choose not to do this, the arbitrary constants would just cancel out anyway.

For example, consider

$$\int_0^{\frac{\pi}{2}} \cos x\,dx = [\sin x + c]_0^{\frac{\pi}{2}} = \left(\sin\frac{\pi}{2} + c\right) - \left(\sin 0 + c\right) = 1 + c - 0 - c = 1,$$

which does not involve c at all.

When we change the variable in the course of finding a definite integral, the normal procedure is to change the values of the limits to the values of the new variable which correspond to the values of the original variable at the limits. Then we substitute these new values into the indefinite integral *without returning to the original variable*.

Example 1. *Evaluate*

$$\int_0^2 x^3 \left(1 + x^4\right)^{\frac{3}{2}} dx.$$

Solution.   We notice that the integrand is in two parts, one of which is a power of $1 + x^4$, the other being a constant times the derivative of $1 + x^4$. This suggests that we should use a substitution in order to find the integral. Specifically, we will put $u = 1 + x^4$, so that $du = 4x^3 dx$, from which we have $x^3 dx = \frac{1}{4} du$. We also calculate that when $x = 0$ then $u = 1$, and when $x = 2$, then $u = 1 + 2^4 = 17$. Hence we have

$$\int_0^2 x^3 \left(1 + x^4\right)^{\frac{3}{2}} dx = \int_{x=0}^{x=2} x^3 \left(1 + x^4\right)^{\frac{3}{2}} dx$$

$$= \frac{1}{4} \int_{u=1}^{u=17} u^{\frac{3}{2}} du$$

$$= \frac{1}{4} \cdot \frac{2}{5} \left[u^{\frac{5}{2}} \right]_{u=1}^{u=17}$$

$$= \frac{1}{10} \left[17^{\frac{5}{2}} - 1^{\frac{5}{2}} \right]$$

$$= \frac{1}{10} \left[289\sqrt{17} - 1 \right].$$

The following facts concerning the evaluation of definite integrals can all be easily checked from the definition. In these formulae, a, b, c and k are all constants, and $f(x)$ is any function having $F(x)$ as an indefinite integral.

$$\int_a^b k f(x) \, dx = k \int_a^b f(x) \, dx,$$

since both of these equal $kF(b) - kF(a)$. This tells us that we may take a constant multiplying a definite integral outside the definite integral, just as we could for indefinite integrals. Examination of the solution of the last example shows that we actually used this fact in the course of that solution.

$$\int_a^b f(x) \, dx = - \int_b^a f(x) \, dx,$$

since both of these are equal to $F(b) - F(a)$. We can think of this as telling us that interchanging the order of the limits of an integral corresponds to multiplying the integral by -1.

$$\int_a^b f(x)\,dx + \int_b^c f(x)\,dx = \int_a^c f(x)\,dx,$$

since both of these are equal to $F(c) - F(a)$. This tells us that integrating from a to b and then from b to c is the same as integrating from a to c in one step.

$$\int_a^a f(x)\,dx = 0,$$

since the integral equals $F(a) - F(a) = 0$.

The other rule that we need is the rule relating to Integration by Parts, where we are dealing with a definite integral. This rule is

$$\int_a^b fg'\,dx = [fg]_a^b - \int_a^b gf'\,dx,$$

where, as before, g denotes *any indefinite integral* of g', so that we can choose g to have arbitrary constant zero.

Example 2.   *Evaluate*

$$\int_0^2 x^2 e^x\,dx.$$

Solution.   The integrand is a product for which there is no obvious connection between the two parts of the integrand. It seems that Integration by Parts is the appropriate method. We shall let $g' = e^x$, so that $g = e^x$ also, while $f = x^2$ so that $f' = 2x$. Hence we have

$$\int_0^2 x^2 e^x\,dx = \left[x^2 e^x\right]_0^2 - \int_0^2 e^x 2x\,dx.$$

To integrate this last term, we use integration by parts again, this time taking $g' = e^x$ so that $g = e^x$, while $f = x$ so that $f' = 1$. So we have

$$\int_0^2 x^2 e^x\,dx = \left[x^2 e^x\right]_0^2 - \int_0^2 e^x 2x\,dx$$

$$= \left[x^2 e^x\right]_0^2 - 2\left([xe^x]_0^2 - \int_0^2 e^x\,dx\right)$$

$$= 2^2 e^2 - 0^2 e^0 - 2\left(2e^2 - 0e^0 - [e^x]_0^2\right)$$

$$= 2^2 e^2 - 0^2 e^0 - 2\left(2e^2 - 0e^0 - e^2 + e^0\right)$$

$$= 4e^2 - 4e^2 + 2e^2 - 2$$

$$= 2e^2 - 2.$$

In the following examples, we shall solve a number of different types of integration problems. One of the most difficult steps when confronted with an integral is to recognise which is the appropriate method to apply.

Example 3. *Evaluate*

$$\int_{\frac{\pi}{6}}^{\frac{\pi}{3}} \sin^2 x \cos x \, dx.$$

Solution.   Since this integral involves an odd power of $\cos x$ together with a power of $\sin x$, the method will be to put $u = \sin x$, so that $du = \cos x \, dx$. When $x = \frac{\pi}{6}$, $u = \sin \frac{\pi}{6} = \frac{1}{2}$, while when $x = \frac{\pi}{3}$, $u = \sin \frac{\pi}{3} = \frac{\sqrt{3}}{2}$. So we have

$$\int_{\frac{\pi}{6}}^{\frac{\pi}{3}} \sin^2 x \cos x \, dx = \int_{x=\frac{\pi}{6}}^{x=\frac{\pi}{3}} \sin^2 x \cos x \, dx$$

$$= \int_{u=\frac{1}{2}}^{u=\frac{\sqrt{3}}{2}} u^2 \, du$$

$$= \frac{1}{3} \left[u^3 \right]_{u=\frac{1}{2}}^{u=\frac{\sqrt{3}}{2}}$$

$$= \frac{1}{3} \left(\left(\frac{\sqrt{3}}{2} \right)^3 - \left(\frac{1}{2} \right)^3 \right)$$

$$= \frac{1}{3} \left(\frac{3\sqrt{3}}{8} - \frac{1}{8} \right)$$

$$= \frac{3\sqrt{3} - 1}{24}.$$

Example 4. *Find*

$$\int_0^1 x \tan^{-1} x \, dx.$$

Solution.   The integrand here is a product of two terms which have no apparent connection. This suggests that Integration by Parts might be the appropriate method. Since integrating $\tan^{-1} x$ is something we would rather avoid, we shall let $g' = x$, so that $g = \frac{1}{2}x^2$, and we shall take $f = \tan^{-1} x$, from which $f' = \dfrac{1}{1+x^2}$. Applying the formula for Integration by Parts, we have

$$\int_0^1 x \tan^{-1} x \, dx = \left[\frac{1}{2}x^2 \tan^{-1} x \right]_0^1 - \int_0^1 \left(\frac{1}{2}x^2 \times \frac{1}{1+x^2} \right) dx.$$

To deal with the integration of $x^2/(1+x^2)$, the best method is to write the numerator as $(1+x^2) - 1$, and then divide each of these two terms by the denominator. This puts the integrand into the form of a sum of two terms, each of which is easily integrated. So we have

$$\int_0^1 x \tan^{-1} x \, dx = \left[\frac{1}{2}x^2 \tan^{-1} x\right]_0^1 - \int_0^1 \frac{1}{2}x^2 \times \frac{1}{1+x^2} \, dx$$

$$= \left[\frac{1}{2}x^2 \tan^{-1} x\right]_0^1 - \frac{1}{2}\int_0^1 \frac{(1+x^2)-1}{1+x^2} \, dx$$

$$= \left[\frac{1}{2}x^2 \tan^{-1} x\right]_0^1 - \frac{1}{2}\int_0^1 \left(1 - \frac{1}{1+x^2}\right) dx$$

$$= \left[\frac{1}{2}x^2 \tan^{-1} x\right]_0^1 - \frac{1}{2}\int_0^1 1 \, dx + \frac{1}{2}\int_0^1 \frac{1}{1+x^2} \, dx$$

$$= \left[\frac{1}{2}x^2 \tan^{-1} x\right]_0^1 - \frac{1}{2}\Big[x\Big]_0^1 + \frac{1}{2}\Big[\tan^{-1} x\Big]_0^1$$

$$= \frac{1}{2}1^2 \tan^{-1} 1 - \frac{1}{2}0^2 \tan^{-1} 0 - \frac{1}{2}(1-0) + \frac{1}{2}(\tan^{-1} 1 - \tan^{-1} 0)$$

$$= \frac{1}{2}\cdot\frac{\pi}{4} - \frac{1}{2} + \frac{1}{2}\cdot\frac{\pi}{4}$$

$$= \frac{\pi}{8} - \frac{1}{2} + \frac{\pi}{8}$$

$$= \frac{\pi}{4} - \frac{1}{2}.$$

Example 5. *Evaluate*

$$\int_0^{\frac{1}{\sqrt{2}}} \frac{x \, dx}{\sqrt{1-x^4}}.$$

Solution.   In this integral, our first reaction is that we are not sure which method is appropriate. However, if we notice that x is related to the derivative of x^2, and that x^4 can be written as $(x^2)^2$, then we have a possible approach. For we can then make a change of variable, putting $u = x^2$, so that $du = 2x \, dx$, and $x \, dx = \frac{1}{2}du$. When we make this change of variable, we see that $u = \frac{1}{2}$ corresponds to $x = \frac{1}{\sqrt{2}}$, while $u = 0$ corresponds to $x = 0$. Hence we have

$$\int_0^{\frac{1}{\sqrt{2}}} \frac{x \, dx}{\sqrt{1-x^4}} = \int_{x=0}^{x=\frac{1}{\sqrt{2}}} \frac{x \, dx}{\sqrt{1-(x^2)^2}}$$

$$= \frac{1}{2}\int_{u=0}^{u=\frac{1}{2}} \frac{du}{\sqrt{1-u^2}}$$

$$= \frac{1}{2}\Big[\sin^{-1} u\Big]_{u=0}^{u=\frac{1}{2}}$$

$$= \frac{1}{2}\left(\sin^{-1}\frac{1}{2} - \sin^{-1} 0\right)$$

$$= \frac{1}{2} \left(\frac{\pi}{6} - 0 \right)$$

$$= \frac{\pi}{12}.$$

In our integrations so far, when we have made a change of variable, we have included the variables x and u with the limits to make it clearer what we are doing. While this is sensible in complicated examples, it is not normal notation. We shall in future use the normal notation, changing the limits as we change the variable, but without putting the names of the variables in the limits.

Example 6.   *Evaluate*

$$\int_{-2}^{1} \frac{dx}{x^2 + 4x + 13}.$$

Solution.   We shall start by completing the square and making a linear change of variable. Now

$$x^2 + 4x + 13 = (x + 2)^2 + 9.$$

So we shall put $u = x + 2$ so that $du = dx$. When $x = -2$ then $u = 0$, while when $x = 1$ we have $u = 3$. Hence we have

$$\int_{-2}^{1} \frac{dx}{x^2 + 4x + 13} = \int_{-2}^{1} \frac{dx}{(x + 2)^2 + 9}$$

$$= \int_{0}^{3} \frac{du}{u^2 + 3^2}$$

$$= \left[\frac{1}{3} \tan^{-1} \frac{u}{3} \right]_{0}^{3}$$

$$= \frac{1}{3} \tan^{-1} \frac{3}{3} - \frac{1}{3} \tan^{-1} \frac{0}{3}$$

$$= \frac{1}{3} \cdot \frac{\pi}{4}$$

$$= \frac{\pi}{12}.$$

Example 7.   *Evaluate*

$$\int_{5}^{8} \frac{3x^2 + 2}{(x - 4)(x + 1)^2} \, dx.$$

Solution.   For a rational function such as we have here, the usual method is to try Partial Fractions. That is what we do here. We will assume that

$$\frac{3x^2 + 2}{(x - 4)(x + 1)^2} = \frac{A}{x - 4} + \frac{B}{x + 1} + \frac{C}{(x + 1)^2}.$$

By the Cover Up Rule, we can see that

$$A = \frac{3 \times 4^2 + 2}{25} = \frac{50}{25} = 2.$$

Also by the Cover Up Rule, we can find

$$C = \frac{3 \times (-1)^2 + 2}{(-5)} = \frac{5}{-5} = -1.$$

To determine B we need to multiply the earlier equation by the expression $(x - 4)(x + 1)^2$. Then we obtain, on substituting $A = 2$ and $C = -1$,

$$3x^2 + 2 = 2(x + 1)^2 + B(x + 1)(x - 4) - 1(x - 4).$$

If we compare the coefficients of x^2 on both sides of this equation, we see that $3 = 2 + B$, so that $B = 1$. Hence we have to find

$$\int_5^8 \left(\frac{2}{x - 4} + \frac{1}{x + 1} - \frac{1}{(x + 1)^2} \right) dx.$$

The first two of these integrals are standard ln-type integrals. The third is also very straight-forward, but involves a linear change of variable. So, for the third integral only, we shall let $u = x + 1$, so that $du = dx$, and when $x = 5$, $u = 6$, while when $x = 8$, $u = 9$. Hence we have

$$\int_5^8 \left(\frac{2}{x - 4} + \frac{1}{x + 1} - \frac{1}{(x + 1)^2} \right) dx$$

$$= \int_5^8 \frac{2}{x - 4} dx + \int_5^8 \frac{1}{x + 1} dx - \int_5^8 \frac{dx}{(x + 1)^2}$$

$$= \left[2 \ln |x - 4| \right]_5^8 + \left[\ln |x + 1| \right]_5^8 - \int_6^9 u^{-2} du$$

$$= \left[2 \ln |x - 4| \right]_5^8 + \left[\ln |x + 1| \right]_5^8 + \left[u^{-1} \right]_6^9$$

$$= (2 \ln |4| - 2 \ln |1|) + (\ln |9| - \ln |6|) + \left(\frac{1}{9} - \frac{1}{6} \right)$$

$$= \ln 16 + \ln 9 - \ln 6 - \frac{1}{18}$$

$$= \ln 24 - \frac{1}{18}.$$

EXAMPLES 20

1. Evaluate each of the following:

(a) $\int_1^4 \left(x^3 - 3x^2 + 4x - 1\right)\, dx$;

(b) $\int_2^3 \left(6x^2 + 2x - 3\right)\, dx$;

(c) $\int_{-1}^1 e^{2x}\, dx$;

(d) $\int_0^{\ln 3} e^{-x}\, dx$;

(e) $\int_0^{\frac{\pi}{4}} \sin 2x\, dx$;

(f) $\int_{-\frac{\pi}{6}}^{\frac{\pi}{6}} \cos 3x\, dx$;

(g) $\int_0^{\frac{\pi}{6}} \sec 2x \tan 2x\, dx$;

(h) $\int_{\frac{\pi}{6}}^{\frac{\pi}{3}} \operatorname{cosec}^2 x\, dx$;

(i) $\int_0^{\frac{\pi}{4}} \sec x\, dx$;

(j) $\int_2^4 \frac{dx}{x+1}$;

(k) $\int_0^{\sqrt{3}} \frac{dx}{\sqrt{4 - x^2}}$;

(l) $\int_0^{4\sqrt{3}} \frac{dx}{16 + x^2}$.

2. Evaluate each of the following definite integrals, by making a suitable change of variable:

(a) $\int_1^9 \frac{dx}{\sqrt{5x + 4}}$;

(b) $\int_3^{11} \frac{dx}{\sqrt{2x + 3}}$;

(c) $\int_1^2 \frac{x}{\left(x^2 + 4\right)^2}\, dx$;

(d) $\int_0^{\frac{\pi}{4}} \frac{\cos x}{1 + \sin^2 x}\, dx$;

(e) $\int_0^{\frac{\pi}{6}} \cos x \sin^{\frac{3}{2}} x\, dx$;

(f) $\int_0^3 x^2 \left(4 + x^3\right)^{\frac{3}{2}}\, dx$;

(g) $\int_1^3 \frac{x^3}{1 + x^4}\, dx$;

(h) $\int_0^2 \frac{2x^3 - 1}{4 - 2x + x^4}\, dx$;

(i) $\int_2^4 \frac{dx}{x^2 - 4x + 8}$;

(j) $\int_2^{\frac{7}{2}} \frac{dx}{\sqrt{5 + 4x - x^2}}$;

(k) $\int_0^{\frac{\pi}{2}} \sin x \cos^3 x\, dx$;

(l) $\int_{\frac{\pi}{6}}^{\frac{\pi}{3}} \sin^4 x \cos x\, dx$;

(m) $\int_0^{\frac{\pi}{6}} \sec^4 2x\, dx$;

(n) $\int_0^{\frac{\pi}{3}} \sec^3 x \tan x\, dx$;

(o) $\int_1^3 \frac{x}{1 + x^4}\, dx$;

(p) $\int_0^2 \frac{x}{\left(4 + x^2\right)^{\frac{3}{2}}}\, dx$.

3.   Use integration by parts to evaluate each of the following:

(a) $\displaystyle\int_0^{\frac{\pi}{2}} x\cos x\,dx;$ (b) $\displaystyle\int_0^2 xe^{-2x}\,dx;$

(c) $\displaystyle\int_1^3 x^2 e^{-2x}\,dx;$ (d) $\displaystyle\int_1^e x^3\ln x\,dx;$

(e) $\displaystyle\int_0^{\frac{\pi}{4}} x\cos 2x\,dx;$ (f) $\displaystyle\int_0^{\frac{\pi}{6}} x^2\sin 2x\,dx;$

(g) $\displaystyle\int_{-2}^4 \ln(x+4)\,dx;$ (h) $\displaystyle\int_0^1 \tan^{-1} x\,dx$.

4.   By using the double angle formulae,

$$\sin^2 A = \frac{1}{2}(1-\cos 2A) \quad \text{and} \quad \cos^2 A = \frac{1}{2}(1+\cos 2A),$$

or otherwise, find each of the following:

(a) $\displaystyle\int_0^{\frac{\pi}{4}} \sin^2 4x\,dx;$ (b) $\displaystyle\int_0^{\frac{\pi}{6}} \cos^2 2x\,dx;$

(c) $\displaystyle\int_0^{\frac{\pi}{3}} \sin^2\frac{x}{2}\cos^2\frac{x}{2}\,dx;$ (d) $\displaystyle\int_0^{\frac{\pi}{4}} \cos^4 x\,dx$.

5.   Use partial fractions to evaluate each of the following integrals:

(a) $\displaystyle\int_2^4 \frac{3x+3}{(x-1)(x+2)}\,dx;$ (b) $\displaystyle\int_4^6 \frac{x+15}{(x-3)(x+3)}\,dx;$

(c) $\displaystyle\int_3^4 \frac{13x-6}{x(x-2)(x+3)}\,dx;$ (d) $\displaystyle\int_3^4 \frac{x^2+2x-2}{(x-2)(x+1)}\,dx;$

(e) $\displaystyle\int_3^5 \frac{x^2-7x+4}{(x-1)^2(x+1)}\,dx;$ (f) $\displaystyle\int_3^8 \frac{12x+6}{(x+2)^2(x-1)}\,dx;$

(g) $\displaystyle\int_0^2 \frac{2x^2+6x-6}{(x+1)(x^2+4)}\,dx;$ (h) $\displaystyle\int_0^1 \frac{6x-4}{(x+1)^2(x^2+1)}\,dx.$

6.   If $f(x)$ is a real function which is continuous on the interval $[a,b]$, then the **average value**, or **mean value**, of $f(x)$ on $[a,b]$ is defined to be

$$\frac{1}{b-a}\int_a^b f(x)\,dx.$$

Find the average value of

(a) x^2 on $[1,4];$ (b) $\cos x$ on $[0,\frac{3\pi}{4}];$

(c) x^3+1 on $[-1,1];$ (d) e^{2x} on $[0,\ln 2].$

CHAPTER 21

The Area under a Curve

Consider the problem of trying to find the area of the region between the curve $y = f(x)$, the x-axis and the lines $x = a$ and $x = b$, where $f(x)$ is a continuous real function such that $f(x) \geq 0$ for all $x \in [a, b]$. We are therefore assuming that the curve $y = f(x)$ lies above or on the x-axis throughout the range of x-values in which we are interested.

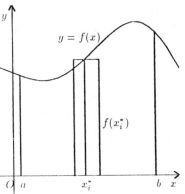

We could obtain an approximation to the above area by means of n rectangles in the following manner.

Let n be a positive integer, and divide the interval $[a, b]$ into n pieces (not necessarily of the same width), where the width of the ith piece is Δx_i.

In the ith subinterval, choose an x-value x_i^*. Form a rectangle with the ith interval as base and of height $f(x_i^*)$ [the height of the function f above the x-axis at $x = x_i^*$]. The area of this rectangle will be

$$f(x_i^*) \times \Delta x_i,$$

and the sum of these areas will be

$$\sum_{i=1}^{n} f(x_i^*) \times \Delta x_i.$$

You may recognise the first steps of the description we gave above. At school, pupils are often asked to cover a semi-circle, or similar shape, approximately with a number of rectangles of coloured gummed paper, usually using rectangles all of the same width. By a simple measurement it is then possible to find an approximate value for the area of the semi-circle.

If we let n, the number of rectangles, tend to infinity in such a way that the width of the widest rectangle tends to zero, then we obtain

$$\lim_{n \to \infty} \sum_{i=1}^{n} f(x_i^*) \times \Delta x_i.$$

We would expect that the method described above would give us a way of evaluating the area we require, although the work required is considerable, except for the case of functions such as x, x^2 and x^3.

Fortunately there is a much better way of evaluating the area under the curve $y = f(x)$.

The **Fundamental Theorem of Integral Calculus** tells us that

$$\lim_{n \to \infty} \sum_{i=1}^{n} f(x_i^*) \times \Delta x_i = [F(x)]_a^b,$$

where $F(x)$ is any function such that $F'(x) = f(x)$ for all $x \in [a, b]$.

Put another way, for a non-negative continuous function, the area of the region between the curve $y = f(x)$, the x-axis, and the lines $x = a$ and $x = b$ is given by the definite integral

$$\int_a^b f(x)\,dx.$$

If we introduce the idea of **signed areas**, which are positive for regions lying above the x-axis and negative for those regions which lie below the x-axis, then, for any real function $f(x)$ which is continuous on the interval $[a, b]$,

$$\int_a^b f(x)\,dx$$

will give the sum of the signed areas between the curve $y = f(x)$, the x-axis, and the lines $x = a$ and $x = b$.

Example 1.   *Find*

$$\int_{-\frac{\pi}{2}}^{\frac{\pi}{2}} \sin x\,dx.$$

Solution.   We can easily see that

$$\int_{-\frac{\pi}{2}}^{\frac{\pi}{2}} \sin x\,dx = [-\cos x]_{-\frac{\pi}{2}}^{\frac{\pi}{2}}$$

$$= \left(-\cos \frac{\pi}{2} + \cos\left(-\frac{\pi}{2}\right)\right)$$

$$= 0 - 0 = 0.$$

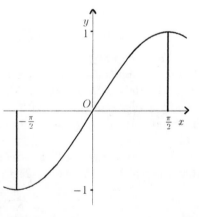

The region in question is formed of two equal pieces which are symmetrically placed with respect to the origin. One of the pieces is above the x-axis, and has a positive signed area, while the other piece is equal in size, but lies below the x-axis. Hence it has a negative signed area. It follows that the sum of the two signed areas, which is what we found by integration, is zero, as we found, because the two signed areas cancel each other out.

If we required to find the physical size of two pieces of cardboard cut out in the shapes shown above, then we would need to find

$$\int_0^{\frac{\pi}{2}} \sin x\,dx - \int_{-\frac{\pi}{2}}^0 \sin x\,dx = [-\cos x]_0^{\frac{\pi}{2}} - [-\cos x]_{-\frac{\pi}{2}}^0$$

$$= \left(-\cos\frac{\pi}{2} + \cos 0\right) - \left(-\cos 0 + \cos\left(-\frac{\pi}{2}\right)\right)$$

$$= 1 - (-1) = 2.$$

Notice that in the above calculation we add the area of the region lying above the x-axis to the negative of the signed area of the region lying below the x-axis. We do this because the negative of a negative signed area will give us the positive value of the physical area we require.

Example 2. *Find the finite area contained between the x-axis and the curve $y = x^2 - 6x + 5$.*

Solution. We can write $x^2 - 6x + 5 = (x-1)(x-5)$. Notice that $y = x^2 - 6x + 5$ is a quadratic function which comes to a minimum value somewhere between $x = 1$ and $x = 5$. It follows that the curve will lie below or on the x-axis for $x \in [1,5]$.

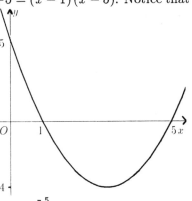

Hence the finite area we require will be the negative of the signed area of the region bounded by the curve $y = x^2 - 6x + 5$ and the x-axis, between the x-values $x = 1$ and $x = 5$. So the required area is

$$-\int_1^5 \left(x^2 - 6x + 5\right) dx = -\left[\frac{1}{3}x^3 - 3x^2 + 5x\right]_1^5$$

$$= -\left(\frac{1}{3}5^3 - 3 \times 5^2 + 5 \times 5\right) + \left(\frac{1}{3}1^3 - 3 + 5\right)$$

$$= -\frac{125}{3} + 75 - 25 + \frac{1}{3} - 3 + 5$$

$$= -\frac{124}{3} + 52 = \frac{156 - 124}{3} = \frac{32}{3}.$$

Example 3. *Find the area of the region contained between the curve $y = \sqrt{9 - x^2}$ and the x-axis. Hence find the area of a circle of radius 3.*

Solution. $y = \sqrt{9 - x^2}$ gives the points on the circle $x^2 + y^2 = 9$ for which $y \geq 0$. In other words, we have those points on the circle which lie above (or on) the x-axis. The required area is therefore given by

$$\int_{-3}^3 \sqrt{9 - x^2}\,dx.$$

The integrand here involves $\sqrt{9 - x^2}$. This is of the type we met in the Chapter on Trigonometric Substitutions, where it was suggested that the appropriate substitution in such a case would be $x = 3\sin\theta$. Then $dx = 3\cos\theta\,d\theta$. When $x = -3$ we need $\sin\theta = -1$, and so $\theta = -\frac{\pi}{2}$. When $x = 3$ we need $\sin\theta = 1$, and so $\theta = \frac{\pi}{2}$. Furthermore $\sqrt{9 - x^2} = \sqrt{9 - 9\sin^2\theta} = \sqrt{9(1 - \sin^2\theta)} = \sqrt{9\cos^2\theta} = 3\cos\theta$. It is valid to take the square-root of $9\cos^2\theta$ as being $3\cos\theta$ since we are considering the interval $-\frac{\pi}{2} \le \theta \le \frac{\pi}{2}$, and on this range of values, $\cos\theta$ will be non-negative.

The required area is

$$\int_{-3}^{3} \sqrt{9 - x^2}\,dx = \int_{-\frac{\pi}{2}}^{\frac{\pi}{2}} 3\cos\theta.\,3\cos\theta\,d\theta$$

$$= 9\int_{-\frac{\pi}{2}}^{\frac{\pi}{2}} \cos^2\theta\,d\theta$$

$$= \frac{9}{2}\int_{-\frac{\pi}{2}}^{\frac{\pi}{2}} (1 + \cos 2\theta)\,d\theta$$

$$= \frac{9}{2}\left[\theta + \frac{1}{2}\sin 2\theta\right]_{-\frac{\pi}{2}}^{\frac{\pi}{2}}$$

$$= \frac{9}{2}\left(\left(\frac{\pi}{2} + \frac{1}{2}\sin\pi\right) - \left(-\frac{\pi}{2} + \frac{1}{2}\sin(-\pi)\right)\right)$$

$$= \frac{9\pi}{2}.$$

Hence the area of the semi-circle above the x-axis is $\frac{9\pi}{2}$, and so the area of the whole circle is 9π. This is of course the result that we would have expected from the formula πr^2 for the area of a circle of radius r. (The justification for that formula, which we were taught at school, is in fact the proof we have just given in the particular case $r = 3$.)

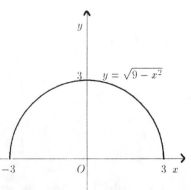

Example 4.   *Find the finite area in the first quadrant contained between the curve $y = x^3$ and the line $y = 4x$.*

Solution.   It is a good idea in examples such as this one to sketch the curves involved, so as to get a clear idea of the area you are trying to calculate.

The curve $y = x^3$ and the line $y = 4x$ meet where $x^3 = 4x$, or $x(x^2 - 4) = 0$, or $x(x - 2)(x + 2) = 0$ which gives $x = 0$, $x = 2$ and $x = -2$.

Let A_1 be the area of the region in the first quadrant between the line $y = 4x$, the line $x = 2$ and the x-axis. Similarly, let A_2 denote the area of the region in the first quadrant between the curve $y = x^3$, the line $x = 2$ and the x-axis. As can be seen from the diagram, the area we require is $A_1 - A_2$. Now

$$A_1 = \int_0^2 4x\,dx = \left[2x^2\right]_0^2 = 8,$$

while

$$A_2 = \int_0^2 x^3\,dx = \left[\frac{1}{4}x^4\right]_0^2 = 4.$$

It follows that the area of the region we need is $8 - 4 = 4$.

The following example is quite similar to the previous example, but we shall adopt a different approach to it. This is purely done for variety, not because there is anything wrong with using the methods we have introduced above.

Example 5.   *Find the area of the region contained between the curve $y = x^2 - 2x - 8$ and the line $y = 2x - 3$.*

Solution.   We can factorise $x^2 - 2x - 8$ as $(x - 4)(x + 2)$. Hence $y = x^2 - 2x - 8$ is a quadratic curve which crosses the x-axis at -2 and 4 as shown. $y = 2x - 3$ is a straight line meeting the axes at the points $(0, -3)$ and $(3/2, 0)$.

The line and the curve meet at the points where

$$x^2 - 2x - 8 = 2x - 3,$$

which is the same as

$$x^2 - 4x - 5 = 0,$$

or

$$(x - 5)(x + 1) = 0.$$

Hence the intersections happen at the points with x-values $x = 5$ and $x = -1$.

We shall approximate the area of the required region by means of a series of rectangles, one of which is shown in the diagram. Its height is $(2x - 3) - (x^2 - 2x - 8)$, and its width is Δx, so that an approximation to the required area would be

$$\sum_{\text{rectangles}} \left((2x - 3) - (x^2 - 2x - 8)\right)\Delta x,$$

and, on taking the limit as we increase the number of rectangles, en-
suring that the width of the widest rectangle tends to zero, the area
is

$$\lim_{n \to \infty} \sum_{\text{rectangles}} \left((2x - 3) - (x^2 - 2x - 8) \right) \Delta x,$$

which, by the Fundamental Theorem of Integral Calculus, can be evaluated as

$$\int_{-1}^{5} \left((2x - 3) - (x^2 - 2x - 8) \right) dx = \int_{-1}^{5} \left(4x + 5 - x^2 \right) dx$$

$$= \left[2x^2 + 5x - \frac{1}{3}x^3 \right]_{-1}^{5}$$

$$= \left(50 + 25 - \frac{125}{3} \right) - \left(2 - 5 + \frac{1}{3} \right)$$

$$= 36.$$

EXAMPLES 21

1.   For each of the following, sketch the given curve, and find the
area of the region between the given curve, the x-axis and the given
lines:

(a) $y = x^2 + 3$, $x = 1$ and $x = 4$;

(b) $y = 6x - x^2$, $x = 1$ and $x = 4$;

(c) $y = 2\cos 2x$, $x = 0$ and $x = \frac{\pi}{6}$.

2.   For each of the following, sketch the given curve, and hence
determine the total area of the region bounded by the given curve, the
x-axis and the given lines:

(a) $y = x^2 - 2x - 8$, $x = 2$ and $x = 6$;

(b) $y = x^3$, $x = -1$ and $x = 3$.

3.   Find the area of the finite region in the first quadrant which is
bounded by the curve $y = x^3$ and the line $y = \frac{1}{4}x$.

4.   Sketch on one diagram the arcs of the curves $y = \cos x$ and
$y = \sin 2x$ for which $0 \le x \le \frac{\pi}{2}$, and hence find the total area of the two
finite regions bounded by these two arcs and the line $x = 0$.

CHAPTER 22

Volumes of Revolution

Let f be a continuous real function of x and suppose that A denotes the region contained between the curve $y = f(x)$, the x-axis, and the lines $x = a$ and $x = b$. If we rotate A through one complete revolution about the x-axis, then we will obtain a solid object, having a volume which we shall denote by V.

We can approximate V as follows. Divide the interval from $x = a$ to $x = b$ into n pieces, the ith of which has width Δx_i. Choose an x_i^* in the ith subinterval, and consider a circular disc, of thickness Δx_i and of radius $f(x_i^*)$. So we are approximating the volume by a series of circular discs, of differing thicknesses, stacked side by side with their centres lying along the x-axis. Now the volume of the ith disc will be

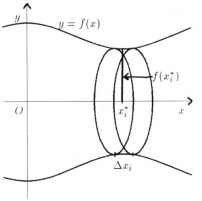

$$\underbrace{\pi\left(f(x_i^*)\right)^2}_{\text{area of circle}} \underbrace{\Delta x_i}_{\text{thickness}} ,$$

so that V can be approximated by

$$\sum_{i=1}^{n} \pi\left(f(x_i^*)\right)^2 \Delta x_i.$$

As in the chapter on areas, we let n tend to infinity in such a way that the thickness of the thickest disc tends to zero. Then we see that

$$V = \lim_{n \to \infty} \sum_{i=1}^{n} \pi\left(f(x_i^*)\right)^2 \Delta x_i,$$

which, by the Fundamental Theorem of Integral Calculus, gives

$$V = \int_a^b \pi\left(f(x)\right)^2 dx = \int_a^b \pi y^2 dx.$$

Example 1. *Find the volume generated by rotating the region bounded by $y = 3x^4$, the x-axis, $x = 0$ and $x = 2$ about the x-axis through one revolution.*

Solution. The required volume is

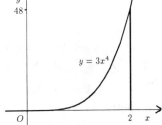

$$\int_0^2 \pi\left(3x^4\right)^2 dx = \pi \int_0^2 9x^8 dx$$
$$= \pi \left[x^9\right]_0^2$$
$$= 2^9 \pi.$$

Example 2.   *By finding the volume obtained by rotating the semi-circle $x^2 + y^2 = r^2$ for which $y \geq 0$ about the x-axis through one revolution, obtain the formula for the volume of a sphere of radius r.*

Solution.   The required volume is

$$\int_{-r}^{r} \pi y^2 \, dx = \int_{-r}^{r} \pi \left(r^2 - x^2\right) dx$$

$$= \pi \left[r^2 x - \frac{1}{3}x^3\right]_{-r}^{r}$$

$$= \pi \left(\left(r^3 - \frac{1}{3}r^3\right) - \left(-r^3 + \frac{1}{3}r^3\right)\right)$$

$$= \frac{4}{3}\pi r^3,$$

which is the well-known formula for the volume of a sphere of radius r.

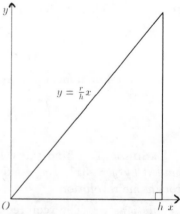

Example 3.   *By finding the volume obtained by rotating the region bounded by the line $y = \frac{r}{h}x$, the x-axis, $x = 0$ and $x = h$ about the x-axis through one complete revolution, show that the volume of a right circular cone of height h and base radius r is $\frac{1}{3}\pi r^2 h$.*

Solution.   If we rotate the region described through one revolution about the x-axis, we will form a right circular cone of base radius r and perpendicular height h, lying on its side.

The volume of the cone will be

$$\int_{0}^{h} \pi y^2 \, dx = \int_{0}^{h} \pi \left(\frac{r}{h}x\right)^2 dx$$

$$= \pi \left(\frac{r}{h}\right)^2 \int_{0}^{h} x^2 \, dx$$

$$= \pi \frac{r^2}{h^2} \left[\frac{1}{3}x^3\right]_{0}^{h}$$

$$= \frac{1}{3}\pi \frac{r^2}{h^2}h^3$$

$$= \frac{1}{3}\pi r^2 h,$$

as required.

This formula, and the formula for the volume of a sphere which we gave earlier, were formulae which we stated in an earlier chapter, promising to prove them later. That promise has now been kept.

Suppose now that we have two continuous real functions $f(x)$ and $g(x)$ such that $f(x) \geq g(x) \geq 0$ for all $x \in [a, b]$. Consider the volume V obtained by rotating about the x-axis the region A contained between the two curves and between the lines $x = a$ and $x = b$. We can think of this volume as being the volume left when we have formed the volume from rotating $f(x)$ about the x-axis and then removed from the centre of this volume a volume obtained by rotating $g(x)$ about the x-axis. So we have a volume with a circular cross-section having through the middle of it a hole also having a circular cross-section.

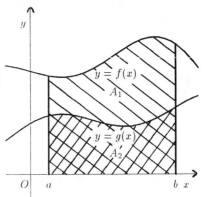

Let A_1 be the region contained between the curve $y = f(x)$, the x-axis, and the lines $x = a$ and $x = b$. Let V_1 denote the volume formed by rotating this volume through one complete revolution about the x-axis.

Let A_2 and V_2 denote the corresponding quantities for $y = g(x)$. Then the required volume is

$$V = V_1 - V_2$$

$$= \int_a^b \pi \left[f(x)\right]^2 dx - \int_a^b \pi \left[g(x)\right]^2 dx$$

$$= \pi \int_a^b \left\{ \left[f(x)\right]^2 - \left[g(x)\right]^2 \right\} dx.$$

Example 4. *Find the volume of the body obtained by rotating about the x-axis through one revolution the finite region enclosed between the curves $y = -3x^2 + 24x - 10$ and $y = x^2 - 8x + 18$.*

Solution. In this type of problem it can be very useful to sketch the curves to see what is happening.

The two curves meet where

$$x^2 - 8x + 18 = -3x^2 + 24x - 10$$

which we can rearrange as

$$4x^2 - 32x + 28 = 0$$

which is the same as

$$x^2 - 8x + 7 = 0$$

or

$$(x - 1)(x - 7) = 0.$$

So the curves meet at the points with x-values $x = 1$ and $x = 7$.

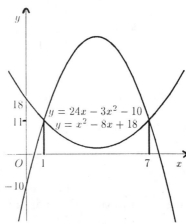

The required volume is therefore

$$\pi \int_1^7 \left\{ \left[-3x^2+24x-10\right]^2 - \left[x^2-8x+18\right]^2 \right\} dx$$

$$= \pi \int_1^7 \left\{ \left[9x^4 - 144x^3 + 636x^2 - 480x + 100\right] \right.$$
$$\left. - \left[x^4 - 16x^3 + 100x^2 - 288x + 324\right] \right\} dx$$

$$= \pi \int_1^7 \left\{ 8x^4 - 128x^3 + 536x^2 - 192x - 224 \right\} dx$$

$$= \pi \left[\frac{8}{5}x^5 - 32x^4 + \frac{536}{3}x^3 - 96x^2 - 224x \right]_1^7$$

$$= \pi \left\{ \left(\frac{8}{5}7^5 - 32 \times 7^4 + \frac{536}{3}7^3 - 96 \times 7^2 - 224 \times 7 \right) \right.$$
$$\left. - \left(\frac{8}{5} - 32 + \frac{536}{3} - 96 - 224 \right) \right\}$$

$$= \frac{26208}{5}\pi.$$

EXAMPLES 22

1.   For each of the following, determine the volume obtained by one revolution about the x-axis of the region bounded by the given curve, the x-axis and the given lines:

(a) $y = x^2$, $x = 0$ and $x = 3$;

(b) $y = x^3$, $x = 1$ and $x = 2$;

(c) $\dfrac{1}{x^2}$, $x = 1$ and $x = 3$;

(d) $y = \tan x$, $x = 0$ and $x = \frac{\pi}{4}$.

2.   Find the volume of the body obtained by rotating, through one revolution about the x-axis, the finite region enclosed by the curve $y = \dfrac{3}{x}$ and the line $2x + y = 7$.

3.   Describe the body obtained by rotating, through one revolution about the x-axis, the smaller of the finite regions enclosed by the circle $x^2 + y^2 = 13$ and the line $y = 2$. Find the volume of the body so formed.

4.   A **torus** is the quoit-shaped body obtained by the rotation, through one revolution about the x-axis, of a circle which does not intersect the x-axis. Find the volume of the torus which would be obtained by rotating, through one revolution about the x-axis, the circle $x^2 + y^2 - 4y + 3 = 0$.

CHAPTER 23

Arc Length and Surface Area of Revolution

Suppose we are given a function $y = f(x)$ which is differentiable for all values of x between the points $A(a, f(a))$ and $B(b, f(b))$ lying on the graph of the function. Suppose that we require to find the **length along the curve** from the point A to B.

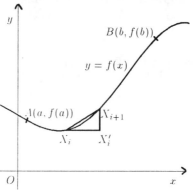

As we have done before, we shall divide the length of curve between A and B into n pieces. Between each consecutive pair X_i and X_{i+1} of division points on the curve, choose a point x_i^* such that the tangent to the curve at the point $(x_i^*, f(x_i^*))$ is parallel to the straight line joining X_i to X_{i+1}. We shall approximate the length of curve between X_i and X_{i+1} by the straight line from X_i to X_{i+1}, which has gradient $f'(x_i^*)$.

As can be seen from the diagram, the length of the curve between X_i and X_{i+1} is approximately

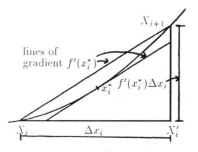

$$\sqrt{1 + [f'(x_i^*)]^2}\, \Delta x_i.$$

Taking the sum over all of the n segments into which the arc length is divided, and then taking the limit as n tends to infinity, with the length of the largest segment tending to zero, we see that the length of curve between A and B is

$$\lim_{n \to \infty} \sum_{A}^{B} \sqrt{1 + [f'(x_i^*)]^2}\, \Delta x_i,$$

which, by the Fundamental Theorem of Integral Calculus, we can evaluate as

$$\int_a^b \sqrt{1 + (y')^2}\, dx.$$

Example 1. *Find the length of the curve $y = x^{\frac{3}{2}}$ between the points $x = 0$ and $x = 2$.*

Solution. If $y = x^{\frac{3}{2}}$ then $\dfrac{dy}{dx} = \dfrac{3}{2}x^{\frac{1}{2}}$, and hence

$$1 + \left(\frac{dy}{dx}\right)^2 = 1 + \left(\frac{3}{2}x^{\frac{1}{2}}\right)^2 = 1 + \frac{9x}{4} = \frac{4 + 9x}{4}.$$

Hence

$$\sqrt{1 + \left(\frac{dy}{dx}\right)^2} = \sqrt{\frac{4 + 9x}{4}} = \frac{1}{2}\sqrt{4 + 9x}.$$

It follows that we need to find

$$\frac{1}{2}\int_0^2 \sqrt{4 + 9x}\,dx.$$

In order to integrate this, we shall let $u = 4 + 9x$, so that $du = 9\,dx$, or $dx = \frac{1}{9}\,du$. We also have to change the limits from $x = 0$ and $x = 2$ to $u = 4$ and $u = 22$. So we have

$$\frac{1}{2}\int_0^2 \sqrt{4 + 9x}\,dx = \frac{1}{2}\int_4^{22} u^{\frac{1}{2}} \times \frac{1}{9}\,du$$

$$= \frac{1}{2}\cdot\frac{1}{9}\cdot\frac{2}{3}\left[u^{\frac{3}{2}}\right]_4^{22}$$

$$= \frac{1}{27}\left(22^{\frac{3}{2}} - 4^{\frac{3}{2}}\right)$$

$$= \frac{1}{27}\left(22\sqrt{22} - 8\right).$$

Example 2. *Find the length of the curve $y = \sqrt{r^2 - x^2}$ between the points $x = 0$ and $x = r$. Hence show that the circumference of a circle of radius r is $2\pi r$.*

Solution.   Notice first of all that $y = \sqrt{r^2 - x^2}$ gives points with a non-negative value of y, and so the length of curve we are asked to find is the length of the part of the circle $x^2 + y^2 = r^2$ which lies in the first quadrant. So the total circumference of the circle will be four times the length in the first quadrant.

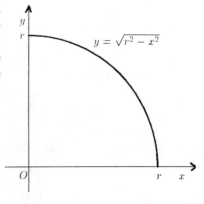

Now $y = \left(r^2 - x^2\right)^{\frac{1}{2}}$, so that

$$\frac{dy}{dx} = \frac{1}{2}\left(r^2 - x^2\right)^{-\frac{1}{2}}(-2x)$$

$$= \frac{-x}{\sqrt{r^2 - x^2}}.$$

Hence

$$1 + \left(\frac{dy}{dx}\right)^2 = 1 + \left(\frac{-x}{\sqrt{r^2 - x^2}}\right)^2$$

$$= 1 + \frac{x^2}{r^2 - x^2}$$

$$= \frac{r^2 - x^2 + x^2}{r^2 - x^2}$$

$$= \frac{r^2}{r^2 - x^2}.$$

Therefore

$$\sqrt{1 + \left(\frac{dy}{dx}\right)^2} = \sqrt{\frac{r^2}{r^2 - x^2}} = \frac{r}{\sqrt{r^2 - x^2}}.$$

Hence the required length of the quarter of the circle is

$$\int_0^r \frac{r}{\sqrt{r^2 - x^2}}\, dx = r\left[\sin^{-1}\frac{x}{r}\right]_0^r$$

$$= r\sin^{-1}\frac{r}{r} - r\sin^{-1}\frac{0}{r}$$

$$= r \times \frac{\pi}{2} - 0$$

$$= \frac{1}{2}\pi r.$$

As explained above, it follows that the total circumference of a circle of radius r is $2\pi r$.

As we saw in the last chapter, if we take a part of a curve and rotate it through one revolution about the x-axis then we obtain a solid body. In the last chapter we found a formula which enables us to find the vol-
ume of such a body. Now we would
like to have a formula which enables
us to calculate the **curved surface
area** of such a body. It should be
carefully noted that the formula gives
the area of the *curved* surface of the
body, and does *not* include the areas
of the circles at the two ends of the
body.

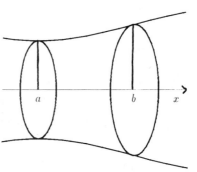

Given a differentiable function
$y = f(x)$, the curved surface area
generated by rotating about the x-axis through one revolution the part
of $y = f(x)$ between the points $x = a$ and $x = b$ is

$$\int_a^b 2\pi|f(x)|\sqrt{1 + (y')^2}\, dx.$$

Example 3. *Find the area of the curved surface generated by
revolving the arc of $y = 2x^{\frac{1}{2}}$ between $x = 1$ and $x = 3$ about the x-axis
through one revolution.*

Solution.   Given that $y = 2x^{\frac{1}{2}}$, then $\dfrac{dy}{dx} = x^{-\frac{1}{2}}$, so that

$$1 + \left(\frac{dy}{dx}\right)^2 = 1 + x^{-1} = \frac{x+1}{x}.$$

Hence

$$\sqrt{1 + \left(\frac{dy}{dx}\right)^2} = \sqrt{\frac{x+1}{x}}.$$

It follows that the surface area generated is

$$\int_1^3 2\pi \left|2x^{\frac{1}{2}}\right| \sqrt{\frac{x+1}{x}}\, dx = 4\pi \int_1^3 x^{\frac{1}{2}} \sqrt{\frac{x+1}{x}}\, dx$$

$$= 4\pi \int_1^3 \sqrt{x+1}\, dx$$

$$= 4\pi \int_2^4 u^{\frac{1}{2}}\, du$$

(on putting $u = x + 1$)

$$= 4\pi . \frac{2}{3} \left[u^{\frac{3}{2}}\right]_2^4$$

$$= \frac{8\pi}{3} \left(4^{\frac{3}{2}} - 2^{\frac{3}{2}}\right)$$

$$= \frac{8\pi}{3} \left(4\sqrt{4} - 2\sqrt{2}\right)$$

$$= \frac{16\pi}{3} \left(4 - \sqrt{2}\right).$$

Example 4. *By rotating the portion of $y = \sqrt{r^2 - x^2}$ for which $-r \le x \le r$ about the x-axis through one complete revolution, find the surface area of a sphere of radius r.*

Solution.   Note that if we take the semi-circle $y = \sqrt{r^2 - x^2}$ (for which $y \ge 0$) and rotate it about the x-axis through one complete revolution, then we shall form a sphere of radius r.

In Example 2, we calculated $\sqrt{1 + \left(\frac{dy}{dx}\right)^2}$ when $y = \sqrt{r^2 - x^2}$, and we use this in the present Example. The required surface area is

$$\int_{-r}^r 2\pi \left|\sqrt{r^2 - x^2}\right| \frac{r}{\sqrt{r^2 - x^2}}\, dx = 2\pi \int_{-r}^r r\, dx$$

$$= 2\pi \left[rx\right]_{-r}^r$$

$$= 2\pi \left(r^2 - r(-r)\right)$$

$$= 4\pi r^2,$$

as we expected.

The formula for the curved surface area of a right circular cone of base radius r and height h can be obtained by applying the above formula to the line $y = \frac{r}{h}x$ between $x = 0$ and $x = h$.

EXAMPLES 23

1.   For each of the following, find the length of the arc of the given curve between the points with the given x-coordinates:

(a) $y = 2x^{\frac{3}{2}}$, $x = 1$ and $x = 4$;

(b) $y = \frac{2}{3}\left(x^2 - 1\right)^{\frac{3}{2}}$, $x = 2$ and $x = 4$;

(c) $y = \dfrac{x^4 + 12}{12x}$, $x = 1$ and $x = 3$;

(d) $y = \ln\left(\cos x\right)$, $x = \frac{\pi}{6}$ and $x = \frac{\pi}{4}$;

(e) $y = \frac{1}{8}x^2 - \ln x$ $x = 2$ and $x = 6$.

2.   Find the area of the surface generated by revolving about the x-axis, through one revolution, the portion of the curve

(a) $y = 2\sqrt{x}$ for which $3 \leq x \leq 8$;

(b) $y = x^3$ for which $0 \leq x \leq 1$;

(c) $y = \frac{1}{2}\left(e^x + e^{-x}\right)$ for which $0 \leq x \leq 1$.

3.   Find the x-coordinate of the point of intersection of the two semi-circles given by the equations $y = \sqrt{16 - x^2}$ and $y = \sqrt{8x - x^2}$. Find the area which lies inside both of these semi-circles. Find also the volume and the surface area of the solid body which is obtained by rotating about the x-axis, through one revolution, the region which lies inside both of the semi-circles.

CHAPTER 24

Numerical Integration

There are four main reasons why we should want to carry out Numerical Integration, which involves determining the approximate value for a definite integral of a function from knowledge of the values of the function at certain x-values.

1) Sometimes it is impossible to find the integral of a particular function. For example, e^{x^2} and $\sqrt{4 - \sin^2 x}$ are both fairly simple functions for which no indefinite integral exists in terms of the standard functions.

2) We can find the values of expressions such as $\ln 2$ or π by finding numerical approximations to definite integrals which equal these values.

3) In an experimental situation we could need to find the integral of a function, because the integral has some significance, while our only knowledge of the function is from taking measurements of the function at various moments in time. It is therefore more sensible to calculate the definite integral directly, if that is what is wanted, rather than going through the detour of determining a function which has the values obtained in the experiment, and then trying to integrate this function.

4) A computer can be very easily programmed to carry out numerical integration, while it is considerably harder to teach a computer (or a person, for that matter) to integrate more than the most straightforward of functions.

An important feature of numerical work is that we can obtain a measure of the possible error involved in the work. This means that if we are finding, say $\ln 2$, then we can show that the value of $\ln 2$ must lie between 2 values. For example, if in using the numerical methods given, we could show that $\ln 2$ must lie between the two values 0.693144 and 0.693149, then we could deduce that the value of $\ln 2$ must be 0.6931 correct to 4 decimal places.

However in this book, we shall not be interested in finding formulae for the errors involved in our numerical approximations.

We shall assume that $f(x)$ is a non-negative continuous function on the interval $[a, b]$, and we shall give two ways of approximating the definite integral

$$\int_a^b f(x)\, dx.$$

Each of the methods is a refinement of the original idea of approximating to the definite integral by means of a number of rectangular strips.

The Trapezium Rule.

We divide the interval $[a, b]$ into n *equal* pieces, each of which will have width $\frac{b-a}{n}$, by using the division points

$$a = x_0 < x_1 < x_2 < \ldots < x_{n-1} < x_n = b.$$

We then approximate the area between the curve, the x-axis, and the lines $x = x_{i-1}$ and $x = x_i$ by means of a trapezium of width $\frac{b-a}{n}$ and height $f(x_{i-1})$ at one side and height $f(x_i)$ at the other. [Note that we are using the word trapezium to describe a quadrilateral figure with two parallel sides. Many American text-books use the word trapezoid to describe this figure, with trapezium being used for something different. Such books refer to the **Trapezoidal Rule**, instead of the Trapezium Rule.]

The area of the ith trapezium will be

$$\underbrace{\left[\frac{f(x_{i-1}) + f(x_i)}{2}\right]}_{\text{average height}} \underbrace{\left[\frac{b-a}{n}\right]}_{\text{width of base}} .$$

Taking the sum of the areas of the n trapezia, we have, as an approximation to the area under the curve between $x = a$ and $x = b$,

$$\left(\frac{b-a}{n}\right)\left[\frac{f(x_0) + f(x_1)}{2} + \frac{f(x_1) + f(x_2)}{2} + \frac{f(x_2) + f(x_3)}{2} + \ldots \right.$$
$$\left. + \frac{f(x_{n-1}) + f(x_n)}{2}\right]$$

$$= \left(\frac{b-a}{2n}\right)\left[f(x_0) + 2f(x_1) + 2f(x_2) + 2f(x_3) + \ldots \right.$$
$$\left. + 2f(x_{n-1}) + f(x_n)\right],$$

and, provided we make n sufficiently large, this should provide a reasonable approximation to

$$\int_a^b f(x)\,dx.$$

We can remember the Trapezium Rule as

$$\int_a^b f(x)\,dx \approx \left(\frac{b-a}{2n}\right)\left[f(\text{Initial point}) + f(\text{Final point})\right.$$
$$\left. + 2 \times \{\text{sum of } f(\text{Intermediate points})\}\right].$$

Here we are using the symbol $\approx$ to denote 'is approximately equal to', in contrast to its earlier use in curve sketching to denote 'behaves asymptotically like'.

Example 1.   *Use the Trapezium Rule with $n = 3$ to approximate*

$$\int_2^5 \frac{2}{x^2 - 1}\,dx,$$

and hence find an approximate value for $\ln 2$.

Solution.   We need to divide the interval $[2, 5]$ into 3 equal pieces, each of which will have length 1. Hence 2, 3, 4 and 5 are the points of division. Taking

$$f(x) = \frac{2}{x^2 - 1},$$

we have $f(2) = \frac{2}{3}$, $f(3) = \frac{2}{8}$, $f(4) = \frac{2}{15}$, and $f(5) = \frac{2}{24}$. Hence, using the Trapezium Rule, we have

$$\begin{aligned}
\int_2^5 \frac{2}{x^2 - 1}\,dx &\approx \frac{5 - 2}{2 \times 3}\left[\frac{2}{3} + 2 \times \frac{2}{8} + 2 \times \frac{2}{15} + \frac{2}{24}\right] \\
&= \frac{3}{6}\left[\frac{2}{3} + \frac{4}{8} + \frac{4}{15} + \frac{2}{24}\right] \\
&= \frac{1}{2}\left[\frac{40}{60} + \frac{30}{60} + \frac{16}{60} + \frac{5}{60}\right] \\
&= \frac{1}{2}\left[\frac{91}{60}\right] \\
&= \frac{91}{120}.
\end{aligned}$$

However, using Example 8 from the chapter on Partial Fractions, we know that

$$\begin{aligned}
\int_2^5 \frac{2}{x^2 - 1}\,dx &= \left[\ln\left|\frac{x - 1}{x + 1}\right|\right]_2^5 \\
&= \left(\ln\left|\frac{5 - 1}{5 + 1}\right|\right) - \left(\ln\left|\frac{2 - 1}{2 + 1}\right|\right) \\
&= \ln\frac{2}{3} - \ln\frac{1}{3} \\
&= \ln 2.
\end{aligned}$$

From this it follows that $\ln 2 \approx \frac{91}{120} \approx 0.7583$. [A calculator gives the value of $\ln 2$ as 0.6931 (correct to 4 decimal places), suggesting that the above approximation is not a particularly good one.] However if we increase the value of n, then we would increase the amount of work involved in finding the approximation, but we should obtain steadily improving approximations to the value of $\ln 2$.

Simpson's Rule.

In the Trapezium Rule we approximated the curve $y = f(x)$ by means of a series of line segments. For Simpson's Rule we shall approximate the curve $y = f(x)$ by means of a series of arcs of quadratic curves $y = ax^2 + bx + c$.

To approximate $\int_a^b f(x)\,dx$, we divide the interval $[a, b]$ into n intervals of equal length $\frac{b-a}{n}$, where n *is an even number.* Suppose that the points of division are

$$a = x_0 < x_1 < x_2 < \ldots < x_{n-1} < x_n = b.$$

For each *even* integer i between 2 and n, we approximate $y = f(x)$ between $x = x_{i-2}$ and $x = x_i$ by a quadratic curve which we choose to pass through points $(x_{i-2}, f(x_{i-2}))$, $(x_{i-1}, f(x_{i-1}))$ and $(x_i, f(x_i))$ on the original curve.

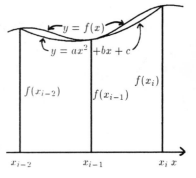

The area beneath the quadratic curve can be expressed in terms of the three points we have made it go through, and we can show that it is

$$\left(\frac{x_i - x_{i-2}}{6}\right) [f(x_{i-2}) + 4f(x_{i-1}) + f(x_i)]$$

$$= \left(\frac{b-a}{3n}\right) [f(x_{i-2}) + 4f(x_{i-1}) + f(x_i)].$$

If we add the area under each of the quadratic curves, we obtain

$$\int_a^b f(x)\,dx = \left(\frac{b-a}{3n}\right) \{[f(x_0) + 4f(x_1) + f(x_2)]$$

$$+ [f(x_2) + 4f(x_3) + f(x_4)] + \ldots$$

$$+ [f(x_{n-2}) + 4f(x_{n-1}) + f(x_n)]\}$$

$$= \left(\frac{b-a}{3n}\right) [f(x_0) + 4f(x_1) + 2f(x_2) + 4f(x_3) + 2f(x_4)$$

$$+ \ldots + 2f(x_{n-2}) + 4f(x_{n-1}) + f(x_n)].$$

This can be remembered as

$$\int_a^b f(x)\,dx \approx \left(\frac{b-a}{3n}\right) [f(\text{Initial point}) + f(\text{Final point})$$

$$+ 4 \times \{\text{sum of } f(\text{Odd points})\} + 2 \times \{\text{sum of } f(\text{Even points})\}].$$

It is important to note that there are several different versions of the formula for Simpson's Rule. This should cause no confusion provided we stick to one version of the formula, and remember what the symbols stand for in the version we are using.

Example 2.   *Use Simpson's Rule with n = 4 to find an approximate value for*

$$\int_0^1 \frac{dx}{\sqrt{4-x^2}},$$

and hence find an approximate value for π.

Solution.   We need to divide the interval $[0,1]$ into 4 equal pieces, and so we need to have 0, $\frac{1}{4}$, $\frac{1}{2}$, $\frac{3}{4}$ and 1 as the points of division.

We shall let

$$f(x) = \frac{1}{\sqrt{4-x^2}},$$

so that $f(0) = \frac{1}{2}$, $f(\frac{1}{4}) = \frac{1}{\sqrt{4-(\frac{1}{4})^2}} = \frac{4}{\sqrt{63}}$, $f(\frac{1}{2}) = \frac{1}{\sqrt{4-(\frac{1}{2})^2}} = \frac{2}{\sqrt{15}}$, $f(\frac{3}{4}) = \frac{1}{\sqrt{4-(\frac{3}{4})^2}} = \frac{4}{\sqrt{55}}$ and $f(1) = \frac{1}{\sqrt{4-1^2}} = \frac{1}{\sqrt{3}}$.

Using Simpson's Rule with $n = 4$, we have

$$\int_0^1 \frac{dx}{\sqrt{4-x^2}} \approx \left(\frac{1-0}{3\times 4}\right)\left[\frac{1}{2} + 4\times\frac{4}{\sqrt{63}} + 2\times\frac{2}{\sqrt{15}} + 4\times\frac{4}{\sqrt{55}} + \frac{1}{\sqrt{3}}\right]$$

$$= \left(\frac{1}{12}\right)\left[\frac{1}{2} + \frac{16}{\sqrt{63}} + \frac{4}{\sqrt{15}} + \frac{16}{\sqrt{55}} + \frac{1}{\sqrt{3}}\right]$$

$$= \left(\frac{1}{12}\right)\left[0.5 + 2.0158105 + 1.0327956 + 2.1574396\right.$$

$$\left. + 0.5773503\right]$$

$$= 0.5236163 \quad \text{(correct to 7 decimal places)},$$

on using a calculator.

Furthermore, we know that

$$\int_0^1 \frac{dx}{\sqrt{4-x^2}} = \left[\sin^{-1}\frac{x}{2}\right]_0^1$$

$$= \sin^{-1}\frac{1}{2} - \sin^{-1}\frac{0}{2}$$

$$= \frac{\pi}{6},$$

and so it follows that

$$\frac{\pi}{6} \approx 0.5236163,$$

and hence

$$\pi \approx 3.1417, \text{ correct to 4 decimal places.}$$

Since the actual value of π is given by the calculator as 3.1416 (correct to 4 decimal places), we have quickly obtained a good approximation to the value of π.

Increasing the value of n would lead to improved accuracy in the approximation we obtained, again at the expense of increasing the work involved.

As a general rule, Simpson's Rule will usually give a better approximation for an integral than the Trapezium Rule will, although, as with any generality, it is possible to find exceptions to that statement.

Sometimes we are asked to apply Simpson's Rule, or the Trapezium Rule, with a specified number of **ordinates**. The number of ordinates is the same as the number of evaluations of the function, which, as in the examples above, is one larger than the value of n. So, for example, if we are told to use 9 ordinates, then we should take $n = 9 - 1 = 8$ in the formulae.

We shall conclude this Chapter with a 'practical' example in which we calculate the integral of a function (approximately) from given values of the function, without trying to determine what the function actually is.

Example 3.   *The velocity v m/sec of a car is noted at time intervals of 20 sec and is as tabulated.*

t sec	0	20	40	60	80	100	120	140	160
v m/sec	0	12	28	16	35	20	35	22	7

By using Simpson's Rule with 9 ordinates to approximate $\int_0^{160} v\, dt$, find the distance travelled by the car in the first 160 seconds.

Solution.   Since we have 9 ordinates, we shall take $n = 8$. Hence

$$\int_0^{160} v\, dt \approx \left(\frac{160 - 0}{3 \times 8} \right) \big[1 \times v(0) + 4 \times v(20) + 2 \times v(40) + 4 \times v(60)$$

$$+ 2 \times v(80) + 4 \times v(100) + 2 \times v(120)$$

$$+ 4 \times v(140) + 1 \times v(160) \big]$$

$$= \left(\frac{20}{3} \right) \big[1 \times 0 + 4 \times 12 + 2 \times 28 + 4 \times 16 + 2 \times 35 + 4 \times 20$$

$$+ 2 \times 35 + 4 \times 22 + 1 \times 7 \big]$$

$$= \left(\frac{20}{3} \right) [0 + 48 + 56 + 64 + 70 + 80 + 70 + 88 + 7]$$

$$= \frac{20}{3} \times 483$$

$$= 3220.$$

Since the integral of the velocity with respect to time will give the distance travelled, we conclude that the car has travelled 3220 meters after 160 seconds.

It may help us to remember the Trapezium Rule and Simpson's Rule if we notice that in the case of the Trapezium Rule we are multiplying the values of the functions by the coefficients

$$1, 2, 1, 2, 1, 2, \ldots, 1, 2, 1,$$

while in the case of Simpson's Rule the coefficients are

$$1, 4, 2, 4, 2, 4, \ldots, 2, 4, 1,$$

and then we are dividing the sum of these terms by the sum of the coefficients we have used.

EXAMPLES 24

1. For each of the following, use
    (α)   the Trapezium Rule, and   (β)   Simpson's Rule,
with the given value of n, to approximate the given integral:

(a) $\displaystyle\int_{-6}^{6} x^2 \, dx,$ $n = 12;$ (b) $\displaystyle\int_{0}^{\pi} \sin^3 x \, dx,$ $n = 4;$

(c) $\displaystyle\int_{0}^{4} \frac{dx}{1 + x^4},$ $n = 4;$ (d) $\displaystyle\int_{0}^{\pi} x \cos^2 x \, dx,$ $n = 6.$

2. For each of the following, use
    (α)   the Trapezium Rule, and   (β)   Simpson's Rule,
with the given value of n, to approximate the given integral. Furthermore, find the exact value of the integral, and hence find an approximation to the given number:

(a) $\displaystyle\int_{0}^{1} \frac{dx}{4 + x^2},$ $n = 4,$ $\tan^{-1} \frac{1}{2};$

(b) $\displaystyle\int_{1}^{9} \frac{dx}{x},$ $n = 8,$ $\ln 3.$

3. For each of the functions tabulated below, use
    (α)   the Trapezium Rule, and   (β)   Simpson's Rule,
to find the best approximations you can to

(a) $\displaystyle\int_{0}^{3} f(x) \, dx;$ (b) $\displaystyle\int_{0}^{1} g(x) \, dx.$

x	0.0	0.5	1.0	1.5	2.0	2.5	3.0
$f(x)$	1.325	1.517	1.755	1.998	2.238	2.554	2.899

x	0.00	0.25	0.50	0.75	1.00
$g(x)$	1.5154	1.8122	2.1003	1.7942	1.5784

4. In order to find the length of the arc of the curve $y = \sin x$ for $0 \le x \le \frac{\pi}{2}$, it is necessary to find

$$\int_{0}^{\frac{\pi}{2}} \sqrt{1 + \cos^2 x} \, dx.$$

Use

(α) the Trapezium Rule, and   (β) Simpson's Rule,
in each case with $n = 2$, to find an approximate value for this arc length.

5. Use

(α) the Trapezium Rule, and   (β) Simpson's Rule,
in each case with $n = 6$, to find an approximate value for the volume obtained by rotating around the x-axis, through one complete revolution, the arc of the curve $y = x(x - 2)e^x$ for which $0 \leq x \leq 2$.

CHAPTER 25

Newton's Method

Many equations that we are asked to solve in mathematics have been contrived to have a nice solution. For example, $x^2 - 3x - 4 = 0$ can be rewritten in factorised form $(x - 4)(x + 1) = 0$, from which we deduce that either $x - 4 = 0$ or $x + 1 = 0$, and so the solutions of the equation are $x = 4$ and $x = -1$.

In practical situations, the equations that arise are not likely to have nice solutions, and so we need to have a method that will enable us to find at least an approximation to one solution of any given equation. There are several such methods, of which the best known is **Newton's Method**.

Let $f(x)$ be a differentiable function of x, and let a be a fixed value of x for which $f'(a) \neq 0$. Newton's Method tells us that if $x = a$ is one approximation to a solution of the equation $f(x) = 0$, then another approximation will be

$$x = a - \frac{f(a)}{f'(a)}.$$

Although it is possible to give conditions under which the approximations provided by Newton's Method improve successively, we shall not concern ourselves with that here, since the conditions are fairly complicated both to remember and to apply. Instead we shall adopt the more pragmatic approach that if the approximations are settling down to approximate more and more closely to a value, then that value is likely to be a solution of the equation.

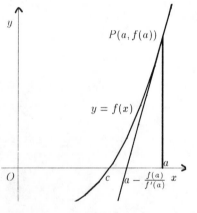

The idea of Newton's Method is seen from the diagram. We approximate the curve $y = f(x)$ by the tangent to it at the point $(a, f(a))$. This tangent will have gradient $f'(a)$ [since the derivative evaluated at $x = a$ gives the gradient of the tangent to the curve at $x = a$]. Hence the equation of the tangent to the curve at $(a, f(a))$ will be

$$y - f(a) = f'(a)(x - a).$$

This tangent meets the x-axis where $y = 0$, and so

$$0 - f(a) = f'(a)(x - a),$$

which, as we require, can be re-arranged as

$$x = a - \frac{f(a)}{f'(a)}.$$

Example 1.   *By applying Newton's Method to $f(x) \equiv x^3 - 7$, with initial value $x = 2$, obtain an approximation to $\sqrt[3]{7}$.*

Solution.   Notice that the only real root of $x^3 - 7 = 0$ will be $\sqrt[3]{7}$. Starting from $x = 2$, and applying Newton's Method, we would hope to obtain an improved approximation to the root. Now if $f(x) = x^3 - 7$ then $f'(x) = 3x^2$, and so $f(2) = 1$ and $f'(2) = 12$. Applying Newton's Method, a new approximation is

$$2 - \frac{1}{12} = \frac{23}{12}.$$

If we applied Newton's Method again, starting from $a = 23/12$ then we would obtain the new approximation $x = 36430/19044$, which the calculator gives as approximately $x = 1.9129385$. Starting from this value, a further use of Newton's Method yields $x = 1.9129312$, which is the value that the calculator gives for $\sqrt[3]{7}$, correct to 7 decimal places.

This is typical of what frequently happens, which is that on using Newton's Method repeatedly to obtain approximations to a certain number then the approximations we obtain will approach (as accurately as we wish or can calculate) the true value of the solution of the equation.

Example 2.   *Find an approximation (correct to 3 decimal places) for the smallest positive value of x for which the graph of $y = \tan x$ meets the line $y = 2x$.*

Solution.   We can sketch the graphs of $y = \tan x$ and $y = 2x$ as in the diagram, and from the diagram we can see that there will be an intersection of the two graphs for a positive value of x somewhere between $x = 1$ and $x = \frac{\pi}{2}$. Remember that we are measuring x in radians. At a point of intersection we will have $\tan x = 2x$, or $\tan x - 2x = 0$. So we shall apply Newton's Method to find an approximation to the smallest positive root of $f(x) = 0$, starting from $x = 1$, where $f(x) \equiv 2x - \tan x$, so that $f'(x) = 2 - \sec^2 x$.

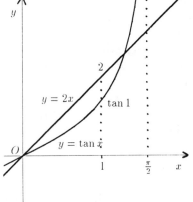

Starting from $x = a$, the next approximation will be given by

$$a - \frac{2a - \tan a}{2 - \sec^2 a} = \frac{2a - a\sec^2 a - 2a + \tan a}{2 - \sec^2 a}$$

$$= \frac{\sin a \cos a - a}{2\cos^2 a - 1}$$

(on multiplying numerator and denominator by $\cos^2 a$)

$$= \frac{\frac{1}{2}\sin 2a - a}{\cos 2a}$$

(on using the double angle formulae)

$$= \frac{\sin 2a - 2a}{2\cos 2a}$$

(on multiplying the numerator and denominator by 2).

Putting $a = 1$ into the above formula as a first approximation, a new approximation will be

$$\frac{\sin 2 - 2}{2\cos 2} \approx 1.310478,$$

from the calculator.

Taking $a = 1.310478$ as a new approximation, the calculator then gives 1.223929 as the next approximation. Substituting this value for a in the above formula, we then obtain 1.176051, followed by 1.165927, then by 1.165562, and finally by 1.165561, which value repeats from then on. In all cases, we are giving the value from the calculator correct to 6 decimal places. It follows that the required root is 1.166 correct to 3 decimal places.

Suppose now that we are given an equation $f(x) = 0$ and asked to find an approximate solution of the equation while given no indication as to where the solution is to be found. What should we do then?

One possible approach would be to take a value at random and apply Newton's Method repeatedly, hoping that the approximations obtained will settle down to one particular value, which will be the required solution.

Another possibility is to use the **Intermediate Value Theorem**. This applies when $f(x)$ is a real function which is continuous on the interval $[a, b]$. Assume that $f(a) > 0$ and $f(b) < 0$ (or that $f(a) < 0$ and $f(b) > 0$.) Then there is at least one value c between a and b such that $f(c) = 0$.

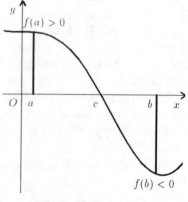

In less formal language, the theorem says that if $y = f(x)$ has a graph with no breaks between $x = a$ and $x = b$, and if $f(a)$ and $f(b)$ are on opposite sides of the x-axis, then the curve must meet the x-axis somewhere between $x = a$ and $x = b$.

Example 3.   *Find the nearest integer to the positive solution of $x^3 + 2x^2 - 5x - 5 = 0$ and use Newton's Method to find the solution correct to 4 decimal places.*

Solution.   Let $f(x) \equiv x^3 + 2x^2 - 5x - 5$. Now $f(0) = -5$, while $f(10) = 1145$. By the Intermediate Value Theorem, the equation $f(x) = 0$ must have a root somewhere between $x = 0$ and $x = 10$. We shall evaluate $f(x)$ for integer values of x between 0 and 10 in order to get a better approximation to the root. Then $f(1) = -7$, $f(2) = 1$. It follows that the root must lie between 1 and 2, by the Intermediate Value Theorem.

To determine which is the nearer integer to the solution, we shall find $f(3/2)$. Now $f(3/2) = -37/8$, which is negative. Hence $y = f(x)$ changes sign between $x = 3/2$ and $x = 2$, and so $x = 2$ is the nearest integer to the solution.

Now we apply Newton's Method to $f(x) = x^3 + 2x^2 - 5x - 5$, so that $f'(x) = 3x^2 + 4x - 5$. Starting from $x = a$, a new approximation to the solution will be

$$a - \frac{a^3 + 2a^2 - 5a - 5}{3a^2 + 4a - 5} = \frac{3a^3 + 4a^2 - 5a - a^3 - 2a^2 + 5a + 5}{3a^2 + 4a - 5}$$
$$= \frac{2a^3 + 2a^2 + 5}{3a^2 + 4a - 5}.$$

Substituting $a = 2$ in this formula, a new approximation is 29/15. If we then substitute this value, we obtain 1.930805, and after a further substitution we obtain 1.930802, which value then repeats itself. Here we have chosen to work correct to 6 decimal places as given by the calculator. It follows that, correct to 4 decimal places, the positive solution of the equation is given by 1.9308.

As a matter of interest, if we had started from the obviously wrong approximation $x = 10$, then it would have taken 8 uses of Newton's Method before we obtained the above value for the solution. The moral of this is that you pay for a poor initial approximation by having extra work to do to obtain an accurate approximation, but in many cases even a poor guess will eventually yield a solution after a sufficient number of applications of Newton's Method.

EXAMPLES 25

1.   By applying Newton's method once to $f(x) \equiv x^2 - 10$, with initial value $a = 3$, obtain an approximation to $\sqrt{10}$.

2.   By applying Newton's method once to $f(x) \equiv x^3 - 9$, with initial value $a = 2$, obtain an approximation to $3^{\frac{2}{3}}$.

3.   Starting from the initial value $a = 1$, find an approximation (correct to 3 decimal places) for the positive value of x for which the graphs of $y = x^2$ and $y = \cos x$ intersect.

4.   Starting from the initial value $a = 1$, find an approximation (correct to 3 decimal places) for the value of x for which the graphs of $y = x^3$ and $y = e^{-x}$ intersect.

5.   Find the nearest integer to the solution of $x^3 - 3x^2 + 5x - 12 = 0$ and use Newton's method to find the solution correct to 3 decimal places.

6.   Find the nearest integer to the positive value of x which is a solution of $x^4 - 4x^3 + 2x^2 - 5x - 20 = 0$ and use Newton's method to find the solution correct to 3 decimal places.

7.   One of the classical problems of Greek mathematics was that of the **duplication of the cube**. This problem was concerned with finding the length of the sides of a cube whose volume was twice that of a given cube. It was eventually proved that the problem of the duplication of the cube did not have an exact solution. Find an approximation (correct to 3 decimal places) for the lengths of the sides of a cube whose volume is to be twice the volume of a cube with sides of length 3 units.

8.   Another of the classical problems of Greek mathematics was that of the **trisection of an angle**. This problem involved constructing two lines which would exactly trisect a given angle. This problem was also eventually shown to be insoluble. In order to trisect an angle of $60°$, it would be necessary to find an exact solution of the equation $8x^3 - 6x - 1 = 0$ having a certain form. Find an approximate solution of this equation, expressing your answer as a decimal (correct to 3 decimal places).

CHAPTER 26

Maclaurin Series

As an alternative to the numerical methods which we have used in the last two Chapters, it is sometimes useful to be able to represent a function by means of a **power series**.

A power series in x is an expression of the form

$$a_0 + a_1 x + a_2 x^2 + a_3 x^3 + \ldots,$$

where the coefficients $a_0, a_1, a_2, \ldots$ are real numbers. So a power series can be thought of as being the same as a polynomial, but extending to an infinite number of terms, rather than stopping at a highest power as a polynomial does.

There is a major difference though between power series and polynomials. If we consider the polynomial

$$f(x) = 1 + x + x^2 + x^3,$$

for example, then we can substitute any value of x that we like, and work out the corresponding value for $f(x)$. However, if we consider the power series

$$g(x) = 1 + x + x^2 + x^3 + x^4 + \ldots,$$

then we find that there are some values of x for which $g(x)$ has a finite value, and other values of x for which it does not. For the series we have chosen is a **geometric progression**, with first term 1 and common ratio x. The sum of this geometric progression is

$$g(x) = \frac{1}{1-x}$$

provided $-1 < x < 1$ and does not exist if $x \geq 1$ or if $x \leq -1$. We say that the series

$$g(x) = 1 + x + x^2 + x^3 + x^4 + \ldots$$

is

$$
\begin{cases}
\text{covergent to } \dfrac{1}{1-x} & \text{if } |x| < 1 \\
\text{divergent} & \text{if } |x| \geq 1.
\end{cases}
$$

A similar result holds for all power series, and so besides knowing a power series it is also important to know for which values of x the power series converges. In this book, we shall state the values for which power series converge, but without trying to justify the results we give.

Suppose now that we are given a function $f(x)$ and we wish to choose constants $a_0, a_1, a_2, a_3, \ldots$ such that

$$f(x) = a_0 + a_1 x + a_2 x^2 + a_3 x^3 + a_4 x^4 + \ldots,$$

at least for values of x close to $x = 0$. The approach we adopt is to make the function and the power series have equal values, equal derivatives, equal second derivatives, equal third derivatives, ... at $x = 0$.

Taking $x = 0$ gives

$$f(0) = a_0.$$

Differentiating with respect to x and then putting $x = 0$ gives

$$f^{(1)}(x) = a_1 + 2a_2 x + 3a_3 x^2 + 4a_4 x^3 + \ldots,$$

from which

$$f^{(1)}(0) = a_1.$$

Differentiating again gives

$$f^{(2)}(x) = 2a_2 + 6a_3 x + 12a_4 x^2 + \ldots,$$

from which we have, on putting $x = 0$,

$$f^{(2)}(0) = 2a_2 \qquad \text{or} \qquad a_2 = \frac{f^{(2)}(0)}{2}.$$

A further differentiation, followed by putting $x = 0$, gives

$$a_3 = \frac{f^{(3)}(0)}{6}.$$

Continuing like this, differentiating with respect to x and then putting $x = 0$, we obtain

$$a_n = \frac{f^{(n)}(0)}{n!},$$

for all $n \geq 1$, where $f^{(n)}(0)$ denotes the nth derivative of $f(x)$ evaluated at $x = 0$.

With the constants chosen as described above, the series

$$a_0 + a_1 x + a_2 x^2 + a_3 x^3 + a_4 x^4 + \ldots$$

is called the **Maclaurin series** for $f(x)$.

Example 1.   *Find the Maclaurin series for $f(x) \equiv e^x$.*

Solution.   If $f(x) = e^x$, then $f^{(1)}(x) = e^x$, and similarly $f^{(2)}(x) = f^{(3)}(x) = f^{(4)}(x) = f^{(5)}(x) = \ldots = e^x$. Hence $f(0) = e^0 = 1$, and $f^{(n)}(0) = e^0 = 1$ for all $n \geq 1$. So we require

$$a_0 = f(0) = 1$$

and

$$a_n = \frac{f^{(n)}(0)}{n!} = \frac{1}{n!},$$

for $n \geq 1$. Hence the Maclaurin series for e^x is

$$1 + \frac{1}{1!}x + \frac{1}{2!}x^2 + \frac{1}{3!}x^3 + \frac{1}{4!}x^4 + \ldots,$$

which is

$$\sum_{n=0}^{\infty} \frac{x^n}{n!}.$$

Example 2. *Find the Maclaurin series for* $f(x) \equiv (125 + x)^{\frac{1}{3}}$, *as far as the term in* x^3, *and use this series to find an approximation for* $2^{\frac{1}{3}}$ *correct to 5 decimal places.*

Solution. We need to differentiate 3 times with respect to x in order to calculate the Maclaurin series as far as the term in x^3. We have

$$f(x) = (125 + x)^{\frac{1}{3}},$$
$$f^{(1)}(x) = \frac{1}{3}(125 + x)^{-\frac{2}{3}},$$
$$f^{(2)}(x) = \frac{1}{3}\left(-\frac{2}{3}\right)(125 + x)^{-\frac{5}{3}},$$
$$f^{(3)}(x) = \frac{1}{3}\left(-\frac{2}{3}\right)\left(-\frac{5}{3}\right)(125 + x)^{-\frac{8}{3}}.$$

Taking $x = 0$ in each of these, and remembering that $125^{\frac{1}{3}} = 5$, we have

$$f(0) = (125)^{\frac{1}{3}} = 5,$$
$$f^{(1)}(0) = \frac{1}{3}(125)^{-\frac{2}{3}} = \frac{1}{3} \cdot \frac{1}{25} = \frac{1}{75},$$
$$f^{(2)}(0) = \frac{1}{3}\left(-\frac{2}{3}\right)(125)^{-\frac{5}{3}} = -\frac{2}{9} \cdot \frac{1}{5^5},$$
$$f^{(3)}(0) = \frac{1}{3}\left(-\frac{2}{3}\right)\left(-\frac{5}{3}\right)(125)^{-\frac{8}{3}} = \frac{10}{27} \cdot \frac{1}{5^8}.$$

Hence the Maclaurin series for $(125 + x)^{\frac{1}{3}}$ is

$$5 + \frac{1}{75}x - \frac{2}{9} \cdot \frac{1}{5^5} \cdot \frac{x^2}{2!} + \frac{10}{27} \cdot \frac{1}{5^8} \cdot \frac{x^3}{3!},$$

as far as the term in x^3.

Assuming that the Maclaurin series gives a good approximation to $f(x)$ for small values of x, we shall substitute $x = 3$ and obtain

$$(125 + 3)^{\frac{1}{3}} \approx 5 + \frac{1}{75} \cdot 3 - \frac{2}{9} \cdot \frac{1}{5^5} \cdot \frac{3^2}{2!} + \frac{10}{27} \cdot \frac{1}{5^8} \cdot \frac{3^3}{3!}$$

from which

$$(128)^{\frac{1}{3}} \approx 5 + \frac{1}{25} - \frac{1}{5^5} + \frac{1}{3 \times 5^7}.$$

Notice that $128 = 64 \times 2$, so that $128^{\frac{1}{3}} = 4 \times 2^{\frac{1}{3}}$, from which we have

$$4 \times 2^{\frac{1}{3}} \approx 5 + 0.04 - 0.00032 + 0.0000042,$$

or, on dividing by 4,

$$2^{\frac{1}{3}} \approx 1.25992,$$

which agrees with the value that the calculator gives for $2^{\frac{1}{3}}$, to 5 decimal places.

In the above example, we substituted the value $x = 3$, and found that the terms in the Maclaurin series rapidly became very small. This meant that we only required to use a small number of terms in order to obtain a good approximation to $2^{\frac{1}{3}}$. On the other hand, if we had substituted a value such as $x = 118$ in order to calculate $3^{\frac{5}{3}}$, we would have needed to take considerably more terms in order to get a reasonable approximation to $3^{\frac{5}{3}}$. Finally, if we took a value such as $x = 131$ in order to find $2^{\frac{8}{3}}$, then the terms in the Maclaurin series would actually increase in size, so that the Maclaurin series would not have a finite sum in this case.

We sum this up by saying that the Maclaurin series for $(125 + x)^{\frac{1}{3}}$, which is

$$5 + \left(\frac{1}{3}\right)\left(\frac{1}{5^2}\right)\frac{x}{1!}$$

$$+ \left(\frac{1}{3}\right)\left(-\frac{2}{3}\right)\left(\frac{1}{5^5}\right)\frac{x^2}{2!}$$

$$+ \left(\frac{1}{3}\right)\left(-\frac{2}{3}\right)\left(-\frac{5}{3}\right)\left(\frac{1}{5^8}\right)\frac{x^3}{3!}$$

$$+ \left(\frac{1}{3}\right)\left(-\frac{2}{3}\right)\left(-\frac{5}{3}\right)\left(-\frac{8}{3}\right)\left(\frac{1}{5^{11}}\right)\frac{x^4}{4!}$$

$$+ \left(\frac{1}{3}\right)\left(-\frac{2}{3}\right)\left(-\frac{5}{3}\right)\left(-\frac{8}{3}\right)\left(-\frac{11}{3}\right)\left(\frac{1}{5^{14}}\right)\frac{x^5}{5!} + \cdots,$$

is

$$\begin{cases} \text{convergent} & \text{when } |x| < 125 \\ \text{divergent} & \text{when } |x| \geq 125. \end{cases}$$

For practical use as an aid to calculation, we need to have series which *converge rapidly*, which happens when x is small.

The following are the Maclaurin series of some of the common mathematical functions, together with a note of the values of x for which the series converge.

The series

$$e^x = 1 + x + \frac{x^2}{2!} + \frac{x^3}{3!} + \frac{x^4}{4!} + \cdots$$

converges for all real values of x, as do the series

$$\sin x = x - \frac{x^3}{3!} + \frac{x^5}{5!} - \frac{x^7}{7!} + \cdots$$

and

$$\cos x = 1 - \frac{x^2}{2!} + \frac{x^4}{4!} - \frac{x^6}{6!} + \dots .$$

However the series

$$\ln(1+x) = x - \frac{x^2}{2} + \frac{x^3}{3} - \frac{x^4}{4} + \frac{x^5}{5} - \dots$$

converges only when $-1 < x \leq 1$, and the series

$$(a+x)^n = a^n + na^{n-1}x + \frac{n(n-1)}{2!}a^{n-2}x^2 + \frac{n(n-1)(n-2)}{3!}a^{n-3}x^3$$
$$+ \frac{n(n-1)(n-2)(n-3)}{4!}a^{n-4}x^4 + \dots$$

converges for $-a < x < a$.

The first of the series given above was found in Example 1 above, while the last one was found in Example 2 [in the particular case $a = 125$ and $n = \frac{1}{3}$, as far as the term involving x^3].

While we cannot prove it here, you may assume that the above Maclaurin series do add up to the functions of which they are power series expansions. So, for example, if we wish to find $\sin x$ for a value of x, it is perfectly in order to substitute that value of x into the Maclaurin series for $\sin x$, evaluate the sum of a number of terms in the series to give the required degree of accuracy, and to assume that in evaluating the Maclaurin series for $\sin x$ you have also found the value of $\sin x$ itself.

The series for $(a+x)^n$ should look familiar as it has exactly the same form as the binomial expansion for n a positive integer. When n is a positive integer, the binomial expansion holds for all values of x, since it is a finite series in this case. Even when n is not a positive integer, the **binomial series** given above will be valid, for the values of x specified above, although in this case the series will be an infinite series.

Notice that if we differentiate the series for e^x term-by-term then we obtain the series for e^x. Differentiating the series for $\sin x$, term-by-term, yields the series for $\cos x$, while the derivative of the series for $\cos x$ is the series for $-\sin x$.

It is also true, but rather more surprising, that if we take the series for e^x and substitute $x = i\theta$, and equate real and imaginary parts, remembering that $e^{i\theta} = \cos\theta + i\sin\theta$, then we obtain the two series for $\cos\theta$ and $\sin\theta$.

Besides differentiating series term-by-term, it can also be shown that we can integrate series term-by-term, and that we can add series, subtract them, and multiply series term-by-term, provided that afterwards we only substitute values of x which lie inside the set of values of x for which all of the original series were convergent. We can extend this to division as well if we add the extra proviso that we must not substitute a value of x which makes the series we are dividing by equal to zero.

There is another useful result which tells us that the power series that represents a function is uniquely determined. This is an important result because it says that if we can find a power series expansion for a function $f(x)$ by some method or other, then this power series must be the Maclaurin series for $f(x)$. We use this fact in the following examples.

Example 3.   *From the power series for e^x and $\sin x$, obtain the Maclaurin series for $e^{\sin x}$ as far as the term in x^4.*

Solution.   We know that

$$e^x = 1 + x + \frac{x^2}{2!} + \frac{x^3}{3!} + \frac{x^4}{4!} + \cdots$$

and

$$\sin x = x - \frac{x^3}{3!} + \frac{x^5}{5!} - \frac{x^7}{7!} + \cdots.$$

Hence, replacing x by $\sin x$ in the series for e^x, we have

$$e^{\sin x} = 1 + (\sin x) + \frac{(\sin x)^2}{2!} + \frac{(\sin x)^3}{3!} + \frac{(\sin x)^4}{4!} + \cdots$$

$$= 1 + \left(x - \frac{x^3}{6} + \cdots\right) + \frac{\left(x - \frac{x^3}{6} + \cdots\right)^2}{2!}$$

$$+ \frac{\left(x - \frac{x^3}{6} + \cdots\right)^3}{3!} + \frac{\left(x - \frac{x^3}{6} + \cdots\right)^4}{4!} + \cdots$$

$$= 1 + \left(x - \frac{x^3}{6} + \cdots\right) + \frac{\left(x^2 - \frac{2x^4}{6} + \cdots\right)}{2!}$$

$$+ \frac{\left(x^3 + \cdots\right)}{3!} + \frac{\left(x^4 + \cdots\right)}{4!} + \cdots$$

$$= 1 + x - \frac{1}{6}x^3 + \frac{1}{2}x^2 - \frac{1}{6}x^4 + \frac{1}{6}x^3 + \frac{1}{24}x^4 + \cdots$$

$$= 1 + x + \frac{1}{2}x^2 - \frac{1}{8}x^4 + \cdots.$$

In the above expansions, we ignored all terms which involved powers of x above x^4, since we were asked for the expansion as far as the term in x^4.

Example 4.   *From the Maclaurin series for* $(1+x)^{-1}$ *find the Maclaurin series for* $\dfrac{1}{1+t^2}$, *and by integrating find the Maclaurin series for* $\tan^{-1} x$.

Solution.   Taking $a = 1$ and $n = -1$ in the binomial series for $(a+x)^n$, we have

$$(1+x)^{-1} = 1^{-1} + (-1)1^{-2}x + \frac{(-1)(-2)}{2!}1^{-3}x^2 + \frac{(-1)(-2)(-3)}{3!}1^{-4}x^3$$
$$+ \frac{(-1)(-2)(-3)(-4)}{4!}1^{-5}x^4 + \dots,$$

which simplifies to

$$(1+x)^{-1} = 1 - x + x^2 - x^3 + x^4 - \dots.$$

Replacing x by t^2 in this formula, we obtain

$$(1+t^2)^{-1} = 1 - t^2 + t^4 - t^6 + t^8 - \dots.$$

We now integrate both sides of this equation. We obtain

$$\int_0^x \frac{1}{1+t^2}\, dt = \int_0^x \left(1 - t^2 + t^4 - t^6 + t^8 - \dots\right) dt,$$

which gives

$$\left[\tan^{-1} t\right]_0^x = \left[t - \frac{t^3}{3} + \frac{t^5}{5} - \frac{t^7}{7} + \frac{t^9}{9} - \dots\right]_0^x.$$

Hence we finish up with the Maclaurin series

$$\tan^{-1} x = x - \frac{x^3}{3} + \frac{x^5}{5} - \frac{x^7}{7} + \frac{x^9}{9} - \dots,$$

which can be shown to be valid for all x strictly between -1 and 1.

EXAMPLES 26

1.   Prove that the Maclaurin series for
        (a) $\sin x$,   (b) $\cos x$,   (c) $\ln(1+x)$
are as given earlier.

2.   Find the Maclaurin series for $f(x) \equiv \sec x$, as far as the term in x^4, by finding $f^{(1)}(x)$, $f^{(2)}(x)$, $f^{(3)}(x)$ and $f^{(4)}(x)$. Hence find an approximation to $\sec\left(\frac{1}{8}\right)$.

3.   Find the Maclaurin series for $f(x) \equiv \dfrac{e^x}{1-x}$, as far as the term in x^3,
    (a)   by finding $f^{(1)}(x)$, $f^{(2)}(x)$ and $f^{(3)}(x)$,
    (b)   by multiplying the Maclaurin series for e^x and for $(1-x)^{-1}$.

4.   Find the Maclaurin series for $f(x) \equiv (1+x)\sin x$, as far as the term in x^4,

(a)   by finding $f^{(1)}(x)$, $f^{(2)}(x)$, $f^{(3)}(x)$ and $f^{(4)}(x)$,

(b)   by multiplying together $1 + x$ and the Maclaurin series for $\sin x$.

5.   Find the Maclaurin series for $f(x) \equiv (27+x)^{\frac{1}{3}}$, as far as the term in x^3, by finding $f^{(1)}(x)$, $f^{(2)}(x)$ and $f^{(3)}(x)$, and hence find an approximation to $5^{\frac{2}{3}}$ by taking $x = -2$ in this series.

6.   From the Maclaurin series for $\ln(1 + x)$, write down a series for $\ln(1 - x)$ and hence write down a series expansion for $\ln\left(\dfrac{1+x}{1-x}\right)$. By taking $x = \frac{1}{10}$ and then $x = \frac{1}{12}$ in this final series, calculate $\ln 11$ and $\ln 13$, each correct to 3 decimal places. [You may assume that $\ln 3 = 1.09861$, correct to 5 decimal places.]

7.   From the Maclaurin series for e^x, write down a series expansion for e^{t^2} and hence find $\displaystyle\int_0^{0.2} e^{t^2}\, dt$, correct to 3 decimal places.

8.   From the Maclaurin series for $\cos x$, write down a series expansion for $t\cos 2t$ and hence find $\displaystyle\int_0^{0.3} t\cos 2t\, dt$, correct to 3 decimal places.

9.   Use the binomial series to write down a series expansion for $(1-t^2)^{-\frac{1}{2}}$, as far as the term in t^8. By finding $\displaystyle\int_0^x \dfrac{dt}{\sqrt{1-t^2}}$ find a series expansion for $\sin^{-1} x$, as far as the term in x^9.

10.   Use the binomial series to write down a series expansion for $(1-t^2)^{-1}$. By finding $\displaystyle\int_0^x \dfrac{dt}{1-t^2}$ find a series expansion for $\ln\left(\dfrac{1+x}{1-x}\right)$.

CHAPTER 27

Differential Equations

We shall start this chapter with an example of a very similar type to the example we solved at the start of the chapter introducing Integration.

Example 1. *The acceleration of a particle at time t is given by* $\dfrac{d^2 x}{dt^2} = t \sin t$, *where x denotes the displacement of the particle from the origin at time t. Find an expression for x in terms of t, given that at time $t = 0$ the particle is at the origin and is moving at 5 units per second in the direction of positive values of x.*

Solution. We start by integrating both sides of the equation $\dfrac{d^2 x}{dt^2} = t \sin t$ with respect to t. We will need to use Integration by Parts to integrate $t \sin t$. We must also remember that $\dfrac{d^2 x}{dt^2}$ is the derivative with respect to t of $\dfrac{dx}{dt}$, so that $\displaystyle\int \dfrac{d^2 x}{dt^2}\, dt = \dfrac{dx}{dt}$. Hence we have

$$\frac{dx}{dt} = t\,(-\cos t) + \int \cos t\, dt$$
$$= -t \cos t + \sin t + c.$$

Now we integrate again with respect to t, and obtain

$$x = -t \sin t - 2\cos t + ct + d.$$

From the initial conditions we are given, we know that when $t = 0$ we have $x = 0$ and $\dfrac{dx}{dt} = 5$, since the distance of the particle from the origin is zero when $t = 0$, and the velocity is 5 units per second at that time. Substituting these values into the above equations we find $c = 5$ and $d = 2$. Hence we conclude that

$$x = -t \sin t - 2\cos t + 5t + 2.$$

In the above example, we solved a **differential equation**, which is an equation involving two variables together with at least one of the derivatives. First of all we found the **general solution**, [which in this case involved two **arbitrary constants** since the equation involved a second derivative], and then we found the **particular solution** that satisfied certain **boundary conditions**, or **initial conditions**.

Differential equations arise in many different practical situations, and the ability to solve such differential equations is crucial to the successful application of mathematics to many practical problems.

In this chapter we shall develop methods for solving some of the simplest types of differential equations. In order to classify different types of differential equations, we shall introduce some notation.

The **order** of a differential equation is *one* if the differential equation involves the derivative $\dfrac{dy}{dx}$ alone, and the **order** is *two* if the differential equation involves the derivative $\dfrac{d^2y}{dx^2}$, and possibly $\dfrac{dy}{dx}$, but no others.

The **degree** of a differential equation is the power to which the highest order derivative in the differential equation is raised.

For example, the differential equation

$$\frac{dy}{dx} = y - \sin x$$

has order 1 and degree 1, while the differential equation

$$\frac{d^2y}{dx^2} + 7\frac{dy}{dx} + (\sin x)y^2 = e^{\cos x}$$

has order 2 and degree 1. Again the equation

$$\frac{d^2y}{dx^2} + \left(\frac{dy}{dx}\right)^4 - y^3 = 3\tan x$$

has order 2 and degree 1, while the differential equation

$$\left(\frac{d^2y}{dx^2}\right)^3 + \left(\frac{dy}{dx}\right)^4 - 2y^3 = e^{\tan x}$$

has order 2 and degree 3.

We shall be concerned here with differential equations of degree 1, and of order 1 or 2.

Type 1.   **First-Order Separable Differential Equations.**

A differential equation of the form

$$\frac{dy}{dx} = f(x)g(y),$$

where $f(x)$ involves x alone, and $g(y)$ involves y alone, is called **separable**. Such equations are solved by separating the variables onto opposite sides of the equality sign, and then integrating both sides of the equation.

Example 2.   *Solve the differential equation*

$$\frac{dy}{dx} = \frac{3x^2}{4y^3}.$$

Solution.   We can rewrite the equation in the form

$$4y^3\frac{dy}{dx} = 3x^2,$$

and if we integrate both sides with respect to x, we obtain

$$\int 4y^3\, dy = \int 3x^2\, dx,$$

from which we have

$$y^4 = x^3 + c.$$

Example 3.   *Find the general solution of the differential equation*

$$\frac{dy}{dx}\left(x^3 + 1\right) = x^2 y^2,$$

and the particular solution for which $y = 2$ when $x = 0$.

   Solution.   If we divide both sides of the equation by $x^3 + 1$ and by y^2 then we will separate the variables. We have

$$\frac{1}{y^2}\frac{dy}{dx} = \frac{x^2}{1 + x^3},$$

and so, integrating both sides with respect to x, we have

$$\int \frac{1}{y^2}\, dy = \int \frac{x^2}{1 + x^3}\, dx,$$

which is equivalent to

$$-\frac{1}{y} = \frac{1}{3}\ln\left|1 + x^3\right| + c.$$

   The left hand side of the equation was integrated by regarding it as $\int y^{-2}\, dy$, which is a standard integral. The right hand side was dealt with by a change of variable. We took $u = 1 + x^3$, so that $du = 3x^2\, dx$.

   The above was the general solution of the differential equation. We need to find the particular solution which is such that $y = 2$ when $x = 0$. Substituting these values into the general solution, we have $-\frac{1}{2} = \frac{1}{3}\ln\left|1 + 0^3\right| + c$. Since $\ln 1 = 0$, we must have $c = -\frac{1}{2}$. Hence the required solution of the differential equation is

$$-\frac{1}{y} = \frac{1}{3}\ln\left|1 + x^3\right| - \frac{1}{2}.$$

Example 4.   *Solve the differential equation*

$$\frac{dy}{dx} = e^{2y - x}.$$

   Solution.   In order to separate the variables in this differential equation, we need to use our knowledge of the index laws, to write $e^{2y - x} = e^{2y} \times e^{-x}$. Then multiplying both sides of the differential equation by e^{-2y} gives

$$e^{-2y}\frac{dy}{dx} = e^{-x},$$

which on integrating with respect to x gives

$$\int e^{-2y}\,dy = \int e^{-x}\,dx,$$

from which we have

$$-\frac{1}{2}e^{-2y} = -e^{-x} + c,$$

which, on multiplying both sides by -2, can be rewritten as

$$e^{-2y} = 2e^{-x} + d,$$

writing $d = -2c$, where both c and d are arbitrary constants.

One type of differential equation which can be made separable is the type which can be expressed in the form

$$\frac{dy}{dx} = f(x,y),$$

where $f(x,y)$ is a **homogeneous** function of x and y. A homogeneous function of x and y is one which can be expressed in the form $g\left(\frac{y}{x}\right)$, for some function g.

One way of checking whether the function $f(x,y)$ is homogeneous is to replace y by vx and then see whether or not $f(x,y)$ can be expressed purely in terms of v. $f(x,y)$ is **homogeneous** if, when we write $y = vx$, then $f(x,y)$ can be expressed purely in terms of the single variable v, with all the x-terms having cancelled out.

In particular, $f(x,y)$ is a homogeneous function when $f(x,y)$ is a quotient of two polynomials where the total degree of each term in each polynomial is the same.

For example,

$$\frac{x^4 - 7x^3y + 3x^2y^2 - 8y^4}{x^2y^2 - 4y^4}$$

is homogeneous since each term in the numerator and denominator has total degree 4. [The **total degree** is the sum of the degrees in x and y in each term.] Notice that if we put $y = vx$ in the above expression we would have

$$\frac{x^4 - 7x^3vx + 3x^2v^2x^2 - 8v^4x^4}{x^2v^2x^2 - 4v^4x^4} = \frac{1 - 7v + 3v^2 - 8v^4}{v^2 - 4v^4},$$

which is a function involving v alone.

On the other hand, the function

$$\frac{x^3 + 5x^2y - 7xy^2 + 8y^3}{2x^2y - 7xy + 4y^3}$$

is not homogeneous, since one of the terms in this function has total degree 2, while all the others have total degree 3. Notice that if we put $y = vx$ in this expression then we would obtain

$$\frac{x^3 + 5x^2vx - 7xv^2x^2 + 8v^3x^3}{2x^2vx - 7xvx + 4v^3x^3} = \frac{x + 5vx - 7xv^2 + 8v^3x}{2vx - 7v + 4v^3x},$$

from which the x-terms cannot be cancelled.

The method for solving a differential equation with a homogeneous right hand side is to put $y = vx$, where v is taken to be a real function of x which we will have to determine. The differential equation can then be solved to find v, using separation of the variables, and then we can find y in terms of x.

Example 5. *Solve the homogeneous differential equation*

$$\frac{dy}{dx} = \frac{3y^2 - 4xy}{2x(y - x)}.$$

Solution.   Since we are told that the differential equation is homogeneous, we know that the method described above is the appropriate one to use.

We put $y = vx$, so that, by the Product Rule for differentiation, we have

$$\frac{dy}{dx} = v\frac{dx}{dx} + x\frac{dv}{dx} = v + x\frac{dv}{dx}.$$

Hence the differential equation becomes

$$v + x\frac{dv}{dx} = \frac{3v^2 x^2 - 4xvx}{2x(vx - x)} = \frac{3v^2 - 4v}{2(v - 1)},$$

on dividing the numerator and denominator of the right hand side by x^2. Subtracting v from both sides of the differential equation we have

$$x\frac{dv}{dx} = \frac{3v^2 - 4v}{2(v - 1)} - v$$

$$= \frac{3v^2 - 4v - v2(v - 1)}{2(v - 1)}$$

$$= \frac{3v^2 - 4v - 2v^2 + 2v}{2(v - 1)}$$

$$= \frac{v^2 - 2v}{2(v - 1)}.$$

We rewrite this equation with the x on the right hand side, and all the terms involving v on the left hand side. To achieve this, we divide both sides by $v^2 - 2v$ and by x, and multiply both sides by $2(v - 1)$. We have

$$\frac{2(v - 1)}{v^2 - 2v}\frac{dv}{dx} = \frac{1}{x},$$

and, on integrating, this gives

$$\int \frac{2(v - 1)}{v(v - 2)}\,dv = \int \frac{1}{x}\,dx.$$

The left hand side of this equation is a rational function for which Partial Fractions is the appropriate method. Using the Cover Up Rule, we have

$$\int \left(\frac{1}{v} + \frac{1}{v-2} \right) dv = \int \frac{1}{x} \, dx,$$

which gives

$$\ln |v| + \ln |v - 2| = \ln |x| + c.$$

We can improve the appearance of this solution if we write $c = \ln C$, where C is an arbitrary constant. So we have

$$\ln |v| + \ln |v - 2| = \ln |x| + \ln C,$$

which we can rewrite, using the rules about logarithms, as

$$\ln |v(v - 2)| = \ln C|x|,$$

or as

$$v(v - 2) = Cx,$$

and on replacing v by $\frac{y}{x}$ this gives

$$y(y - 2x) = Cx^3.$$

You will notice that in the above we dropped the $|\ |$ symbols. From now on we shall normally omit the $|\ |$ symbols when integrals lead to ln-terms. This is not strictly accurate, but we shall find one permissible solution of a given differential equation. We do not wish, in this simplified treatment, to get involved in questions concerning whether expressions involved in the solutions are positive or negative. Notice however that if there is a condition from which we can find a particular solution, we will then let the choice of the arbitrary constant decide on the form of the particular solution.

Type 2.   First-Order Linear Differential Equations.

Equations of degree 1 of this type will all be expressible in the form

$$\frac{dy}{dx} + P(x)y = Q(x),$$

where $P(x)$ and $Q(x)$ are functions which involve x and not y. Examples of this form are:

$$\frac{dy}{dx} + 5y = 2x^3,$$

$$\frac{dy}{dx} + y \sin x = e^{2x},$$

$$\frac{dy}{dx} - x^2 y = \ln x.$$

Sometimes it may be necessary to rearrange the terms in the equation, in order to put the equation in the form

$$\frac{dy}{dx} + P(x)y = Q(x),$$

where $P(x)$ and $Q(x)$ are functions which involve x and not y.

The method of solution is then as follows.

1)   Find $\int P(x)\, dx$.

2)   Find the **integrating factor** $e^{\int P(x)\, dx}$.

3)   Multiply both sides of the differential equation by the integrating factor.

4)   Write the left hand side of the differential equation in the form $\dfrac{d}{dx}(y \times \text{Integrating Factor})$.

5)   Integrate both sides with respect to x.

We shall see this method in action in the following examples.

Example 6.   *Solve the differential equation*

$$\frac{dy}{dx} + 3x^2 y = x^2 + x^5.$$

Solution.   In the notation given above, we have $P(x) = 3x^2$, and so

$$\int P(x)\, dx = \int 3x^2\, dx = x^3.$$

We are just trying to find any one of a number of possible integrating factors. Introducing an arbitrary constant in the above integration would lead to multiplying the integrating factor we are going to use by a constant. Since this is not going to affect the answer we obtain, we shall, in this and all future examples, ignore the arbitrary constant when finding $\int P(x)\, dx$.

The integrating factor is e^{x^3}. If we multiply both sides of the differential equation by this integrating factor, we obtain

$$e^{x^3}\frac{dy}{dx} + 3x^2 y e^{x^3} = \left(x^2 + x^5\right)e^{x^3},$$

which we can rewrite as

$$\frac{d}{dx}\left(y e^{x^3}\right) = \left(x^2 + x^5\right)e^{x^3}.$$

The reason for choosing the integrating factor we did is so that the left hand side of the differential equation can be written in the form given. To check this, try differentiating $y e^{x^3}$ with respect to x, using the Product Rule.

If we integrate both sides of the above equation, we see that

$$y e^{x^3} = \int \left(x^2 + x^5\right)e^{x^3}\, dx = \int \left(1 + x^3\right)e^{x^3}x^2\, dx.$$

In order to integrate the right hand side of this equation, we will put $u = x^3$, so that $du = 3x^2 dx$. Then we need to find

$$\int \frac{1}{3}(1+u)e^u \, du = \frac{1}{3}ue^u + c,$$

where we use Integration by Parts in order to integrate ue^u. So we have

$$ye^{x^3} = \frac{1}{3}x^3 e^{x^3} + c,$$

or, on multiplying by e^{-x^3}, we have

$$y = \frac{1}{3}x^3 + ce^{-x^3}.$$

Example 7. *Find the general solution of the differential equation*

$$x\frac{dy}{dx} + 2y = 6x^4,$$

and the particular solution for which $y = 2$ when $x = 1$.

Solution.   In order to put this differential equation into the standard form, we need to divide both sides of the differential equation by x. Then we have

$$\frac{dy}{dx} + \frac{2}{x}y = 6x^3.$$

Comparing this with the standard form, we have $P(x) = \dfrac{2}{x}$. Hence

$$\int P(x)\, dx = \int \frac{2}{x}\, dx = 2\ln|x| = \ln|x^2| = \ln x^2.$$

(As before, we do not need to include an arbitrary constant here, since it would have no effect on the final answer we obtain.)

The integrating factor is

$$e^{\ln x^2} = x^2,$$

on using the connection between the logarithmic and exponential functions.

We must now multiply the equation *in standard form* by the integrating factor. This gives

$$x^2\frac{dy}{dx} + x^2\frac{2}{x}y = x^2 6x^3,$$

or

$$x^2\frac{dy}{dx} + 2xy = 6x^5,$$

which we express as

$$\frac{d}{dx}\left(yx^2\right) = 6x^5,$$

on noticing that the derivative of yx^2 is $x^2\dfrac{dy}{dx} + 2xy$.

If we integrate both sides with respect to x, then we obtain

$$yx^2 = \int 6x^5 dx = x^6 + c,$$

which, on dividing both sides by x^2, yields

$$y = x^4 + cx^{-2}.$$

This is the general solution of the given differential equation.

For the required particular integral, we substitute the given values. So we want $y = 2$ when $x = 1$. This gives $2 = 1 + c$, from which $c = 1$. Hence the required particular solution is

$$y = x^4 + x^{-2}.$$

Before seeing how to apply the techniques for solving differential equations to various practical problems, we shall examine methods for solving one final type of differential equation.

Type 3. Second-Order Linear Differential Equations with Constant Coefficients.

An example of a differential equation of this form is the differential equation

$$2\frac{d^2 y}{dx^2} + 4\frac{dy}{dx} - 7y = 5x^3.$$

In general, a typical differential equation of the type we are going to consider has the form

$$a\frac{d^2 y}{dx^2} + b\frac{dy}{dx} + cy = f(x),$$

where a, b and c are constants (with $a \neq 0$), and $f(x)$ is a function involving x alone.

The method for solving such differential equations can be broken into three convenient stages.

    1) Find the **complementary function.**
    2) Find the **particular integral.**
    3) Find the general solution, which is

$$y = \text{complementary function} + \text{particular integral.}$$

We shall now examine the methods involved in each of these steps, applied to the general differential equation of the type under consideration,

$$a\frac{d^2 y}{dx^2} + b\frac{dy}{dx} + cy = f(x).$$

1) a) Write down the **auxiliary equation,**

$$az^2 + bz + c = 0,$$

obtained by replacing $\dfrac{d^2y}{dx^2}$ by z^2, $\dfrac{dy}{dx}$ by z, y by 1 and $f(x)$ by 0.

1) b)   Find the solutions of the auxiliary equation.

1) c)   Write down the complementary function in a form which will depend upon the solutions of the auxiliary equation found in b). There are three possible cases to consider.

Case 1.   The auxiliary equation has two distinct real solutions z_1 and z_2. In this case, the complementary function is $y = Ae^{z_1x} + Be^{z_2x}$, where A and B are arbitrary constants.

Case 2.   The auxiliary equation has two distinct complex conjugate solutions $\alpha \pm i\beta$. In this case, the complementary function is $y = e^{\alpha x}(A\cos\beta x + B\sin\beta x)$, where A and B are arbitrary constants.

Case 3.   The auxiliary equation has one (repeated) real solution z_1. In this case, the complementary function is $y = (A + Bx)e^{z_1x}$, where A and B are arbitrary constants.

Before proceeding to the next stage of our method of solution, we shall work through stage 1 for several typical differential equations of the type we are considering.

Example 8.   *Find the complementary functions for each of the differential equations*

$$a) \quad 2\frac{d^2y}{dx^2} + \frac{dy}{dx} - 6y = 15e^{3x};$$

$$b) \quad \frac{d^2y}{dx^2} - 2\frac{dy}{dx} + 10y = 250x^2 + 52\sin 2x;$$

$$c) \quad \frac{d^2y}{dx^2} - 4\frac{dy}{dx} + 4y = 4e^{2x} + 50\sin x.$$

Solution.   a)   The auxiliary equation is $2z^2 + z - 6 = 0$, which can be written as $(2z - 3)(z + 2) = 0$, which has the two distinct real solutions $z = -2$ and $z = \frac{3}{2}$. Hence the complementary function is

$$y = Ae^{-2x} + Be^{\frac{3}{2}x},$$

where A and B are arbitrary constants.

b)   The auxiliary equation is $z^2 - 2z + 10 = 0$, which has two distinct complex conjugate solutions $z = 1 \pm 3i$. Hence the complementary function is

$$y = e^x(A\cos 3x + B\sin 3x),$$

where A and B are arbitrary constants.

c)   The auxiliary equation is $z^2 - 4z + 4 = 0$, which can be written as $(z - 2)^2 = 0$, having one repeated real root $z = 2$. Hence the complementary function is

$$y = (A + Bx)e^{2x},$$

where A and B are arbitrary constants.

Before turning to the next stage in our solution—the finding of the particular integral—we should note that the complementary function contains two arbitrary constants. Since we would expect that solving a second-order differential equation would involve two integrations and therefore two arbitrary constants, it follows that we would not expect our particular integral to contain any unknown constants.

Now we describe the routine for finding the particular integral for the differential equation. The operation of this routine depends upon both sides of the original equation. It is as follows.

2) a)   Guess the correct form of the particular integral, depending upon the form of the function $f(x)$ on the right hand side of the differential equation.

2 b)   Differentiate the particular integral you have guessed and substitute it into the differential equation, so as to determine any unknown constants from the requirement that the particular integral satisfies the original differential equation.

In choosing the form of the particular integral, there are many different cases that can arise. Amongst these are the following.

Case 1)   If $f(x) = 0$, then take $y = 0$ as the particular integral.

Case 2)   If the function $f(x)$ is a sum of terms then take a particular integral which is a sum of the particular integrals which arise from each term.

Case 3)   If $f(x)$ is a polynomial in x, then try a polynomial of the same degree. For example, try $y = ax^2 + bx + c$ if $f(x)$ is a polynomial of degree 2, where a, b and c are constants to be found.

Case 4)   If $f(x)$ involves a sine or cosine term, then try a particular integral involving both the corresponding sine and cosine terms. For example, if $f(x)$ involves $\sin 5x$, then try $y = c \sin 5x + d \cos 5x$, where c and d are constants to be found.

Case 5)   If $f(x)$ involves an exponential term, then try a similar exponential term. For example, if $f(x)$ includes e^{4x}, then try $y = ce^{4x}$, where c is a constant to be found.

Note however that any term which occurs in the complementary function cannot also occur in the particular integral. If our suggested particular integral does contain a term we already have in the complementary function then we multiply the suggested term in the particular integral by either x or x^2, so as to get a different term. For example, if a complementary function is $y = A \cos 2x + B \sin 2x$ and $f(x) = 4 \cos 2x$, then for a particular integral we would try $y = cx \sin 2x + dx \cos 2x$, so as to avoid repeating terms already included in the complementary function.

Probably the best way to understand the method is to work through some examples.

Example 9. *Find the particular integrals for each of the differential equations in Example 8.*

Solution.   a)   The differential equation

$$2\frac{d^2y}{dx^2} + \frac{dy}{dx} - 6y = 15e^{3x}$$

had complementary function

$$y = Ae^{-2x} + Be^{\frac{3}{2}x},$$

where A and B are arbitrary constants. Since e^{3x} does not appear in the complementary function, it may appear in the particular integral, and so as particular integral we shall try $y = ce^{3x}$, where c is a constant we wish to choose in order that the differential equation may be satisfied.

If $y = ce^{3x}$, then $\frac{dy}{dx} = 3ce^{3x}$ and $\frac{d^2y}{dx^2} = 9ce^{3x}$, and so, on substituting, we need

$$2\left[9ce^{3x}\right] + \left[3ce^{3x}\right] - 6\left[ce^{3x}\right] = 15e^{3x}.$$

From this we see that we need

$$(18c + 3c - 6c)\, e^{3x} = 15e^{3x},$$

from which we need $15c = 15$, or $c = 1$. Hence the particular integral is $y = e^{3x}$.

b)   The differential equation

$$\frac{d^2y}{dx^2} - 2\frac{dy}{dx} + 10y = 250x^2 + 52\sin 2x$$

had complementary function

$$y = e^x \left(A\cos 3x + B\sin 3x\right),$$

where A and B are arbitrary constants. As $\sin 2x$ and $\cos 2x$ do not occur in the complementary function, and neither does any power of x, we shall try as our particular integral,

$$y = cx^2 + dx + e + f\sin 2x + g\cos 2x.$$

Differentiating, we have

$$\frac{dy}{dx} = 2cx + d + 2f\cos 2x - 2g\sin 2x,$$

and on differentiating again we have

$$\frac{d^2y}{dx^2} = 2c - 4f\sin 2x - 4g\cos 2x.$$

We now substitute these into the differential equation, and compare corresponding terms, in order to determine the unknown constants. We have

$$[2c - 4f\sin 2x - 4g\cos 2x] - 2[2cx + d + 2f\cos 2x - 2g\sin 2x]$$
$$+ 10\left[cx^2 + dx + e + f\sin 2x + g\cos 2x\right] = 250x^2 + 52\sin 2x.$$

Rearranging the terms we have

$$(10c) x^2 + (-4c + 10d) x + (10e - 2d + 2c) + (-4f + 4g + 10f) \sin 2x$$
$$+ (-4g - 4f + 10g) \cos 2x = 250x^2 + 52 \sin 2x.$$

From this, we need $10c = 250$, $-4c + 10d = 0$, $10e - 2d + 2c = 0$, $6f + 4g = 52$ and $6g - 4f = 0$. We can solve these equations and find $c = 25$, $d = 10$, $e = -3$, $f = 6$ and $g = 4$. Hence the required particular integral is

$$y = 25x^2 + 10x - 3 + 6 \sin 2x + 4 \cos 2x.$$

c) The differential equation

$$\frac{d^2y}{dx^2} - 4\frac{dy}{dx} + 4y = 4e^{2x} + 50 \sin x$$

had complementary function

$$y = (A + Bx) e^{2x},$$

where A and B are arbitrary constants. Since e^{2x} and xe^{2x} both occur in the complementary function, we will need to try $x^2 e^{2x}$ as part of the particular integral. To correspond to the term $50 \sin x$ we will need to try both a $\sin x$ and a $\cos x$ term. Hence we have as a particular integral

$$y = cx^2 e^{2x} + d \sin x + e \cos x.$$

Differentiating with respect to x, we have

$$\frac{dy}{dx} = 2cxe^{2x} + 2cx^2 e^{2x} + d \cos x - e \sin x,$$

and, on differentiating again, we have

$$\frac{d^2y}{dx^2} = 2ce^{2x} + 4cxe^{2x} + 4cxe^{2x} + 4cx^2 e^{2x} - d \sin x - e \cos x.$$

We now substitute these into the differential equation, and we obtain

$$\left[2ce^{2x} + 4cxe^{2x} + 4cxe^{2x} + 4cx^2 e^{2x} - d \sin x - e \cos x \right]$$
$$- 4 \left[2cxe^{2x} + 2cx^2 e^{2x} + d \cos x - e \sin x \right]$$
$$+ 4 \left[cx^2 e^{2x} + d \sin x + e \cos x \right] = \left[4e^{2x} + 50 \sin x \right],$$

which we can rewrite in the form

$$(2c) e^{2x} + (4c + 4c - 8c) xe^{2x} + (4c - 8c + 4c) x^2 e^{2x}$$
$$+ (-d + 4e + 4d) \sin x + (-e - 4d + 4e) \cos x = 4e^{2x} + 50 \sin x.$$

It follows from this that we need $2c = 4$, $4c + 4c - 8c = 0$, $4c - 8c + 4c = 0$, $3d + 4e = 50$ and $3e - 4d = 0$. From these equations we find that $c = 2$, $d = 6$ and $e = 8$. Hence the particular integral is

$$y = 2x^2 e^{2x} + 6 \sin x + 8 \cos x.$$

Notice that it was not an accident that the equations from comparing the xe^{2x} and x^2e^{2x} terms both collapsed to $0 = 0$. This must happen in the situation we have here, where we have needed to include extra powers of x in order to avoid a term which had already appeared in the complementary function.

Stage 3 in the solution of these differential equations is the simplest of all. We write down the general solution of the differential equation, simply by adding together the complementary function and the particular integral that we have already found. We then find the values of the arbitrary constants required to give a particular solution if we are required to find a solution satisfying given boundary conditions.

Example 10. *Find the general solutions of the differential equations occuring in Example 8, and find the particular solution of a) for which $y = 6$ and $\dfrac{dy}{dx} = 0$ when $x = 0$, and the particular solution of b) for which $y = 0$ when $x = 0$ and $y = 5\pi - 7$ when $x = \frac{\pi}{2}$.*

Solution.   a)   The differential equation

$$2\frac{d^2y}{dx^2} + \frac{dy}{dx} - 6y = 15e^{3x}$$

had complementary function

$$y = Ae^{-2x} + Be^{\frac{3}{2}x},$$

and particular integral

$$y = e^{3x},$$

so that the general solution of the differential equation will be

$$y = Ae^{-2x} + Be^{\frac{3}{2}x} + e^{3x}.$$

To determine the required particular solution, we need to differentiate y, and substitute the given values for y, x and $\dfrac{dy}{dx}$. We have

$$\frac{dy}{dx} = -2Ae^{-2x} + \frac{3}{2}Be^{\frac{3}{2}x} + 3e^{3x},$$

and so we need $6 = A + B + 1$ and $0 = -2A + \frac{3}{2}B + 3$. Solving these simultaneous equations, we see that $A = 3$ and $B = 2$. Hence the required particular solution is

$$y = 3e^{-2x} + 2e^{\frac{3}{2}x} + e^{3x}.$$

b)   The differential equation

$$\frac{d^2y}{dx^2} - 2\frac{dy}{dx} + 10y = 250x^2 + 52\sin 2x$$

has complementary function

$$y = e^x\left(A\cos 3x + B\sin 3x\right)$$

and particular integral

$$y = 25x^2 + 10x - 3 + 6\sin 2x + 4\cos 2x.$$

Hence the general solution of the differential equation is

$$y = e^x \left(A\cos 3x + B\sin 3x \right) + 25x^2 + 10x - 3 + 6\sin 2x + 4\cos 2x.$$

To find the particular solution which satisfies the boundary conditions we are given, we substitute these values into the formula for y. We have $0 = A - 3 + 4$, from which $A = -1$, and also

$$5\pi - 7 = e^{\frac{\pi}{2}} \left(-B \right) + 25 \left(\frac{\pi}{2} \right)^2 + 10\frac{\pi}{2} - 3 - 4,$$

from which

$$Be^{\frac{\pi}{2}} = \frac{25\pi^2}{4},$$

or

$$B = \frac{25\pi^2}{4e^{\frac{\pi}{2}}}.$$

Hence the particular solution which satisfies the boundary conditions we were given is

$$y = e^x \left(-\cos 3x + \left(\frac{25\pi^2}{4e^{\frac{\pi}{2}}} \right) \sin 3x \right) + 25x^2 + 10x - 3 + 6\sin 2x + 4\cos 2x.$$

c)   The differential equation

$$\frac{d^2y}{dx^2} - 4\frac{dy}{dx} + 4y = 4e^{2x} + 50\sin x$$

has complementary function

$$y = (A + Bx)e^{2x},$$

and particular integral

$$y = 2x^2e^{2x} + 6\sin x + 8\cos x.$$

Hence the general solution of the differential equation is

$$y = (A + Bx)e^{2x} + 2x^2e^{2x} + 6\sin x + 8\cos x.$$

EXAMPLES 27

1.   The acceleration of a particle at time t is given by the equation $\frac{d^2x}{dt^2} = 2\cos t + 6t - 2e^{-2t}$, where x denotes the displacement of the particle from the origin. Find an expression for x in terms of t, given that, at time $t = 0$, the particle is at the origin and is at rest.

2.   Find the general solution of each of the following first-order separable differential equations:

(a) $\dfrac{dy}{dx} = x^2 y^2$;

(b) $\dfrac{dy}{dx} = x(y + y^2)$;

(c) $\dfrac{dy}{dx} = \dfrac{\sin^2 y}{\sqrt{1 - x^2}}$;

(d) $\dfrac{dy}{dx} = e^{2x}(1 + y^2)$;

(e) $\dfrac{dy}{dx} = \dfrac{\cos x - x^2}{y - \sin y}$;

(f) $\dfrac{dy}{dx} = e^{2x - 4y}$;

(g) $\dfrac{dy}{dx} = \dfrac{1 + y^2}{1 + x^2}$;

(h) $\dfrac{dy}{dx} = \dfrac{1}{x \tan y}$.

3.   For each of the following first-order separable differential equations, find the general solution and also the particular solution satisfying the given boundary condition:

(a) $\dfrac{dy}{dx} = \sin x \sec y$; $y = \frac{\pi}{6}$ when $x = \frac{\pi}{3}$;

(b) $\dfrac{dy}{dx} = x^2(1 + y)$; $y = 0$ when $x = 1$;

(c) $\dfrac{dy}{dx} = x^3 y^3$; $y = -2$ when $x = 3$;

(d) $\dfrac{dy}{dx} = \dfrac{\cos 2x}{\sin 3y}$; $y = \frac{\pi}{6}$ when $x = \frac{\pi}{4}$.

4.   By putting $y = vx$, where v is a function of x, find the general solution of each of the following first-order differential equations of the homogeneous type:

(a) $x(x + y)\dfrac{dy}{dx} = y^2$;

(b) $(x - y)\dfrac{dy}{dx} = x + y$;

(c) $\dfrac{dy}{dx} = \dfrac{2y^3}{x(x^2 + 2y^2)}$;

(d) $x\dfrac{dy}{dx} = y + y \ln\left(\dfrac{y}{x}\right)$.

5.   For each of the following first-order linear differential equations, find the general solution and also the particular solution satisfying the given boundary condition:

(a) $\dfrac{dy}{dx} + 2y = 4$; $y = 3$ when $x = 0$;

(b) $x\dfrac{dy}{dx} - 2y = 3x^5$; $y = 4$ when $x = 2$;

(c) $\dfrac{dy}{dx} + 4y = xe^{-2x}$; $y = 3$ when $x = 0$;

(d) $\dfrac{dy}{dx} + y = \sin 2x$; $y = 4$ when $x = 0$.

6. For each of the following second-order linear differential equations having constant coefficients, find

(α)   the complementary function,
(β)   the particular integral,
(γ)   the general solution,

and, where appropriate,

(δ)   the particular solution satisfying the given initial conditions:

(a) $\dfrac{d^2y}{dx^2} - 5\dfrac{dy}{dx} + 6y = 18x^2 - 18x - 28$;

(b) $\dfrac{d^2y}{dx^2} + \dfrac{dy}{dx} - 6y = 22\cos 2x - 6\sin 2x$;

(c) $\dfrac{d^2y}{dx^2} - 4\dfrac{dy}{dx} - 5y = 9e^{2x}$; $y = 4$ and $\dfrac{dy}{dx} = 5$ when $x = 0$;

(d) $\dfrac{d^2y}{dx^2} - 9y = -9x^3 + 9x^2 + 15x - 20$;

(e) $\dfrac{d^2y}{dx^2} - 4\dfrac{dy}{dx} + 3y = 12e^x$;

(f) $\dfrac{d^2y}{dx^2} + \dfrac{dy}{dx} - 2y = 9e^{-2x}$; $y = 2$ and $\dfrac{dy}{dx} = 5$ when $x = 0$;

(g) $\dfrac{d^2y}{dx^2} - 4\dfrac{dy}{dx} + 4y = 4x^2 - 8x + 14$;

(h) $\dfrac{d^2y}{dx^2} + 6\dfrac{dy}{dx} + 9y = 9x^2 - 6x + 17$;

(i) $\dfrac{d^2y}{dx^2} - 2\dfrac{dy}{dx} + y = 4e^x$; $y = e$ and $\dfrac{dy}{dx} = 6e$ when $x = 1$;

(j) $\dfrac{d^2y}{dx^2} + 9y = 13e^{-2x}$;

(k) $\dfrac{d^2y}{dx^2} + 16y = 36\sin 2x - 12\cos 2x$;

(l) $\dfrac{d^2y}{dx^2} - 4\dfrac{dy}{dx} + 5y = 5x^2 - 3x - 12$;

(m) $\dfrac{d^2y}{dx^2} - 2\dfrac{dy}{dx} + 10y = 9e^x$; $y = 3$ and $\dfrac{dy}{dx} = 0$ when $x = 0$;

(n) $\dfrac{d^2y}{dx^2} - 4\dfrac{dy}{dx} + 8y = 8x^2 - 8x - 22$;

(o) $\dfrac{d^2y}{dx^2} - 4\dfrac{dy}{dx} + 3y = 6x - 11 + 2e^{2x}$;

(p) $\dfrac{d^2y}{dx^2} + 5\dfrac{dy}{dx} + 6y = 12e^x + e^{-2x}$.

CHAPTER 28

Applications of Differential Equations

In this Chapter, we will use our ability to solve different types of differential equations in order to solve some 'practical' problems.

Example 1. *Find the curve in the x, y-plane which passes through the point $(3, 1)$ and whose tangent at the point (x, y) has gradient $x^2 y^2$.*

Solution. The slope of the tangent to the curve at the point (x, y) is given by $\dfrac{dy}{dx}$. Hence we are given that

$$\frac{dy}{dx} = x^2 y^2.$$

This differential equation is of the separable type, and so we solve it by separating the variables, and then finding the particular solution which satisfies the given condition.

Separating the variables and integrating gives

$$\int \frac{dy}{y^2} = \int x^2 \, dx$$

from which

$$-y^{-1} = \frac{1}{3} x^3 + c.$$

We require $y = 1$ when $x = 3$, from which $c = -10$. Hence the required curve has equation

$$\frac{1}{y} + \frac{x^3}{3} = 10.$$

One of the most common types of growth and decay is that covered by the laws of **exponential growth** and **exponential decay**. This happens in those situations where the rate of change of a quantity at any given time is directly proportional to the value of the quantity at that time. This happens for example where the rate of change of a population is directly proportional to the size of the population, or where the rate of growth through interest of money deposited in the bank is directly proportional to the amount of money deposited.

To see that such situations lead to the laws of exponential growth and decay, let us consider the following example.

Example 2. *Let y denote the value of a quantity present at time t. Assume that the rate of change of y is directly proportional to the value of y at time t. Find an expression for y in terms of t.*

Solution. We know that the rate of change of y with respect to t, which is given by $\dfrac{dy}{dt}$, is directly proportional to the value of y. This implies that

$$\frac{dy}{dt} = ky,$$

where k is the constant of proportionality. This differential equation is separable, and on rearranging the terms we have

$$\int \frac{dy}{y} = \int k\, dt$$

from which

$$\ln y = kt + c,$$

where c is an arbitrary constant.

If we apply the exponential function to both sides of this equation, then we have

$$e^{\ln y} = e^{kt+c}$$

or, using the index laws,

$$y = e^{kt} \times e^{c},$$

from which

$$y = Ae^{kt},$$

writing $A = e^{c}$, where A will be an arbitrary constant. This is the well-known rule giving exponential growth and decay.

A gives the value of y at time $t = 0$, while the constant k determines whether y is increasing (when $k > 0$), or decreasing (when $k < 0$). Also the size of k determines how rapidly or slowly y is increasing or decreasing.

Newton's law of cooling states that the rate at which a body cools is directly proportional to the difference in temperatures between the body and the surrounding medium. The following example shows that this leads to a modified form of exponential decay.

Example 3.   *A cake is mixed at room temperature of 75°F. It is then placed in an oven which has been heated to 375°F. Assuming that the oven maintains its temperature throughout the 20 minutes that the cake is baking, find the temperature of the cake when it is removed from the oven. The temperature of the cake is known to be 275°F two minutes after it is placed in the oven.*

Solution.   Let T°F be the temperature of the cake t minutes after it is placed in the oven. Then we are given that $T = 75$ at $t = 0$, and that $T = 275$ when $t = 2$. We need to determine the value of T when $t = 20$.

We may assume that $\dfrac{dT}{dt}$, the rate of change of the temperature of the cake, is directly proportional to $375 - T$, the difference in temperature between the cake and the air in the oven which is surrounding it. This is a modified form of Newton's law of cooling which will apply to things which are getting hotter.

H

Hence we know that

$$\frac{dT}{dt} = k\,(375 - T)$$

from which, on separating the variables, we have

$$\int \frac{dT}{375 - T} = \int k\,dt$$

so that, on finding the integrals, we have

$$-\ln\,(375 - T) = kt + c,$$

which we can rewrite as

$$375 - T = Ae^{-kt},$$

if we let $A = e^{-c}$.

We now substitute the two pieces of information that we were given into this equation in order to find k and A.

When $t = 0$, we have $T = 75$, and so, on substituting we find $375 - 75 = Ae^{-k0}$, from which we have $A = 300$.

When $t = 2$, we have $T = 275$, and so, on substituting we find $375 - 275 = Ae^{-2k}$, from which we have $100 = 300e^{-2k}$. Using the index laws, we can rewrite this as

$$\left(e^{-k}\right)^2 = \frac{1}{3} \quad \text{from which} \quad e^{-k} = \sqrt{\frac{1}{3}}.$$

At time $t = 20$, the temperature T is given by the equation

$$375 - T = 300e^{-20k},$$

which we can rewrite as

$$T = 375 - 300\left(e^{-k}\right)^{20},$$

or as

$$T = 375 - 300\left(\sqrt{\frac{1}{3}}\right)^{20},$$

which is equivalent to

$$T = 375 - 300\left(\frac{1}{3}\right)^{10},$$

or, on using a calulator,

$$T \approx 374.99.$$

It follows that, in the circumstances described, the cake has reached a temperature of 374.99°F after 20 minutes in an oven maintained at a constant temperature of 375°F.

It is worth noting that in the above example we avoided finding k, managing instead to use the index laws so that we could work with e^{-k}. The advantage of this is that it cuts out one step from the solution, and also removes a potential source of inaccuracy, arising from finding a (necessarily approximate) value for k. However, there would be no objection to a solution that did find the value of k as a step towards finding T.

Before the example, it was described as a modification of exponential growth. The way in which it can be regarded as being an example of exponential growth is that if we measure temperatures from a base of 375°F rather than from the base of 0°F then we would have exponential growth of the temperature from the relative value $-300°$ towards the value $0°$.

Example 4.   *A body is falling under the action of gravity through a resisting medium which applies a retarding force to the movement which is related to the square of the velocity of the body. Assuming that the body starts from rest at time $t = 0$, and that the velocity v at time t satisfies the differential equation*

$$\frac{dv}{dt} = \frac{1}{6}\left(81 - v^2\right),$$

find the velocity of the body at time $t = 0.5$.

Solution.   We can separate the variables in this differential equation and rewrite it as

$$\int \frac{dv}{81 - v^2} = \frac{1}{6}\int dt$$

so that, using Partial Fractions on the left hand side, we have

$$\frac{1}{18}\int \left(\frac{1}{9 + v} + \frac{1}{9 - v}\right)dv = \frac{1}{6}\int dt$$

and on integrating both sides we have

$$\frac{1}{18}\left(\ln|v + 9| - \ln|9 - v|\right) = \frac{1}{6}t + c.$$

We know that $v = 0$ when $t = 0$ and so on substituting we have

$$\frac{1}{18}\left(\ln|0 + 9| - \ln|9 - 0|\right) = \frac{1}{6}0 + c,$$

from which we must have $c = 0$.

Assuming that the velocity v will always stay below the value 9, we have $|9 - v| = 9 - v$, while from the given differential equation, if v always stays below 9 then the acceleration of the body will stay positive, and so in particular the velocity of the body will stay positive. Hence also we may write $|9 + v| = 9 + v$. We can therefore rewrite the above equation as

$$\ln(9 + v) - \ln(9 - v) = 3t,$$

which we can put in the alternative form

$$\ln\left(\frac{9 + v}{9 - v}\right) = 3t,$$

or

$$\frac{9+v}{9-v} = e^{3t}.$$

Solving this equation for v in terms of t, we have

$$v = 9\left(\frac{e^{3t}-1}{e^{3t}+1}\right).$$

Substituting $t = 0.5$ into this equation, to find the velocity of the body at $t = 0.5$, and using a calculator, we have

$$v = 9\left(\frac{e^{1.5}-1}{e^{1.5}+1}\right) \approx 5.716,$$

correct to 3 decimal places.

Example 5.   *The current x in a certain electrical circuit at time t is given by the differential equation*

$$\frac{dx}{dt} + 5x = 1 - \cos t.$$

Find x in terms of t, given that $x = 0$ at time $t = 0$.

Solution.   The given differential equation is a first order linear differential equation, which we shall solve by the integrating factor method. Now the integrating factor will be

$$e^{\int 5\,dt} = e^{5t}.$$

Multiplying the differential equation by the integrating factor, we have

$$e^{5t}\frac{dx}{dt} + 5xe^{5t} = e^{5t} - e^{5t}\cos t,$$

which we can rewrite in the form

$$\frac{d}{dt}\left(xe^{5t}\right) = e^{5t} - e^{5t}\cos t.$$

Integrating both sides of this equation with respect to t gives

$$xe^{5t} = \frac{1}{5}e^{5t} - \int e^{5t}\cos t\,dt.$$

To complete the solution, we need to find $I = \int e^{5t}\cos t\,dt$. Earlier we found an integral like this one by using complex numbers. This time, for comparison, we shall use Integration by Parts twice. We have

$$I = e^{5t}\sin t - 5\int e^{5t}\sin t\,dt$$

$$= e^{5t}\sin t - 5\left[-e^{5t}\cos t + 5\int e^{5t}\cos t\,dt\right]$$

$$= e^{5t}\sin t + 5e^{5t}\cos t - 25\int e^{5t}\cos t\,dt$$

$$= e^{5t}\sin t + 5e^{5t}\cos t - 25I - 26c.$$

Solving this equation to find I gives

$$26I = e^{5t} \sin t + 5e^{5t} \cos t - 26c,$$

from which

$$I = \frac{1}{26} \left(e^{5t} \sin t + 5e^{5t} \cos t\right) - c.$$

Substituting back into the equation, we have

$$xe^{5t} = \frac{1}{5}e^{5t} - \frac{1}{26} \left(e^{5t} \sin t + 5e^{5t} \cos t\right) + c,$$

We now need to substitute the initial values $x = 0$ and $t = 0$ in order to find the value of c. Then we have $0 = \frac{1}{5} - \frac{5}{26} + c$, from which we have $c = -\frac{1}{130}$. Hence we conclude that

$$x = \frac{1}{5} - \frac{1}{26} \left(\sin t + 5 \cos t\right) - \frac{1}{130}e^{-5t},$$

or

$$x = \frac{1}{130} \left(26 - 5 \sin t - 25 \cos t - e^{-5t}\right).$$

Example 6.   *A weight is attached to the lower end of a spring, the upper end of which is attached to the ceiling. Let y cm denote the vertical distance of the weight from the ceiling at time t sec. Suppose that the relation between y and t is determined by the differential equation*

$$\frac{d^2y}{dt^2} + 10\frac{dy}{dt} + 41y = 410.$$

Find y in terms of t, given that at time $t = 0$ the weight is at rest and is a distance of 20 cm below the ceiling.

Solution.   For this second order linear differential equation with constant coefficients, the method of solution involves finding a complementary function and a particular integral. Now the auxiliary equation is $z^2 + 10z + 41 = 0$, which will have the two complex solutions $z = -5 \pm 4i$. Hence the complementary function will be

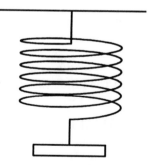

$$y = e^{-5t} \left(A \cos 4t + B \sin 4t\right).$$

As a particular integral we shall take $y = c$, where c is a constant. Then we know that $\frac{dy}{dt} = 0 = \frac{d^2y}{dt^2}$, and so we need $41c = 410$, from which we have $c = 10$. Hence the particular integral is $y = 10$.

The general solution of the differential equation is therefore

$$y = 10 + e^{-5t} \left(A \cos 4t + B \sin 4t \right).$$

We are looking for the particular solution which satisfies the initial conditions $y = 20$ and $\dfrac{dy}{dt} = 0$ at $t = 0$, since we know that the distance from the ceiling is $20\,\text{cm}$ and that the weight has velocity 0 at time $t = 0$.

Substituting $y = 20$ at $t = 0$ we have

$$20 = 10 + A, \quad \text{so that} \quad A = 10.$$

We differentiate in order to find $\dfrac{dy}{dt}$. We have

$$\frac{dy}{dt} = -5e^{-5t} \left(A \cos 4t + B \sin 4t \right) + e^{-5t} \left(-4A \sin 4t + 4B \cos 4t \right).$$

Substituting $\dfrac{dy}{dt} = 0$ at $t = 0$ we have

$$0 = -5A + 4B, \quad \text{so that} \quad B = \frac{25}{2}.$$

We finally conclude that the required solution of the differential equation is

$$y = 10 + e^{-5t} \left(10 \cos 4t + \frac{25}{2} \sin 4t \right).$$

This solution gives us the result that experience tells us would happen. We start with the spring and weight stretched beyond their equilibrium position. When the weight is released at time $t = 0$, it will oscillate about its equilibrium position, with the magnitude of the oscillations gradually reducing, until finally the weight will appear to be motionless at its equilibrium position. This is precisely the behaviour of the function we have found in the above solution.

EXAMPLES 28

1. Find the equation of the curve in the x,y-plane which passes through the point $(2,1)$ and whose tangent at the point (x,y) has gradient $x^3 y$.

2. Find the equation of the curve in the x,y-plane which passes through the point $(1,0)$ and whose tangent at the point (x,y) has gradient $\dfrac{x+y}{x-y}$.

3. A joint of meat has been cooked in an oven at $400°\text{F}$ for a long time, so that the whole joint has reached this temperature. It is then removed from the oven and carved in the kitchen where the temperature is a constant $70°\text{F}$. Given that it takes the housewife two

minutes to carve the meat, and that when she has finished carving it the temperature of the meat has dropped to 300°F, how long can the family delay further before coming to the table, if the housewife likes to present their meals 'piping hot', which in this case means at a temperature of at least 150°F?

4.   In a room maintained at a constant temperature of 20°C, a heated body cools from 100°C to 70°C in 15 minutes. How long will it take the body to cool to 40°C?

5.   A solution of chemical A reacts with a solution of chemical B. If x is the concentration of A which has reacted in time t, and K is a constant determining the rate of the reaction, then

$$\frac{dx}{dt} = K(0.01 - x)(0.02 - x).$$

Given that $x = 0$ when $t = 0$, find the particular solution of this differential equation.

6.   The radioactive decay of Uranium 238 is a complicated process, part of which is governed by the differential equation

$$\frac{dy}{dt} + Ky = ALe^{-Lt},$$

where K, A and L are constants with $K \neq L$. Given that $y = 0$ when $t = 0$, solve this differential equation to find an expression for y in terms of t.

7.   A reservoir contains a volume V of water, which flows into it and out of it at a constant rate v. Suppose that c measures the concentration of pollution in the water flowing into the reservoir, and that y measures the concentration of pollution in the water flowing out of the reservoir.

Given that the reservoir is initially not polluted, so that $y = 0$ when $t = 0$, and that c is a constant, find an expression for y in terms of t, given that they are related by the differential equation

$$\frac{dy}{dt} + \frac{vy}{V} = \frac{vc}{V}.$$

8.   If glucose is being fed intravenously at a constant rate, the concentration y of glucose in the blood at time t is given by the differential equation

$$\frac{dy}{dt} = C - ky,$$

where C and k are positive constants. Solve this differential equation to find y in terms of t, given that at time $t = 0$, $y = A$, where A is a constant.

9.   The current i at time t in a certain electrical circuit is given by the equation

$$R\frac{di}{dt} + \frac{i}{C} = \frac{dE}{dt},$$

where R, C are constants. Find i in terms of t if $i = i_0$ at time $t = 0$ and $E = E_0(1 - \cos \omega t)$, where E_0 and ω are constants.

10.   The equation of motion of a certain body is

$$5\frac{dv}{dt} + 4v = e^{-2t}.$$

If $v = 0$ at time $t = 0$, find an expression for v in terms of t.

11.   In a certain galvanometer, the deflection θ satisfies the differential equation

$$\frac{d^2\theta}{dt^2} + 4\frac{d\theta}{dt} + 4\theta = 2e^{-4t}.$$

Given that $\theta = 0$ and $\frac{d\theta}{dt} = 0$ when $t = 0$, find an expression for θ in terms of t.

12.   A particle is performing as a damped harmonic oscillator, subject to the differential equation

$$\frac{d^2x}{dt^2} + 12\frac{dx}{dt} + 32x = 0.$$

Find an expression for x in terms of t, given that $x = 0$ and $\frac{dx}{dt} = 8$ when $t = 0$.

CHAPTER 29
Basic Techniques

In some of the earlier chapters, we promised to deal with certain further details which we put off then so as not to disrupt the continuity of the course. This chapter is divided into various unconnected sections, each of which deals with one of the topics mentioned earlier in the book.

Section 1. **Factorisation.**

Given a quadratic expression such as $x^2 - 7x + 6$, we frequently wish to write it as a product of two factors. The reason for wishing to do this is that if we can write

$$x^2 - 7x + 6 = (x - 6)(x - 1),$$

as we can, then we can find the roots of the equation $x^2 - 7x + 6 = 0$, since $(x - 6)(x - 1) = 0$ precisely when either $x - 6 = 0$ or $x - 1 = 0$. Hence the solutions of the equation $x^2 - 7x + 6 = 0$ are the two real numbers $x = 6$ and $x = 1$.

It follows that factorisation can be a help on the way to finding the solutions of an equation.

The reverse is also true. If we know that α is a root of an equation of the form $f(x) = 0$, where $f(x)$ is a polynomial in x, then it can be shown that $x - \alpha$ will be a factor of the polynomial $f(x)$.

There is a result which says that if we can factorise a polynomial which has integers as its coefficients, then all of the numbers involved must either be integers or real numbers which are not rational. Suppose that $f(x)$ is a polynomial having integer coefficients which can be factored into linear factors not involving irrational numbers. Then the implication of the above result is that all the coefficients in the factorisation can be assumed to be integers. Furthermore the numbers at the beginning and end of each bracket must divide the coefficients of the highest and lowest powers of x involved in the original polynomial.

Suppose then that we are given a quadratic polynomial such as $x^2 + x - 6$, and we are asked to factorise this quadratic as a product of two linear factors. By the result quoted above, we must try to write

$$x^2 + x - 6 = (ax + b)(cx + d),$$

where a and c divide 1, and where b and d divide -6, with a, b, c and d being integers. We might as well take it that $a = 1$ and $c = 1$. What are the possibilities for b and d?

We can choose $b = \pm 6$, $b = \pm 3$, $b = \pm 2$ and $b = \pm 1$. These are the only integers which divide -6. Once b is determined, the value of d will be fixed because we need $bd = -6$. So for example, if $b = -2$, we would have to have $d = 3$.

Now on expanding $(x + b)(x + d)$, we have

$$(x + b)(x + d) = x^2 + (b + d)x + bd,$$

and so we need to choose b and d with $bd = -6$ and $b + d = 1$. We want b and d to be roughly the same in size in order that $b + d = 1$. This suggests that $b = \pm 2$ or $b = \pm 3$ might be more suitable than $b = \pm 1$ (which means $d = \mp 6$), or $b = \pm 6$ (which means $d = \mp 1$).

We now use trial-and-error to try to find the appropriate values for b and d. If we take $b = 2$ then $d = -3$, so that $b + d = -1$, which is not what is wanted. If we take $b = -2$ then $d = 3$ so that $b + d = 1$, which is what is wanted. Hence we have the factorisation

$$x^2 + x - 6 = (x - 2)(x + 3).$$

Let us now try a slightly more difficult example. Suppose we wish to factorise $3x^2 - 2x - 8$. We shall assume that

$$3x^2 - 2x - 8 = (ax + b)(cx + d),$$

where we shall assume that a, b, c and d are integers. (By the theorem quoted earlier, if these numbers are rational numbers, then they must in fact be integers.)

Now if the identity above holds, then we must have $ac = 3$, with a and c being integers. Hence one of the numbers must be ± 3 and the other must be ± 1. We shall assume that $a = 3$ and $c = 1$.

Next we need to choose b and d such that $bd = -8$ and also such that $ad + bc = -2$. b and d must be factors of -8, if they are integers, and so we must have either $b = \pm 1$, $b = \pm 2$, $b = \pm 4$ or $b = \pm 8$, with $d = -8/b$.

Remembering that we have already chosen $a = 3$ and $c = 1$, we use trial-and-error to find that $b = 4$ and $d = -2$. Hence we have the factorisation

$$3x^2 - 2x - 8 = (3x + 4)(x - 2).$$

It is important to check at the end of examples like the above that the factorisation you have written down is correct. It is all too common to see students guess at what they think is a correct factorisation, and proceed to work on carrying a mistake, because their guess was wrong and they omitted to check their guess properly.

Section 2.   **Right Angled Triangles.**

In the first diagram, O is the centre of a circle of radius r, and A is the point where the circle cuts the x-axis. P is the point on the circumference of the circle chosen so that the angle AOP is $\frac{\pi}{6}$. X is the foot of the perpendicular from P onto the x-axis. Since the angles of a triangle add up to π (radians), and since the angle PXO is $\frac{\pi}{2}$, it follows that the angle OPX will be $\frac{\pi}{3}$. P' is the reflection of P in the x-axis. By congruent triangles, we can see that the angle $OP'X$ will also be $\frac{\pi}{3}$. Furthermore the angle $P'OP$ will also be $\frac{\pi}{3}$. Hence the triangle OPP' will be an **equilateral triangle** (one with all sides having the same size and with all angles being equal).

Now the length of OP is the radius of the circle, which we took to be r. Hence PP' will have length r also, and so, by symmetry, PX will have length $\frac{r}{2}$ (since X is the mid-point of PP'). Using Pythagoras' theorem on the right-angled triangle OPX, we see that

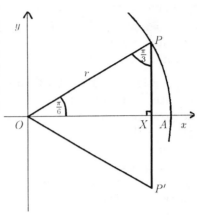

$$|OX|^2 + |XP|^2 = |OP|^2,$$

so that

$$|OX|^2 + \left(\frac{r}{2}\right)^2 = r^2,$$

from which we conclude that

$$|OX| = \frac{\sqrt{3}}{2}\, r.$$

In the second diagram, O, A and r are as defined above. This time the point P is chosen so that the angle AOP is $\frac{\pi}{4}$. As before, X will be the foot of the perpendicular from P onto OA. Hence the angle PXO will be $\frac{\pi}{2}$ and so we see that the angle OPX will also be $\frac{\pi}{4}$.

The triangle OPX is an **isosceles triangle**, which is one having two sides of equal length, since the sides opposite to the equal angles OPX and XOP must be equal. We now apply Pythagoras' Theorem to the triangle OPX, remembering that $|OP| = r$, and that $|PX| = |OX|$.

We easily see that

$$|PX|^2 = |OX|^2 = \frac{r^2}{2},$$

and so

$$|PX| = |OX| = \frac{r}{\sqrt{2}}.$$

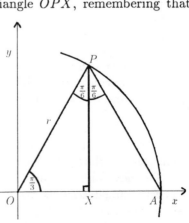

The third diagram is similar to the first, except that A, the point where the circle meets the x-axis, is also the reflection of O in the line PX, and the angle XOP is $\frac{\pi}{3}$. Then the triangle OPA is equilateral, and by a similar argument to that used earlier we conclude that $|OP| = r$, $|OX| = \frac{r}{2}$ and $|PX| = \frac{\sqrt{3}}{2} r$.

Now we use the definitions of sine, cosine, and tangent given in Chapter 2 to obtain the values given in the table there.

Section 3.   The Addition Formulae.

We shall prove the addition formulae only in the case where x and y are positive angles whose sum is less than a right-angle. We refer to the diagram shown.

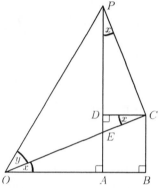

In this diagram, the line OCE is chosen such that the angle AOC is x radians, while OP is chosen such that the angle COP is y radians. Let P be chosen so that $|OP| = r$, and let C be the foot of the perpendicular from P onto the line OEC, while A and B are the feet of the perpendiculars from P and C respectively onto the line OAB. D is the foot of the perpendicular from C onto AP, while E is the point of intersection of the lines OC and AP.

Since the lines OB and CD are parallel, both being perpendicular to AP, it follows that the angles AOC and ECD are equal. Hence $ECD = x$.

From the right-angled triangle CDE we can deduce that the angle CED is $\frac{\pi}{2} - x$. Now, by considering the right-angled triangle ECP, we see that the angle CPD is x.

Now we consider the right-angled triangle OCP, in which $|OP| = r$ and the angle COP is y. Applying the definitions of sine and cosine to this triangle, we can deduce that

$$\cos y = \frac{|OC|}{|OP|} \quad \text{and} \quad \sin y = \frac{|CP|}{|OP|}$$

from which we can see that $|OC| = r \cos y$ and that $|CP| = r \sin y$.

Next we consider the right-angled triangle OBC in which the angle BOC is x and $|OC| = r \cos y$. From this triangle, we can deduce that

$$\cos x = \frac{|OB|}{|OC|} \quad \text{and} \quad \sin x = \frac{|BC|}{|OC|}$$

from which we have $|OB| = r \cos y \cos x$ and $|BC| = r \cos y \sin x$.

The next right-angled triangle we consider is the triangle DPC in which the angle DPC is x and $|PC| = r \sin y$. From this triangle, we can deduce that

$$\cos x = \frac{|PD|}{|PC|} \quad \text{and} \quad \sin x = \frac{|DC|}{|PC|}$$

from which we deduce that $|PD| = r \sin y \cos x$ and $|DC| = r \sin y \sin x$.

Notice that $ABCD$ is a rectangle, and so in particular we know that $|AD| = |BC| = r \cos y \sin x$, and also that $|AB| = |DC| = r \sin y \sin x$.

Now we are ready to calculate $\sin(x + y)$ and $\cos(x + y)$. We have

$$\cos(x + y) = \frac{|OA|}{|OP|}$$

from which

$$\cos(x + y) = \frac{|OB| - |AB|}{|OP|}$$
$$= \frac{r \cos y \cos x - r \sin y \sin x}{r}$$
$$= \cos y \cos x - \sin y \sin x,$$

as required. Also

$$\sin(x + y) = \frac{|AP|}{|OP|}$$
$$= \frac{|AD| + |DP|}{|OP|}$$
$$= \frac{r \cos y \sin x + r \sin y \cos x}{r}$$
$$= \cos y \sin x + \sin y \cos x.$$

The extension of these results to numbers x and y which do not satisfy the conditions given above follows by consideration of a number of special cases, none of which is particularly difficult, using formulae such as

$$\sin(\pi + x) = -\sin x.$$

Although it was suggested earlier in the book that formulae such as this could be deduced from the addition formulae, they can also be readily deduced directly from the definitions of the sine and cosine function that were given. This avoids the need to use the addition formulae in trying to prove the addition formulae, which would of course lead to a circular argument.

Section 4. **The Sine Rule.**

Suppose we are given a triangle ABC in which the lengths of the sides opposite to A, B and C are a, b and c respectively. Let the angles in the triangle ABC at the vertices be A, B and C respectively. Then the **Sine Rule** states that

$$\frac{a}{\sin A} = \frac{b}{\sin B} = \frac{c}{\sin C}.$$

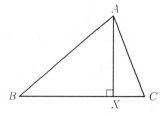

To prove the Sine Rule, we consider the diagram shown, where AX is the perpendicular from A onto the line BC, extended if necessary. Then

$$\sin B = \frac{|AX|}{|AB|} \quad \text{and} \quad \sin C = \frac{|AX|}{|AC|}.$$

From these two equations we have

$$|AX| = c\sin B \quad \text{and} \quad |AX| = b\sin C.$$

Equating these expressions for $|AX|$, and dividing by $\sin B \sin C$ we conclude that

$$\frac{b}{\sin B} = \frac{c}{\sin C}.$$

By dropping the perpendicular from B onto AC, we can conclude similarly that

$$\frac{a}{\sin A} = \frac{c}{\sin C}.$$

The Sine Rule follows immediately from these two equations.

Section 5. The Product and Quotient Rules.

Let $f(x)$ and $g(x)$ be differentiable functions, and let us consider the product fg, which is defined by $(fg)(x) = f(x) \times g(x)$. Suppose that $h \neq 0$. Consider

$$\frac{(fg)(x+h) - (fg)(x)}{h} = \frac{f(x+h)g(x+h) - f(x)g(x)}{h}$$

$$= \frac{f(x+h)g(x+h) - f(x+h)g(x) + f(x+h)g(x) - f(x)g(x)}{h}$$

$$= \frac{f(x+h)g(x+h) - f(x+h)g(x)}{h} + \frac{f(x+h)g(x) - f(x)g(x)}{h}$$

$$= f(x+h)\left(\frac{g(x+h) - g(x)}{h}\right) + g(x)\left(\frac{f(x+h) - f(x)}{h}\right).$$

Now we assume that $h \to 0$. Since $f(x)$ is a differentiable function of x, $f(x)$ will be continuous. Hence it follows that $f(x+h) \to f(x)$ as $h \to 0$. Furthermore, since f and g are differentiable functions of x, we know that, as $h \to 0$,

$$\frac{f(x+h) - f(x)}{h} \to \frac{df}{dx} \quad \text{and} \quad \frac{g(x+h) - g(x)}{h} \to \frac{dg}{dx}.$$

From these results we conclude that, as $h \to 0$,

$$\frac{(fg)(x+h) - (fg)(x)}{h} \to f(x) \times \frac{dg}{dx} + g(x) \times \frac{df}{dx},$$

as required.

Now we consider the differentiable functions $f(x)$ and $g(x)$, and we consider the quotient $\dfrac{f}{g}$, which is defined to be the function such that

$$\left(\frac{f}{g}\right)(x) = \frac{f(x)}{g(x)},$$

where we are assuming that $g(x) \neq 0$. Suppose that $h \neq 0$, and that h is sufficiently small so that g is not zero between x and $x + h$. Consider

$$\frac{\left(\dfrac{f}{g}\right)(x + h) - \left(\dfrac{f}{g}\right)(x)}{h} = \frac{\dfrac{f(x + h)}{g(x + h)} - \dfrac{f(x)}{g(x)}}{h}$$

$$= \frac{f(x + h)g(x) - f(x)g(x + h)}{hg(x + h)g(x)}$$

$$= \frac{f(x + h)g(x) - f(x)g(x) + f(x)g(x) - f(x)g(x + h)}{hg(x + h)g(x)}$$

$$= \frac{f(x + h)g(x) - f(x)g(x)}{hg(x + h)g(x)} + \frac{f(x)g(x) - f(x)g(x + h)}{hg(x + h)g(x)}$$

$$= \frac{g(x)\left(\dfrac{f(x + h) - f(x)}{h}\right) - f(x)\left(\dfrac{g(x + h) - g(x)}{h}\right)}{g(x + h)g(x)}.$$

As in the last proof, as $h \to 0$, we know that $g(x + h) \to g(x)$, and also that

$$\frac{f(x + h) - f(x)}{h} \to \frac{df}{dx} \quad \text{and} \quad \frac{g(x + h) - g(x)}{h} \to \frac{dg}{dx}.$$

Hence we conclude that, as $h \to 0$,

$$\frac{\left(\dfrac{f}{g}\right)(x + h) - \left(\dfrac{f}{g}\right)(x)}{h} \to \frac{g(x) \times \dfrac{df}{dx} - f(x) \times \dfrac{dg}{dx}}{[g(x)]^2},$$

as required.

Section 6. **Long Division of Polynomials.**

Earlier on, we saw that the technique of long division of polynomials can be very helpful. The method is very similar to the method of long division of numbers, which sadly is no longer as familiar as it was, in these days when calculators are so common.

Suppose we are required to divide $x^5 + 5x^4 + 5x^3 + 3x + 2$ by $x^3 + 3x^2 - 2x + 4$. We start by setting up the familiar long division format. In order to keep corresponding terms in the correct positions, we put the term $0x^2$ into the dividend. As we calculate, we concentrate on the highest powered terms in the divisor and dividend.

$$x^3 + 3x^2 - 2x + 4 \,\overline{\big)\, x^5 + 5x^4 + 5x^3 + 0x^2 + 3x + 2}$$

Since x^5 divided by x^3 is x^2, we put x^2 in the quotient and we multiply each term of the divisor by x^2, writing the answer in the appropriate columns under the dividend. So we have

$$
\begin{array}{r}
x^2 \hspace{10em} \\
\hline
x^3 + 3x^2 - 2x + 4 \,\big|\; x^5 + 5x^4 + 5x^3 + 0x^2 + 3x + 2 \\
x^5 + 3x^4 - 2x^3 + 4x^2 \hspace{6em}
\end{array}
$$

Now we subtract the result of the multiplication from the dividend, and then bring down the term involving the next power of x. So we have

$$
\begin{array}{r}
x^2 \hspace{10em} \\
\hline
x^3 + 3x^2 - 2x + 4 \,\big|\; x^5 + 5x^4 + 5x^3 + 0x^2 + 3x + 2 \\
x^5 + 3x^4 - 2x^3 + 4x^2 \hspace{6em} \\
\hline
2x^4 + 7x^3 - 4x^2 + 3x \hspace{3em}
\end{array}
$$

Now we repeat the above process. We start by dividing $2x^4$ by x^3, so that we have $2x$ which we put into the quotient and then we multiply the divisor by this $2x$, subtracting the result as before, and finally bringing down the next term.

$$
\begin{array}{r}
x^2 + 2x \hspace{8em} \\
\hline
x^3 + 3x^2 - 2x + 4 \,\big|\; x^5 + 5x^4 + 5x^3 + 0x^2 + 3x + 2 \\
x^5 + 3x^4 - 2x^3 + 4x^2 \hspace{6em} \\
\hline
2x^4 + 7x^3 - 4x^2 + 3x \hspace{3em} \\
2x^4 + 6x^3 - 4x^2 + 8x \hspace{3em} \\
\hline
x^3 + 0x^2 - 5x + 2
\end{array}
$$

Finally we repeat the process once more, when we will reach the point where the degree of the remainder is less than the degree of the divisor. At this point we could only continue by introducing negative powers of x. For some purposes this is meaningful, but here we shall just leave the solution with a quotient and remainder which are polynomials in x. We have

$$
\begin{array}{r}
x^2 + 2x + 1 \hspace{6em} \\
\hline
x^3 + 3x^2 - 2x + 4 \,\big|\; x^5 + 5x^4 + 5x^3 + 0x^2 + 3x + 2 \\
x^5 + 3x^4 - 2x^3 + 4x^2 \hspace{6em} \\
\hline
2x^4 + 7x^3 - 4x^2 + 3x \hspace{3em} \\
2x^4 + 6x^3 - 4x^2 + 8x \hspace{3em} \\
\hline
x^3 + 0x^2 - 5x + 2 \\
x^3 + 3x^2 - 2x + 4 \\
\hline
- 3x^2 - 3x - 2
\end{array}
$$

From this we conclude that, when $x^5 + 5x^4 + 5x^3 + 3x + 2$ is divided by $x^3 + 3x^2 - 2x + 4$, the quotient is $x^2 + 2x + 1$ and the remainder is $-3x^2 - 3x - 2$.

EXAMPLES 29

1.   Factorise each of the following as a product of two real linear terms, where possible:

(a) $x^2 + 4x - 5$;   (b) $x^2 + 5x + 4$;

(c) $x^2 + 5x + 6$;   (d) $x^2 + x - 12$;

(e) $2x^2 + 5x + 3$;   (f) $3x^2 + 13x + 4$;

(g) $2x^2 + 7x + 13$;   (h) $3x^2 - 3x + 12$;

(i) $4x^2 - 8x + 3$;   (j) $3x^2 + 5x - 2$;

(k) $3x^2 + 4x + 2$;   (l) $3x^2 + 4x + 1$.

2.   In each of the triangles ABC described below, use the Sine Rule to determine those of the lengths a, b and c of the sides and the angles A, B and C which are not given:

(a) $A = 50°$, $C = 55°$ and $a = 3$;

(b) $A = 40°$, $a = 3$ and $c = 4$ with $0° \leq C° \leq 90°$;

(c) $A = 30°$, $b = 2$ and $a = 7$ with $90° \leq C° \leq 180°$.

Numerical Answers to the Examples

This section provides numerical answers to the examples in the book, together with hints for the most difficult examples.

Examples 1.

3. (a) $(x-3)^2-2$; (b) $(x+2)^2-8$; (c) $3(x-1)^2+4$; (d) $-2(x-1)^2+11$.
4. (a) $y=(x-2)^2-4$; (b) $y=(x-1)^2-4$. **5.** (a), (d) No real roots; (b) 2 distinct real roots -4, $1/3$; (c) 2 distinct real roots $-1/2$, 3.
6. (a) $y=(x-2)^2-1$; (b) $y=4-(x+1)^2$; (c) $y=12-3(x-2)^2$; (d) $y=16-4(x-1)^2$. **8.** $(-\infty,-2)\cup(1,3)$. **9.** $[-4,-1]\cup[3,\infty)$.
10. $(-2,3)\cup(3,\infty)$. **11.** $(-\infty,-1]\cup[5,\infty)$.

Examples 2.

1. (a) $\frac{1}{2}$, $\frac{\sqrt{3}}{2}$, $\frac{1}{\sqrt{3}}$, 2, $\frac{2}{\sqrt{3}}$, $\sqrt{3}$; (b) $\frac{1}{\sqrt{2}}$, $\frac{1}{\sqrt{2}}$, 1, $\sqrt{2}$, $\sqrt{2}$, 1; (c) $\frac{\sqrt{3}}{2}$, $\frac{1}{2}$, $\sqrt{3}$, $\frac{2}{\sqrt{3}}$, 2, $\frac{1}{\sqrt{3}}$; (d) 1, 0, ND, 1, ND, 0; (e) $-\frac{1}{2}$, $\frac{\sqrt{3}}{2}$, $-\frac{1}{\sqrt{3}}$, -2, $\frac{2}{\sqrt{3}}$, $-\sqrt{3}$; (f) $\frac{\sqrt{3}}{2}$, $-\frac{1}{2}$, $-\sqrt{3}$, $\frac{2}{\sqrt{3}}$, -2, $-\frac{1}{\sqrt{3}}$; (g) $-\frac{\sqrt{3}}{2}$, $-\frac{1}{2}$, $\sqrt{3}$, $-\frac{2}{\sqrt{3}}$, -2, $\frac{1}{\sqrt{3}}$; (h) 0, -1, 0, ND, -1, ND; (i) 0, -1, 0, ND, -1, ND; (j) $-\frac{\sqrt{3}}{2}$, $-\frac{1}{2}$, $\sqrt{3}$, $-\frac{2}{\sqrt{3}}$, -2, $\frac{1}{\sqrt{3}}$; (k) $-\frac{1}{2}$, $-\frac{\sqrt{3}}{2}$, $\frac{1}{\sqrt{3}}$, -2, $-\frac{2}{\sqrt{3}}$, $\sqrt{3}$; (l) $-\frac{1}{\sqrt{2}}$, $-\frac{1}{\sqrt{2}}$, 1, $-\sqrt{2}$, $-\sqrt{2}$, 1; (m) -1, 0, ND, -1, ND, 0; (n) $-\frac{1}{\sqrt{2}}$, $\frac{1}{\sqrt{2}}$, -1, $-\sqrt{2}$, $\sqrt{2}$, -1; (o) -1, 0, ND, -1, ND, 0. **2.** $-\frac{\sqrt{3}}{2}$, $-\frac{1}{\sqrt{3}}$, $-\frac{2}{\sqrt{3}}$, 2, $-\sqrt{3}$. **3.** $-\frac{3}{5}$, $-\frac{4}{5}$, $-\frac{5}{4}$, $-\frac{5}{3}$, $\frac{4}{3}$.
4. (a) 2π, $\pi/3$, 2; (b) $2\pi/3$, 0, 3; (c) $\pi/2$, 0; (d) $2\pi/3$, $\pi/4$, 3. **5.** 18 m.
6. 8.9 km. **7.** 6.8 cm. **8.** 79.9 ft. **9.** 409.5 m. **10.** $\frac{\sqrt{6}-\sqrt{2}}{4}$, $\frac{\sqrt{6}+\sqrt{2}}{4}$, $2-\sqrt{3}$. **11.** $\frac{\sqrt{6}+\sqrt{2}}{4}$, $\frac{\sqrt{2}-\sqrt{6}}{4}$, $-2-\sqrt{3}$. **12.** $\frac{1}{2}\sqrt{2-\sqrt{2}}$, $\frac{1}{2}\sqrt{2+\sqrt{2}}$, $\sqrt{2}-1$. **19.** $2A\sin(t/T)\cos(x/X)$.

Examples 3.

1. $y=\sqrt{2}\sin\left(4x+\frac{\pi}{4}\right)$, $\sqrt{2}$, $-\frac{\pi}{16}$, $\frac{\pi}{2}$. **2.** $y=17\sin\left(2x-\theta\right)$, 17, 0.54, π. **3.** $\frac{\pi}{9}$. **4.** $1/\sqrt{1+x^2}$. **5.** $\sqrt{1-x^2}$. **6.** $\frac{1}{3}\sqrt{5-4x-x^2}$, $(x+2)/\sqrt{5-4x-x^2}$. **7.** $(x-3)/\sqrt{13-6x+x^2}$, $2/\sqrt{13-6x+x^2}$.
8. (a) $\frac{\pi}{3}$; (b) $-\frac{\pi}{6}$; (c) $\frac{\pi}{6}$; (d) $\frac{\pi}{6}$. **9.** (a) $\frac{\sqrt{2}}{3}$; (b) $-\frac{\sqrt{5}}{4}$. **10.** (a) $x=2k\pi\pm\frac{\pi}{6}$ $(k\in\mathbb{Z})$; (b) $x=k\pi+\frac{\pi}{12}$ or $x=k\pi+\frac{5\pi}{12}$ $(k\in\mathbb{Z})$; (c) $x=\frac{2k\pi}{3}-\frac{\pi}{18}$ or $x=\frac{2k\pi}{3}+\frac{7\pi}{18}$ $(k\in\mathbb{Z})$; (d) $x=\frac{k\pi}{2}-\frac{\pi}{48}$ or $x=\frac{k\pi}{2}+\frac{5\pi}{48}$ $(k\in\mathbb{Z})$.
11. (a) $x=\frac{2k\pi}{3}\pm\frac{\pi}{6}$ or $x=k\pi-\frac{\pi}{6}$ or $x=k\pi+\frac{2\pi}{3}$ $(k\in\mathbb{Z})$; (b) $x=\frac{k\pi}{2}$ or $x=k\pi\pm\frac{\pi}{6}$ $(k\in\mathbb{Z})$; (c) $x=2k\pi$ or $x=2k\pi+\frac{\pi}{2}$ $(k\in\mathbb{Z})$; (d) $x=k\pi+\frac{\pi}{6}$ or $x=k\pi+\frac{\pi}{2}$ $(k\in\mathbb{Z})$. **12.** $91.2°$, $1.2°$. **13.** $18°$.

Examples 4.

1. (a) $35x^4-16x^3+24x^2-10x+2$; (b) $20x^4-15x^2+14x-8$; (c) $18x^2-6x+5-\dfrac{4}{x^3}+\dfrac{12}{x^4}$; (d) $36x^3-24x^2+3-\dfrac{4}{x^2}+\dfrac{4}{x^3}+\dfrac{20}{x^5}$.

2. (a) $7x^6 - 30x^5 + 24x^3 + 9x^2 - 54x + 14$; (b) $90x^5 + 220x^4 + 132x^3 + 219x^2 + 124x + 57$; (c) $(x^3 + 4x)\cos x + (3x^2 + 4)\sin x$;

(d) $(10x^4 - 27x^2)\ln x + 2x^4 - 9x^2$.   **3.** (a) $\dfrac{x^4 + 29x^2 + 82x - 18}{(x^2 + 9)^2}$;

(b) $4(x-2)(x+2)/(x^2 - 3x + 4)^2$; (c) $\dfrac{2\cos x + x^3\cos x - 3x^2\sin x}{(2 + x^3)^2}$;

(d) $(3x^2 - 5 - 6x^2\ln x)/x(3x^2 - 5)^2$. **4.** (a) $7(2x^3 - 3x^2 - 5x + 2) \times (x^4 - 2x^3 - 5x^2 + 4x - 7)^{\frac{5}{2}}$; (b) $(5/4) \times (3x^5 - 4x^3 - 7x^2 + 3x + 2)^{\frac{1}{4}} \times (15x^4 - 12x^2 - 14x + 3)$; (c) $3\sec^2 x\tan^2 x$; (d) $5\sec^5 x\tan x$; (e) $(4 - 10x)\sin(5x^2 - 4x + 7)$; (f) $\sec^2(x^2 - 4x + 2)\cos(\tan(x^2 - 4x + 2)) \times (2x - 4)$. **5.** (a) $2(7x - 3)(x - 5)^7(x + 3)^5$; (b) $42(3x + 4)^6(7x - 2)^2 \times (5x + 1)$; (c) $3\cos^2 x\cos 4x$; (d) $4\sin^3 x\cos 5x$; (e) $6\sin^5 x\cos^2 2x\cos 3x$; (f) $2\sec 2x\,\mathrm{cosec}^2 x(\tan 2x - \cot x)$; (g) $(3\sec^2\sqrt{x}\tan^2\sqrt{x})/(2\sqrt{x})$; (h) $-\tfrac{2}{5}x^{-\frac{3}{5}}\sin x^{\frac{2}{5}}$; (i) $-\tfrac{4}{3}x^{\frac{1}{3}}\,\mathrm{cosec}\,x^{\frac{4}{3}}\cot x^{\frac{4}{3}}$; (j) $-3\tan x\sec^2 x \times (1 - \tan^2 x)^{\frac{1}{2}}$; (k) $-x^2/(x\sin x + \cos x)^2$; (l) $3\sin^2 x\cos 2x/\cos^3 3x$; (m) $5\cos 4x/\cos^6 x$; (n) $-6\cos 3x\cos x/\sin^4 2x$; (o) $3/\sqrt{1 - 9x^2}$; (p) $-5/\sqrt{1 - 25x^2}$; (q) $3/\sqrt{-(3 + 12x + 9x^2)}$; (r) $4/(1 + 16x^2)$; (s) $3(\sin^{-1}x)^2/\sqrt{1 - x^2}$; (t) $2/(13 + 6x + x^2)$. **6.** (a) $3/(3x - 5)$; (b) $6x^2/(1 + 2x^3)$; (c) $x/(6 + x^2)$; (d) $8x/(3x^2 - 7)$; (e) $-\tan x$; (f) $x + 2x\ln 2x$; (g) $\tfrac{1}{x}\sec^2(\ln x)$; (h) $4(\cos 4x + \sin 4x)/(\sin 4x - \cos 4x)$;

(i) $x(3x - 10)\ln(x^2 + 3) + \dfrac{2x(x^3 - 5x^2)}{x^2 + 3}$; (j) $\dfrac{(x + 7)(6x^2 - 5)}{(2x^2 - 5)} + $

$(2x + 7)\ln(2x^3 - 5x)$;   (k) $\dfrac{2x}{x^2 + 4} - \dfrac{4x^3}{x^4 + 7}$;   (l) $\dfrac{6x}{(3x^2 + 4)\ln 10}$;

(m) $-\tfrac{4}{\ln 4}\tan 4x$; (n) $\tfrac{4}{\ln 10}\,\mathrm{cosec}\,4x$; (o) $\dfrac{1}{\ln 2}\left(\dfrac{x - 2}{x + 4}\right) + \log_2(x + 4)$;

(p) $7e^{7x}$; (q) $-3e^{4-3x}$; (r) $4x^3 e^{x^4}$; (s) $e^{\sin x}\cos x$; (t) $e^{\sec x}\sec x\tan x$; (u) $2x(1 + 2x)e^{4x}$; (v) $x^3(3x^3 - 2x + 4)e^{x^3 - 2x + 5}$; (w) $4 \times 2^{4x}\ln 2$;

(x) $\sec^2 x \times \ln 5 \times 5^{\tan x}$; (y) $\dfrac{\ln 3}{x}3^{\ln x}$; (z) $x^2.7^{5x}(3 + 5x\ln 7)$.

7. (a) $\left(\dfrac{\tan x}{x} + \sec^2 x\ln x\right)x^{\tan x}$;   (b) $\left(\dfrac{\sin x}{x} + \cos x\ln x\right)x^{\sin x}$;

(c) $(\ln\sin x + x\cot x)(\sin x)^x$; (d) $\left[\dfrac{(x - 2)(2x + 2)}{(x^2 + 2x + 5)} + \ln(x^2 + 2x + 5)\right] \times$

$(x^2 + 2x + 5)^{x-2}$.

Examples 5.

1. $(-1, -2)$. **2.** $x = \frac{2k\pi}{3} - \frac{\pi}{18}$ or $\frac{2k\pi}{3} + \frac{7\pi}{18}$ $(k \in \mathbb{Z})$. **3.** (a) $y = 3 - x$, $y = x + 1$, $(2, 1)$; (b) $y = 18 - 11x$, $11y = x - 46$, $(1, 7)$, $(-2, 40)$.
4. (a) 4, $(0, -2)$; (b) -32, $(3, -125)$, $(-2, -90)$. **5.** (a) $2\sin x\cos 3x$, $x = k\pi$ or $x = \frac{2k\pi}{3} \pm \frac{\pi}{6}$ $(k \in \mathbb{Z})$, 0, $\pi/6$, $\pi/2$, $5\pi/6$, π, $7\pi/6$, $3\pi/2$, $11\pi/6$, 2π; (b) $-4\cos^3 x\sin 5x$, $x = 2k\pi \pm \frac{\pi}{2}$ or $\frac{k\pi}{5}$ $(k \in \mathbb{Z})$,

0, $\pi/5$, $2\pi/5$, $\pi/2$, $3\pi/5$, $4\pi/5$, π, $6\pi/5$, $7\pi/5$, $3\pi/2$, $8\pi/5$, $9\pi/5$, 2π;
(c) $3\sin^2 x \cos 2x/\cos^2 3x$, $x = k\pi$ or $k\pi \pm \frac{\pi}{4}$ ($k \in \mathbb{Z}$), 0, $\pi/4$, $3\pi/4$, π,
$5\pi/4$, $7\pi/4$, 2π; (d) $-4\cos 6x/(\sin^3 2x \cos^2 4x)$, $x = \frac{k\pi}{3} \pm \frac{\pi}{12}$ ($k \in \mathbb{Z}$),
$\pi/12$, $\pi/4$, $5\pi/12$, $7\pi/12$, $3\pi/4$, $11\pi/12$, $13\pi/12$, $5\pi/4$, $17\pi/12$, $19\pi/12$,
$7\pi/4$, $23\pi/12$. **6.** 48, 142. **7.** $10 - 2\cos 3$, $12 + 2\sin 3$. **8.** 14504. **9.** -26.
10. $50 + 6e^6$. **11.** $A = \frac{1}{2}x^2$, 5. **12.** 36π.

Examples 6.

1. (a) $-2\sin 2x$, $-4\cos 2x$, $8\sin 2x$, $16\cos 2x$; (b) $\sin 3x + 3x\cos 3x$,
$6\cos 3x - 9x\sin 3x$, $-27\sin 3x - 27x\cos 3x$, $81x\sin 3x - 108\cos 3x$; (c) $x +$
$2x\ln x$, $3 + 2\ln x$, $2/x$, $-2/x^2$; (d) $-3e^{-3x}$, $9e^{-3x}$, $-27e^{-3x}$, $81e^{-3x}$.

Examples 7.

1. $(2y - 2x - 5)/(6y - 2x - 4)$. **2.** $(y\cos x - \sin y)/(x\cos y - \sin x)$.
3. 4, -25. **4.** 3, 16. **5.** $4y + x = 6$, $y = 4x + 10$. **6.** $y + 3x = 7\pi/6$.

Examples 8.

No numerical answers.

Examples 9.

1. $(-\infty, 4)$. **2.** $(-\infty, -1) \cup (2, \infty)$. **3.** $(1, -3)$ and $(-3, -19)$. Both
are points of inflection. **4.** $(-1, 6)$ is a point of inflection; $(1, -2)$ is
not. **5.** 0, -48; concave down, and concave down becoming concave up.
6. $(2, 26)$: -10, 18, 22; concave up in each case. **7.** $(-2, -172)$, $(3, 43)$;
142, -48, 168 and -82; concave down, up, up becoming down and down
becoming up.

Examples 10.

1. $(-\infty, -2) \cup (1, \infty)$. **2.** $(-\infty, -3) \cup (-2, 2)$. **3.** $(-\infty, 1) \cup (4, \infty)$.
4. $(\pi/6, \pi/2) \cup (5\pi/6, \pi)$. Hint: Use a table of sign to find when
$2\sin x \cos 3x > 0$. **5.** (a) $(-1, 0)$, $(1, 0)$, $(3, 0)$ and $(0, 3)$; $x = 1 - \frac{2\sqrt{3}}{3}$,
maximum, $x = 1 + \frac{2\sqrt{3}}{3}$, minimum; $(1, 0)$; (b) $(1, 0)$, $(4, 0)$ and $(0, -4)$;
$x = 1$, maximum, $x = 3$, minimum; $(2, -2)$. **6.** (a) $(4, 4)$, maxi-
mum, $(10, 16)$, minimum; $(-2, 0)$, $(6, 0)$ and $(0, 12/7)$; $x = 7$; $y \approx x$.
7. (a) $(-1, 8)$, maximum, $(5, 32)$, minimum; $(-7, 0)$, $(1, 0)$ and $(0, 7)$;
$x = 2$; $y \approx 2x$. **8.** (a) $(5, 1/8)$, maximum; $(7, 1/9)$; $(3, 0)$ and
$(0, -3)$; $x = 1$; $y \approx 1/x$. **9.** (a) $(-4, -1/4)$, minimum; $(-5, -2/9)$;
$(-3, 0)$ and $(0, 3/4)$; $x = -2$; $y \approx 1/x$. **10.** (a) $(0, 4)$, minimum;
$(-4, 0)$, $(4, 0)$ and $(0, 4)$; $x = \pm 2$; $y \approx 1$. **11.** (a) $(3, 16)$, minimum;
$(-5, 0)$, $(11, 0)$ and $(0, -11)$; $x = 1$, $x = 5$; $y \approx 1$. **12.** (1) (a),
(e); (2) (c), (g); (3) (b), (d), (f), (h). **13.** (a) $(4, e^{-4})$, maximum;
$(5, 2e^{-5})$; $(3, 0)$, $(0, -3)$; $y \to 0^+$ as $x \to \infty$; $y \to -\infty$ as $x \to -\infty$.
(b) $(-3, -e^{-3})$, minimum; $(-4, -2e^{-4})$; $(-2, 0)$, $(0, 2)$; $y \to \infty$ as
$x \to \infty$; $y \to 0^-$ as $x \to -\infty$. (c) $(0, 1)$, maximum, $(1, 0)$, minimum;
$\left(-\frac{1}{\sqrt{2}}, \left(-\frac{1}{\sqrt{2}} - 1\right)^2 e^{-\sqrt{2}}\right)$, $\left(\frac{1}{\sqrt{2}}, \left(\frac{1}{\sqrt{2}} - 1\right)^2 e^{\sqrt{2}}\right)$; $(1, 0)$, $(0, 1)$; $y \to \infty$

$\ln|x-3|-5\ln|x+1|+c$; (c) $\frac{1}{2}x^2+2x-3\ln|x-2|+\ln|x+1|+3/(x-2)+c$;
(d) $x+\ln|x-1|+\ln|x^2+4|-\frac{1}{2}\tan^{-1}\frac{x}{2}-1/(x-1)+c$.

Examples 18.

1. $\frac{1}{8}, -\frac{1}{2}, \frac{3}{8}, \frac{3}{8}x-\frac{1}{4}\sin 2x+\frac{1}{32}\sin 4x+c$. **2.** $\frac{1}{8}, \frac{1}{2}, \frac{3}{8}, \frac{3}{8}x+\frac{1}{4}\sin 2x+$
$\frac{1}{32}\sin 4x+c$. **3.** $\frac{1}{32}, -\frac{1}{16}, -\frac{1}{32}, \frac{1}{16}, \frac{1}{192}\sin 6x-\frac{1}{64}\sin 4x-\frac{1}{64}\sin 2x+$
$\frac{1}{16}x+c$. **4.** (a) $\frac{1}{25}e^{3x}(4\sin 4x+3\cos 4x)+c$; (b) $\frac{1}{4}e^{2x}(\sin 2x+\cos 2x)+c$;
(c) $-\frac{1}{10}e^{-x}(\sin 3x+3\cos 3x)+c$; (d) $\frac{1}{17}e^{4x}(4\sin x-\cos x)+c$.

Examples 19.

1. (a) $\sqrt{9+4x^2}-3\ln\left|\dfrac{3+\sqrt{9+4x^2}}{2x}\right|+c$; (b) $-\frac{1}{2}\ln\left|\dfrac{2+\sqrt{4+x^2}}{x}\right|+c$;

(c) $-\frac{1}{8}x\left(2x^2-125\right)\sqrt{25-x^2}+\frac{1875}{8}\sin^{-1}\frac{x}{5}+c$; (d) $-\frac{1}{8}\sin^3 2x\cos 2x-$
$\frac{3}{16}\sin 2x\cos 2x+\frac{3}{8}x+c$; (e) $\frac{1}{18}\cos^5 3x\sin 3x+\frac{5}{72}\cos^3 3x\sin 3x+$
$\frac{5}{48}\cos 3x\sin 3x+\frac{5}{16}x+c$; (f) $\frac{1}{8}\sec^3 2x\tan 2x+\frac{3}{16}\sec 2x\tan 2x+$
$\frac{3}{16}\ln|\sec 2x+\tan 2x|+c$; (g) $-\frac{1}{20}\cos 10x-\frac{1}{8}\cos 4x+c$; (h) $\frac{1}{5}x^5\ln x-$
$\frac{1}{25}x^5+c$; (i) $-\sin^{-1}\frac{x}{2}-\sqrt{4-x^2}/x+c$; (j) $\frac{1}{29}e^{5x}(5\sin 2x-2\cos 2x)+c$;
(k) $\left(-\frac{1}{2}x^4+\frac{3}{2}x^2-\frac{3}{4}\right)\cos 2x+\left(x^3-\frac{3}{2}x\right)\sin 2x+c$; (l) $-\frac{1}{6}\cot^2 3x-$
$\frac{1}{3}\ln|\sin 3x|+c$;   (m) $-\dfrac{\sqrt{4x+3}}{3x}-\dfrac{2}{3\sqrt{3}}\ln\left|\dfrac{\sqrt{4x+3}-\sqrt{3}}{\sqrt{4x+3}+\sqrt{3}}\right|+c$;

(n) $\left(\frac{2}{27}x^3-\frac{20}{189}x^2+\frac{80}{567}x-\frac{800}{5103}\right)(3x+5)^{\frac{3}{2}}+c$.

Examples 20.

1. (a) $\frac{111}{4}$; (b) 40; (c) $\frac{1}{2}\left(e^2-e^{-2}\right)$; (d) $\frac{2}{3}$; (e) $\frac{1}{2}$; (f) $\frac{2}{3}$; (g) $\frac{1}{2}$;
(h) $\frac{2}{\sqrt{3}}$; (i) $\ln|1+\sqrt{2}|$; (j) $\ln\left|\frac{5}{3}\right|$; (k) $\frac{\pi}{3}$; (l) $\frac{\pi}{12}$. **2.** (a) $\frac{8}{5}$; (b) 2; (c) $\frac{3}{80}$;
(d) $\tan^{-1}\frac{1}{\sqrt{2}}$; (e) $\frac{\sqrt{2}}{20}$; (f) $\frac{2}{15}\left(31^{\frac{5}{2}}-32\right)$; (g) $\frac{1}{4}\ln 41$; (h) $\ln 2$; (i) $\frac{\pi}{8}$;
(j) $\frac{\pi}{6}$; (k) $\frac{1}{4}$; (l) $\frac{9\sqrt{3}-1}{160}$; (m) $\sqrt{3}$; (n) $\frac{7}{3}$; (o) $\frac{1}{2}\left(\tan^{-1}9-\frac{\pi}{4}\right)$; (p) $\frac{2-\sqrt{2}}{4}$.
3. (a) $\frac{\pi}{2}-1$; (b) $\frac{1}{4}-\frac{5}{4}e^{-4}$; (c) $\frac{5}{4e^6}\left(e^4-5\right)$; (d) $\frac{3}{16}e^4+\frac{1}{16}$; (e) $\frac{\pi}{8}-\frac{1}{4}$;
(f) $\frac{\pi\sqrt{3}}{24}-\frac{\pi^2}{144}-\frac{1}{8}$; (g) $22\ln 2-6$; (h) $\frac{\pi}{4}-\frac{1}{2}\ln 2$. **4.** (a) $\frac{\pi}{8}$; (b) $\frac{\pi}{12}+\frac{\sqrt{3}}{16}$;
(c) $\frac{\pi}{24}-\frac{\sqrt{3}}{32}$; (d) $\frac{3\pi}{32}+\frac{1}{4}$. **5.** (a) $\ln\frac{27}{2}$; (b) $\ln\frac{49}{3}$; (c) $\ln\left(\frac{2^7.3^2}{7^3}\right)$; (d) $1+\ln 5$;
(e) $\ln\frac{27}{32}-\frac{1}{4}$; (f) $\ln\frac{49}{16}+\frac{3}{5}$; (g) $\frac{\pi}{4}+2\ln\frac{2}{3}$; (h) $\frac{3\pi}{4}-\frac{5}{2}-\ln 2$. **6.** (a) 7;
(b) $\frac{2\sqrt{2}}{3\pi}$; (c) 1; (d) $\frac{3}{2\ln 2}$.

Examples 21.

1. (a) 30; (b) 24; (c) $\frac{\sqrt{3}}{2}$. **2.** (a) 24; (b) $\frac{41}{2}$. **3.** $\frac{1}{64}$. **4.** $\frac{1}{2}$.

Examples 22.

1. (a) $\frac{243\pi}{5}$; (b) $\frac{127\pi}{7}$; (c) $\frac{26\pi}{81}$; (d) $\pi\left(1-\frac{\pi}{4}\right)$. **2.** $\frac{125\pi}{6}$. **3.** 36π.
4. $4\pi^2$. Hint: think of the circle as formed by the two curves $y=2+\sqrt{1-x^2}$ and $y=2-\sqrt{1-x^2}$. Then find the volume obtained by rotating the area between these two curves about the x-axis.

Examples 23.

1. (a) $\frac{2}{27}\left(37^{\frac{3}{2}} - 10^{\frac{3}{2}}\right)$; (b) $\frac{106}{3}$; Hint: $\frac{ds}{dx}$ simplifies to $2x^2 - 1$ for

$2 \le x \le 4$; (c) $\frac{17}{6}$; Hint: $\frac{ds}{dx}$ simplifies to $\frac{3x^4 + 12}{12x^2}$; (d) $\ln\left(\frac{\sqrt{3} + \sqrt{6}}{3}\right)$;

(e) $4 + \ln 3$; Hint: $\frac{ds}{dx}$ simplifies to $\frac{x}{4} + \frac{1}{x}$. **2.** (a) $\frac{152\pi}{3}$; Hint: Show

that the surface area is $4\pi \int_3^8 \sqrt{1 + x}\, dx$; (b) $\frac{\pi}{27}\left(10^{\frac{3}{2}} - 1\right)$; Hint: Show

that the surface area is $2\pi \int_0^1 x^3 \sqrt{1 + 9x^4}\, dx$; (c) $\frac{\pi}{4}\left(e^2 + 4 - e^{-2}\right)$; Hint:

Show that the surface area is $\frac{\pi}{2}\int_0^1 \left(e^x + e^{-x}\right)^2 dx$. **3.** 2, $\frac{4}{3}\left(4\pi - 3\sqrt{3}\right)$,

$\frac{80\pi}{3}$, 32π; Hint: In each of the integrations, you need to deal separately

with the cases $0 \le x \le 2$ and $2 \le x \le 4$. For the curved surface areas,

you finish up needing to find $2\pi \int 4\, dx$ in each case, with appropriate

limits.

Examples 24.

1. (a) (α) 146, (β) 144; (b) (α) $\frac{\pi}{8}\left(2 + \sqrt{2}\right)$, ($\beta$) $\frac{\pi}{6}\left(1 + \sqrt{2}\right)$;

(c) (α) 1.073 (to 3 dec. pl.), (β) 1.057 (to 3 dec. pl.); (d) (α) $\frac{\pi^2}{4}$, (β) $\frac{\pi^2}{4}$.

2. (a) (α) $0.2314065\ldots, 0.4628130\ldots$, ($\beta$) $0.2318263\ldots, 0.4636526\ldots$,

$\frac{1}{2}\tan^{-1}\frac{1}{2}$; (b) ($\alpha$) $2.2734126\ldots$, $1.1367063\ldots$, (β) $2.210052\ldots$,

$1.1050264\ldots$, $2\ln 3$. **3.** (a) (α) 6.087, (β) 6.081; (b) (α) 1.8134,

(β) 1.8100. **4.** (α) $\frac{\pi}{8}\left(\sqrt{2} + \sqrt{6} + 1\right)$, ($\beta$) $\frac{\pi}{12}\left(\sqrt{2} + 2\sqrt{6} + 1\right)$.

5. (α) $32.474435\ldots$, (β) $33.267892\ldots$.

Examples 25.

1. $\frac{19}{6}$. **2.** $\frac{25}{12}$. **3.** 0.824. **4.** 0.773. **5.** 3, 2.762. **6.** 4, 4.100. **7.** 3.780.

8. 0.940.

Examples 26.

2. $1 + \frac{1}{2}x^2 + \frac{5}{24}x^4 + \ldots$, $1.00786\ldots$. **3.** $1 + 2x + \frac{5}{2}x^2 + \frac{8}{3}x^3 + \ldots$.

4. $x + x^2 - \frac{1}{6}x^3 - \frac{1}{6}x^4 + \ldots$. **5.** $3 + \frac{1}{27}x - \frac{1}{37}x^2 + \frac{5}{312}x^3$, $2.9240216\ldots$.

6. $-\left(x + \frac{1}{2}x^2 + \frac{1}{3}x^3 + \frac{1}{4}x^4 + \ldots\right)$, $2\left(x + \frac{1}{3}x^3 + \frac{1}{5}x^5 + \ldots\right)$, 2.398,

2.565. **7.** $1 + t^2 + \frac{1}{2}t^4 + \frac{1}{6}t^6 + \frac{1}{24}t^8 + \ldots$, 0.203. **8.** $t - 2t^3 + \frac{2}{3}t^5 - \frac{4}{45}t^7 + \ldots$,

0.041. **9.** $1 + \frac{1}{2}t^2 + \frac{3}{8}t^4 + \frac{5}{16}t^6 + \frac{35}{128}t^8$, $x + \frac{1}{6}x^3 + \frac{3}{40}x^5 + \frac{5}{112}x^7 + \frac{35}{1152}x^9$.

10. $1 + t^2 + t^4 + t^6 + t^8 + \ldots$, $2\left(x + \frac{1}{3}x^3 + \frac{1}{5}x^5 + \frac{1}{7}x^7 + \frac{1}{9}x^9 + \ldots\right)$.

Examples 27.

1. $-2\cos t + t^3 - \frac{1}{2}e^{-2t} - t + \frac{5}{2}$. **2.** (a) $-y^{-1} = \frac{1}{3}x^3 + c$;

(b) $\ln|y/(1 + y)| = \frac{1}{2}x^2 + c$; (c) $-\cot y = \sin^{-1} x + c$; (d) $\tan^{-1} y = \frac{1}{2}e^{2x} + c$; (e) $\frac{1}{2}y^2 + \cos y = \sin x - \frac{1}{3}x^3 + c$; (f) $e^{4y} = 2e^{2x} + c$; (g) $\tan^{-1} y = \tan^{-1} x + c$; (h) $\sec y = cx$. **3.** (a) $\sin y = c - \cos x$, $\sin y = 1 - \cos x$;

(b) $\ln|1 + y| = \frac{1}{3}\left(x^3 + c\right)$, $\ln|1 + y| = \frac{1}{3}\left(x^3 - 1\right)$; (c) $x^4 + 2y^{-2} = c$,

$x^4 + 2y^{-2} = \frac{163}{2}$; (d) $3\sin 2x + 2\cos 3y = c$, $3\sin 2x + 2\cos 3y = 3$.

4. (a) $\ln|y| = c - x^{-1}y$;   (b) $\tan^{-1}\frac{y}{x} = \ln|c\sqrt{x^2 + y^2}|$;
(c) $y^2 + x^2 \ln|y| = cx^2$;   (d) $\ln|y/x| = cx$; Hint: Put $u = \ln v$ to solve
the harder integral. **5.** (a) $y = 2 + ce^{-2x}$, $y = 2 + e^{-2x}$; (b) $y = x^5 + cx^2$,
$y = x^5 - 7x^2$; (c) $y = \frac{1}{4}(2x - 1)e^{-2x} + ce^{-4x}$, $y = \frac{1}{4}(2x - 1)e^{-2x} + \frac{13}{4}e^{-4x}$;
(d) $y = \frac{1}{5}(\sin 2x - 2\cos 2x) + ce^{-x}$, $y = \frac{1}{5}(\sin 2x - 2\cos 2x) + \frac{22}{5}e^{-x}$.

6. (a) (α) $y = Ae^{3x} + Be^{2x}$, (β) $y = 3x^2 + 2x - 4$, (γ) $y = Ae^{3x} + Be^{2x} + 3x^2 + 2x - 4$; (b) ($\alpha$) $y = Ae^{2x} + Be^{-3x}$, (β) $y = \sin 2x - 2\cos 2x$,
(γ) $y = Ae^{2x} + Be^{-3x} + \sin 2x - 2\cos 2x$; (c) ($\alpha$) $y = Ae^{5x} + Be^{-x}$,
(β) $y = -e^{2x}$, (γ) $y = Ae^{5x} + Be^{-x} - e^{2x}$, ($\delta$) $y = 2e^{5x} + 3e^{-x} - e^{2x}$;
(d) (α) $y = Ae^{3x} + Be^{-3x}$, (β) $y = x^3 - x^2 - x + 2$, (γ) $y = Ae^{3x} + Be^{-3x} + x^3 - x^2 - x + 2$; (e) ($\alpha$) $y = Ae^{3x} + Be^x$, (β) $y = -6xe^x$,
(γ) $y = Ae^{3x} + Be^x - 6xe^x$; (f) ($\alpha$) $y = Ae^{-2x} + Be^x$, (β) $y = -3xe^{-2x}$,
(γ) $y = Ae^{-2x} + Be^x - 3xe^{-2x}$, ($\delta$) $y = -2e^{-2x} + 4e^x - 3xe^{-2x}$; (g) ($\alpha$) $y = (A + Bx)e^{2x}$, (β) $y = x^2 + 3$, (γ) $y = (A + Bx)e^{2x} + x^2 + 3$; (h) ($\alpha$) $y = (A + Bx)e^{-3x}$, (β) $y = x^2 - 2x + 3$, (γ) $y = (A + Bx)e^{-3x} + x^2 - 2x + 3$;
(i) (α) $y = (A + Bx)e^x$, (β) $y = 2x^2e^x$, (γ) $y = (A + Bx + 2x^2)e^x$,
(δ) $y = (2x^2 + x - 2)e^x$; (j) (α) $y = A\cos 3x + B\sin 3x$, (β) $y = e^{-2x}$,
(γ) $y = A\cos 3x + B\sin 3x + e^{-2x}$; (k) ($\alpha$) $y = A\cos 4x + B\sin 4x$,
(β) $y = 3\sin 2x - \cos 2x$, (γ) $y = A\cos 4x + B\sin 4x + 3\sin 2x - \cos 2x$;
(l) (α) $y = e^{2x}(A\cos x + B\sin x)$, ($\beta$) $y = x^2 + x - 2$, (γ) $y = e^{2x}(A\cos x + B\sin x) + x^2 + x - 2$; (m) ($\alpha$) $y = e^x(A\cos 3x + B\sin 3x)$,
(β) $y = e^x$, (γ) $y = e^x(A\cos 3x + B\sin 3x + 1)$, ($\delta$) $y = e^x(2\cos 3x - \sin 3x + 1)$; (n) ($\alpha$) $y = e^{2x}(A\cos 2x + B\sin 2x)$, ($\beta$) $y = x^2 - 3$,
(γ) $y = e^{2x}(A\cos 2x + B\sin 2x) + x^2 - 3$; (o) ($\alpha$) $y = Ae^x + Be^{3x}$,
(β) $y = 2x - 1 - 2e^{2x}$, (γ) $y = Ae^x + Be^{3x} + 2x - 1 - 2e^{2x}$; (p) ($\alpha$) $y = Ae^{-2x} + Be^{-3x}$, (β) $y = e^x + xe^{-2x}$, (γ) $y = Ae^{-2x} + Be^{-3x} + e^x + xe^{-2x}$.

Examples 28.

1. $\ln y = \frac{1}{4}x^4 - 4$. **2.** $\tan^{-1}\frac{y}{x} = \ln\sqrt{x^2 + y^2}$. **3.** $5.8504910\ldots$.

4. $44.243095\ldots$. **5.** $x = \dfrac{1}{50}\left(1 - e^{\frac{Kt}{100}}\right)\Big/\left(1 - 2e^{\frac{Kt}{100}}\right)$. **6.** $y = \dfrac{AL}{K-L}\left(e^{-Lt} - e^{-Kt}\right)$. **7.** $y = c\left(1 - e^{-\frac{v}{V}t}\right)$. **8.** $y = Ae^{-kt} + \frac{c}{k}\left(1 - e^{-kt}\right)$.

9. $i = \dfrac{E_0\omega C}{\omega^2 R^2 C^2 + 1}\left(\sin\omega t - \omega RC\cos\omega t + \omega RCe^{-\frac{t}{RC}}\right) + i_0 e^{-\frac{t}{RC}}$. Hint:
Use integration by parts twice, or the complex number method, to find
$\int e^{\frac{t}{RC}}\sin\omega t\, dt$. **10.** $v = \frac{5}{6}\left(e^{-\frac{4}{5}t} - e^{-2t}\right)$. **11.** $\theta = \left(t - \frac{1}{2}\right)e^{-2t} + \frac{1}{2}e^{-4t}$.
12. $x = 2\left(e^{-4t} - e^{-8t}\right)$.

Examples 29.

1. (a) $(x - 1)(x + 5)$; (b) $(x + 1)(x + 4)$; (c) $(x + 3)(x + 2)$;
(d) $(x + 4)(x - 3)$; (e) $(2x + 3)(x + 1)$; (f) $(3x + 1)(x + 4)$; (g), (h) not
possible; (i) $(2x - 3)(2x - 1)$; (j) $(3x - 1)(x + 2)$; (k) not possible;
(l) $(3x + 1)(x + 1)$. **2.** (a) $B = 75$, $b = 3.7827798\ldots$, $c = 3.2079811\ldots$;
(b) $C = 58.98696\ldots$, $B = 81.01303\ldots$, $b = 4.6098767\ldots$;
(c) $B = 8.2132107\ldots$, $C = 141.78678\ldots$, $c = 8.660254\ldots$.

Some Standard Integrals

In the following formulae, a is a constant.

$f(x)$	$\int f(x)\,dx$	Note
a	$ax + c$	
x^n	$\dfrac{1}{n+1}x^{n+1} + c$	$n \neq 0,\ n \neq -1$
$\dfrac{1}{x}$	$\ln|x| + c$	$x \neq 0$
e^x	$e^x + c$	
a^x	$\dfrac{1}{\ln a}a^x + c$	$a \neq 1,\ a > 0$
$\cos x$	$\sin x + c$	
$\sin x$	$-\cos x + c$	
$\tan x$	$\ln|\sec x| + c$	
$\sec x$	$\ln|\sec x + \tan x| + c$	
$\operatorname{cosec} x$	$\ln|\operatorname{cosec} x - \cot x| + c$	
$\cot x$	$\ln|\sin x| + c$	
$\sec^2 x$	$\tan x + c$	
$\operatorname{cosec}^2 x$	$-\cot x + c$	
$\sec x \tan x$	$\sec x + c$	
$\operatorname{cosec} x \cot x$	$-\operatorname{cosec} x + c$	
$\dfrac{1}{\sqrt{1-x^2}}$	$\sin^{-1} x + c$ or $-\cos^{-1} x + c$	$x \in (-1, 1)$
$\dfrac{1}{1+x^2}$	$\tan^{-1} x + c$	
$\dfrac{1}{x^2 - a^2}$	$\dfrac{1}{2a}\ln\left|\dfrac{x-a}{x+a}\right| + c$	$x^2 \neq a^2$

Index

The numbers refer to pages in the text

ALSO AVAILABLE IN THIS SERIES ARE THE FOLLOWING:

ADVANCED CALCULUS FOR ENGINEERING AND SCIENCE STUDENTS

Ian S. Murphy.   Third Edition, 1989.   248 pages.

Arklay Publishers, 64 Murray Place, Stirling.

Contents: Double and Triple Integration, Beta and Gamma Functions, Differential Equations, Laplace Transforms, Partial Differentiation, Errors and Exact Differentials, Vector Calculus, Line and Surface Integrals, Fourier Series, Maxima and Minima of Functions of Several Variables, Eigenvalues and Eigenvectors of Matrices, Systems of Linear Differential Equations, Lagrange Multipliers, Hints and answers to the examples, Index.

BASIC MATHEMATICAL ANALYSIS: THE FACTS

Ian S. Murphy.   Third Edition, 1991.   246 pages.

Arklay Publishers, 64 Murray Place, Stirling.

Contents: Basic ideas, Limits of sequences, Limits of real functions, Continuity, Metric spaces and compactness, Derivatives and applications, Series, Taylor and Maclaurin expansions, More on series, Power series, Exponential, logarithmic, trigonometric and hyperbolic functions, Integration, More on the convergence of sequences and series, Miscellaneous examples, Hints and answers to the examples, Index.

PROBABILITY: A FIRST COURSE

Ian S. Murphy.   First Edition, 1991.   120 pages.

Arklay Publishers, 64 Murray Place, Stirling.

Contents: Basic ideas, Counting cases, Equally likely outcomes, Hypergeometric distribution, Conditional probability, Bayes' theorem, Independence, Discrete and continuous random variables, Binomial, Poisson and Normal random variables, Expected value, Variance and standard deviation, Normal and Poisson approximations to the Binomial, Two dimensional random variables, Chebyshev Inequality, The Central Limit Theorem, Appendix on the Gamma function, Table for the Normal Distribution, Hints and answers to the examples, Index.
